VAX 8800

VAX 8650

VAX 8600

VAX 8500

VAX 8300

VAX-11/785

VAX 8200

MicroVAX II

11/725

MicroVAX I

1985   1990

VAX Architecture
Reference Manual

VAX Architecture Reference Manual

Edited by
Timothy E. Leonard

Contributing Authors

Dileep P. Bhandarkar
Peter F. Conklin
David N. Cutler
Thomas W. Eggers
Thomas N. Hastings
Richard I. Hustvedt
Judson S. Leonard
Peter Lipman
Thomas Rarich
David P. Rodgers
Steven Rothman
William D. Strecker
Theodore B. Taylor

digital

DECbooks

9 8 7 6 5 4 3

Printed in the United States of America.

Order number EY-3459E-DP

DEC, DECnet, the Digital logo, MASSBUS, MicroVAX, PDP, RSX, SBI, UNIBUS, VAX, and VMS are trademarks of Digital Equipment Corporation.

UNIX is a trademark of Bell Laboratories.

Library of Congress Cataloging-in-Publication Data

VAX architecture reference manual

    Includes index.
    1. VAX-11 (Computer) 2. Computer architecture.
I. Leonard, Timothy E. (Timothy Edwin), 1954–
II. Bhandarkar, Dileep P.
QA76.8.V37V38   1987   004.1'45   86-13559
ISBN 0-932376-86-X

Contents

4 Memory Management   199

5 Exceptions and Interrupts   223

6 Process Structure   259

11 Architectural Subsetting   359

A Opcode Assignments   367

B Implementation Dependencies   373

Index

Foreword

By any practical measure, the VAX family of computers is one of the most successful series of computer systems ever developed. At the time of this writing, over 100,000 machines have been installed, ranging in size from the MicroVAX II to the VAX 8800—a number that even surpasses that for the pioneering IBM SYSTEM 360/370 series. The VAX design has been implemented from scratch over seven times in the past decade to capitalize on advances in technology as well as the changing needs of our customers. These different implementations have used a variety of technologies, organizational techniques, and configurations to create the broad set of systems shown in the chart printed as the endpapers of this book. And though work on the first machine began in 1975, we expect VAX computers to remain the backbone of Digital's product offerings for many years into the future.

To a considerable extent, the success of the VAX family is due to this book, the *VAX Architecture Reference Manual.* Not only does it describe a computer architecture that is outstanding in its own right, but it does so in a manner that is more unambiguous, precise, and complete than for any other computer architecture. With this document, diverse hardware groups throughout Digital have been able to create compatible machines using different technologies, at different periods of time, and in widely separated locations. The book has also served as the control document for approved design modifications, and over the years we have both extended and provided for subsets of its content to improve performance and to pave the way for smaller, yet compatible, implementations.[1]

Of course, the main reason for the success of the VAX family lies in the design itself. The VAX architecture is a computer architecture in the classic sense, a design for a hardware/software interface that is meant to remain consistent, from the point of view of a machine

1. For discussions of two recent implementations—the VAX 8600 and the MicroVAX II—and the special problems they posed, see *Digital Technical Journal,* nos. 1 and 2 (September 1985 and March 1986). Both issues are available from Digital Press, 12 Crosby Drive, Bedford, MA 01730.

language program, across machines of varying price, performance, and technology.

Such a well-defined interface was first used by IBM in its SYSTEM 360/370 family of computers; it was described in 1964 in a seminal paper by G. A. Blauw and F. P. Brooks, Jr., two of its principal designers. At that time, six models had been announced, and all, according to the authors, were "logically identical . . . Even though the allowable (I/O) channels or storage capacity may vary from model to model . . . the logical structure can be discussed without reference to specific models."[2]

This is precisely the goal we set for the VAX design. By defining an architecture that would apply to all members of the VAX family, hardware engineers would be free to build different hardware instantiations or implementations "up" to the specification, while application and system programmers could safely program "down" to it, confident that any program conforming to the specification would run on any present or future machine.

That goal has, in fact, been achieved. Today, any program that conforms to the VAX architecture will run on any VAX with the necessary resources. And hardware engineers, without getting involved in the details of software, can build new generations of VAXes, confident that the billions of dollars invested in existing VAX applications will not be jeopardized.

As for the success of the VAX architecture itself, there are a number of reasons for its widespread acceptance and longevity.

One major reason is the enormous size of the VAX virtual address space. Lack of virtual address space has been the Achilles' heel of most computer architectures. Not long after we announced the first PDP-11 in 1969, we realized that customers were going to demand minicomputers with more than 64 kilobytes of memory, the maximum amount that can be addressed directly by a 16-bit address. We could see that relentless progress in memory chip densities was going to lead to a quadrupling of bits per chip every three to four years. Increasing densities yield decreasing memory costs and computers at minicomputer prices would be able to have more than 64 Kbytes. So, over the years we first extended the PDP-11's physical memory

2. G. A. Blauw and F. P. Brooks, Jr., "The Structure of SYSTEM/360: Part I— Outline of the Logical Structure," *IBM Systems Journal*, vol. 3, no. 2 (1964), pp. 119–135. This is the first published description of a commercial computer architecture with multiple implementations. See also Andrew S. Tanenbaum, *Structured Computer Organization* (Prentice-Hall, 1984), for an introduction to the notion of computer architecture, including comparisons of several contemporary designs.

to 256 Kbytes and then to 2 megabytes. However, the *virtual address* of the PDP-11 remains at 64 Kbytes and the programmer often faces the tedious task of mapping, and then remapping, the PDP-11's small virtual address into a much larger physical memory.

The VAX acronym itself (which originally stood for Virtual Address eXtension) clearly indicated a major design goal of the project: to dramatically increase the address space of the popular PDP-11 computer architecture. The desire to build a machine with enough address space to satisfy customers for years to come led to the decision to create a new 32-bit architecture. With 32-bit addresses, 4 billion bytes of address space were available. The first VAX-11/780 machines shipped in early 1978 with one quarter of a megabyte of physical memory, built from 4K-bit memory chips. By contrast the VAX 8650, one of our more recent large computers, can be configured with 68 megabytes of physical memory, built this time from 256K-bit memory chips.

Each time the physical memory of a machine quadruples, an additional 2 bits of address are required to reference it. To address 64 million bytes on a VAX 8650, 26 bits are needed. If the density of memory chips continues to quadruple every three to four years, then the 32-bit address of the VAX architecture will be adequate for at least another decade without requiring programmers to map virtual memory onto a larger physical memory.

In addition to its expanded address space, the VAX architecture built upon the elegant instruction set and addressing modes of the PDP-11. Additional data formats and corresponding instructions were added to support the needs of compiler writers, as well as scientific and commercial application programmers. A standard calling interface was designed to allow modules written in different languages to call one another. And finally, most importantly, the architecture was carefully designed to support the needs of a modern virtual-memory operating system.[3]

The result of this design work has been gratifying to all of us who have contributed. Customers can choose among three operating systems: VMS, Digital's operating system designed to take full advantage of the VAX architecture; ULTRIX, an implementation of the industry-standard UNIX operating system; and ELN, a system

3. See H. M. Levy and Richard H. Eckhouse, *Computer Programming and Architecture: The VAX-11* (Digital Press, 1980), which gives special attention to the manner in which architectural features support a virtual memory operating system such as VMS. Lawrence Kenah and Simon F. Bate, *VAX/VMS Internals and Data Structures* (Digital Press, 1984), provides a thorough discussion of the algorithms and data structures of the VAX/VMS operating system, including their interactions.

designed to support the development of dedicated, real-time applications. Programmers can choose from a large family of industry-standard, compatible languages, all of which make use of the calling standard and can access the supporting library routines and system services. The architecture has also allowed development of DECnet, Digital's network architecture, and an incredibly rich set of Digital, third party, and customer applications.

An architectural specification can make for dry reading. Nevertheless, this book should be of real interest to at least three audiences. For the serious computer engineer who aspires to design a machine as good as (or better than) a VAX, the *VAX Architecture Reference Manual* is an outstanding example of a successful computer architecture and how it should be documented. For the serious application or systems programmer of VAX computers, this is also the book of "last resort," providing the most precise, authoritative, and complete description of the machine language interface with which he or she will work. Finally, for serious students of either computer science or engineering, the *VAX Architectural Manual* is an excellent supplementary reference, to be consulted as a case study in design or for additional detail regarding computer organization or assembly language programming.

Computer design continues to be a dynamic field; I expect we will see more rather than less change and innovation in the decades ahead. No matter how computers evolve, however, it is clear that the VAX architecture is a major contribution to progress in the field. It will be as important to study and understand a generation from now as it is today.

Samuel H. Fuller
Vice President, Research & Architecture
Digital Equipment Corporation
Maynard, Massachusetts
June 1986

Introduction

The VAX architecture represents a significant extension of the PDP-11 family architecture. It shares byte addressing with the PDP-11, similar I/O and interrupt structures, and identical data formats. Although the instruction set is not strictly compatible with the PDP-11, it is related and can be mastered easily by a PDP-11 programmer. Likewise, the similarity allows straightforward manual conversion of existing PDP-11 programs to the VAX system. Existing user-mode PDP-11 programs which do not need the extended features of VAX can run unchanged in the PDP-11 compatibility mode provided in VAX architecture.

As compared to the PDP-11, VAX offers a greatly extended virtual address space, additional instructions and data types, and new addressing modes. VAX architecture also provides a sophisticated memory management and protection mechanism, and hardware-assisted process scheduling and synchronization.

A number of specific goals are achieved in the VAX design:

- VAX architecture has maximal compatibility with the PDP-11 consistent with a significant extension of the virtual address space and a significant functional enhancement.

- High bit efficiency is achieved by a wide range of data types and new addressing modes.

- The systematic, elegant instruction set with orthogonality of operators, data types, and addressing modes can be exploited easily, particularly by high-level language processors.

- The VAX system is extensible. The instruction set is designed so that new data types and operators can be included efficiently in a manner consistent with the currently defined operators and data types.

- The architecture is suitable in terms of price and performance over a wide range of computer system implementations sold by Digital Equipment Corporation.

TERMINOLOGY AND CONVENTIONS

The terminology and conventions used in this book include the following:

Numbering

All numbers unless otherwise indicated are decimal. Where there is ambiguity, the radix is explicitly stated, as in 48 (hex), or 1001000 (binary).

UNPREDICT-ABLE and UNDEFINED

Results specified as UNPREDICTABLE may vary from moment to moment, implementation to implementation, and instruction to instruction within implementations. Software can never depend on results specified as UNPREDICTABLE. Operations specified as UNDEFINED may vary from moment to moment, implementation to implementation, and instruction to instruction within implementations. The operation may vary in effect from nothing to stopping system operation. UNDEFINED operations must not cause the processor to hang (reach an unhalted state from which there is no transition to a normal state in which the processor executes instructions). Note the distinction between result and operation: non-privileged software cannot invoke UNDEFINED operations.

Ranges and Extents

Ranges are specified in English and are inclusive. For example, a range of integers 0 through 4 includes the integers 0, 1, 2, 3, and 4. Extents are specified by a pair of numbers separated by a colon and are inclusive. For example, bits <7:3> specifies an extent of bits including bits 7, 6, 5, 4, and 3.

MBZ

Fields specified as MBZ (Must Be Zero) should never be filled by software with a non-zero value. If the processor encounters a non-zero value in a field specified as MBZ, a reserved operand fault or abort occurs (see Chapter 5, Exceptions and Interrupts) if that field is accessible to non-privileged software. MBZ fields that are accessible only to privileged software (kernel mode) may not be checked for non-zero value by some or all VAX implementations. Non-zero values in MBZ fields accessible only to privileged software may produce UNDEFINED operation.

Reserved

Unassigned values of fields are reserved for future use. In many cases, some values are indicated as reserved for the customer, that is, the equipment owner. Only these values should be used for non-standard applications. The values indicated as reserved for DIGITAL and all MBZ fields are to be used only to extend the standard architecture in the future.

Figure Conventions

Figures depicting registers or memory follow the convention that increasing addresses run right to left and top to bottom.

Basic Architecture

1

The basic addressable unit in the VAX architecture is the 8-bit byte. Virtual addresses are 32 bits long: hence the virtual address space is 2^{32} (approximately 4.3 billion) bytes. Virtual addresses as seen by the program are translated into physical memory addresses by the memory management mechanism described in Chapter 4.

DATA TYPES

Following are descriptions of the VAX architecture data types.

Byte

A byte is 8 contiguous bits starting on an addressable byte boundary. The bits are numbered from the right $\langle 0 \rangle$ through $\langle 7 \rangle$, as shown in Figure 1.1. A byte is specified by its address A. When interpreted arithmetically, a byte is a two's complement integer with bits of increasing significance from $\langle 0 \rangle$ through $\langle 6 \rangle$ and bit $\langle 7 \rangle$, the sign bit. The value of the integer is in the range -128 through 127. For the purposes of addition, subtraction, and comparison, VAX instructions also provide direct support for the interpretation of a byte as an unsigned integer with bits of increasing significance from $\langle 0 \rangle$ through $\langle 7 \rangle$. The value of the unsigned integer is in the range 0 through 255.

Word

A word is 2 contiguous bytes starting on an arbitrary byte boundary. The bits are numbered from the right $\langle 0 \rangle$ through $\langle 15 \rangle$. See Figure 1.1. A word is specified by its address A, the address of the byte containing bit $\langle 0 \rangle$. When interpreted arithmetically, a word is a two's complement integer with bits of increasing significance from $\langle 0 \rangle$ through $\langle 14 \rangle$ and bit $\langle 15 \rangle$, the sign bit. The value of the integer is in the range $-32,768$ through 32,767. For the purposes of addition, subtraction, and comparison, VAX instructions also provide direct support for the interpretation of a word as an unsigned integer with bits of increasing significance from $\langle 0 \rangle$ through $\langle 15 \rangle$. The value of the unsigned integer is in the range 0 through 65,535.

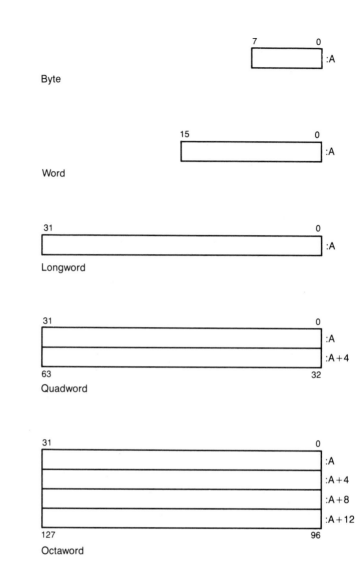

Byte

Word

Longword

Quadword

Octaword

Figure 1.1
Data Types

Longword

A longword is 4 contiguous bytes starting on an arbitrary byte boundary. The bits are numbered from the right ⟨0⟩ through ⟨31⟩, as shown in Figure 1.1. A longword is specified by its address A, the address of the byte containing bit ⟨0⟩. When interpreted arithmetically, a longword is a two's complement integer with bits of increasing significance from ⟨0⟩ through ⟨30⟩ and bit ⟨31⟩, the sign bit. The value of the integer is in the range −2,147,483,648 through 2,147,483,647. For the purposes of addition, subtraction, and comparison, VAX instructions also provide direct support for the interpretation of a longword as an unsigned integer with bits of increasing significance from ⟨0⟩ through ⟨31⟩. The value of the unsigned integer is in the range 0 through 4,294,967,295.

Quadword

A quadword is 8 contiguous bytes starting on an arbitrary byte boundary. The bits are numbered from the right ⟨0⟩ through ⟨63⟩, as shown in Figure 1.1. A quadword is specified by its address A, the address of the byte containing bit ⟨0⟩. When interpreted arithmetically, a quadword is a two's complement integer with bits of increasing significance from ⟨0⟩ through ⟨62⟩ and bit ⟨63⟩, the sign bit. The value of the integer is in the range -2^{63} to $2^{63} - 1$. only a subset of the full complement of operators is provided for quadword.

Octaword

This data type need not be supported in a subset implementation. An octaword is 16 contiguous bytes starting on an arbitrary byte boundary. The bits are numbered from the right ⟨0⟩ through ⟨127⟩, as shown in Figure 1.1. An octaword is specified by its address A, the address of the byte containing bit ⟨0⟩. When interpreted arithmetically, an octaword is a two's complement integer with bits of increasing significance from ⟨0⟩ through ⟨126⟩ and bit ⟨127⟩, the sign bit. The value of the integer is in the range -2^{127} to $2^{127} - 1$. Only a subset of the full complement of operators is provided for octaword.

F__floating

The F__floating data type need not be supported in a subset implementation. An F__floating datum is 4 contiguous bytes starting on an arbitrary byte boundary. The bits are labeled from the right ⟨0⟩ through ⟨31⟩, as shown in Figure 1.2. An F__floating datum is specified by its address A, the address of the byte containing bit ⟨0⟩. The form of an F__floating datum is sign magnitude with bit ⟨15⟩, the sign bit; bits ⟨14:7⟩, an excess 128 binary exponent; and bits ⟨6:0⟩ and ⟨31:16⟩, a normalized 24-bit fraction with the redundant most-significant fraction bit not represented. Within the fraction, bits of increasing significance go from ⟨16⟩ through ⟨31⟩ and ⟨0⟩ through ⟨6⟩. The 8-bit exponent field encodes the values 0 through 255. An exponent value of 0 together with a sign bit of 0 is taken to indicate that the F__floating datum has a value of 0. Exponent values of 1 through 255 indicate true binary exponents of -127 through $+127$. An exponent value of 0 together with a sign bit of 1 is taken as reserved. Floating-point instructions processing a reserved operand take a reserved operand fault (see Chapters 3 and 5). The value of an F__floating datum is in the approximate range $.29*10^{-38}$ through $1.7*10^{38}$. The precision of an F__floating datum is approximately one part in 2^{23}, typically 7 decimal digits.

```
31                    16 15 14        7 6            0
┌──────────────────┬─┬──────────┬──────────┐
│    fraction      │S│ exponent │ fraction │  :A
└──────────────────┴─┴──────────┴──────────┘
```

F__floating Data Type (Single Precision)

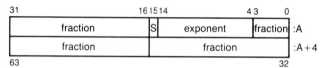

```
31                    16 15 14        7 6            0
┌──────────────────┬─┬──────────┬──────────┐
│    fraction      │S│ exponent │ fraction │  :A
├──────────────────┴─┴──────────┴──────────┤
│    fraction              fraction         │  :A+4
└───────────────────────────────────────────┘
63                                          32
```

D__floating Data Type (Double Precision)

```
31                    16 15 14         4 3          0
┌──────────────────┬─┬──────────┬──────────┐
│    fraction      │S│ exponent │ fraction │  :A
├──────────────────┴─┴──────────┴──────────┤
│    fraction              fraction         │  :A+4
└───────────────────────────────────────────┘
63                                          32
```

G__floating Data Type (Extended-Range Double Precision)

```
31                    16 15 14                       0
┌──────────────────┬─┬────────────────────┐
│    fraction      │S│      exponent       │  :A
├──────────────────┴─┴────────────────────┤
│    fraction              fraction         │  :A+4
├───────────────────────────────────────────┤
│    fraction              fraction         │  :A+8
├───────────────────────────────────────────┤
│    fraction              fraction         │  :A+12
└───────────────────────────────────────────┘
127                                         96
```

H__floating Data Type (Extended-Range Quadruple Precision)

Figure 1.2
Floating Data Types

D__floating

This data type need not be supported in a subset implementation. A D__floating datum is 8 contiguous bytes starting on an arbitrary byte boundary. The bits are labeled from the right ⟨0⟩ through ⟨63⟩, as shown in Figure 1.2. A D__floating datum is specified by its address A, the address of the byte containing bit ⟨0⟩. The form of a D__floating datum is identical to a floating datum except for an additional 32 low-significance fraction bits. Within the fraction, bits of increasing significance are from ⟨48⟩ through ⟨63⟩, ⟨32⟩ through ⟨47⟩, ⟨16⟩ through ⟨31⟩, and ⟨0⟩ through ⟨6⟩. The exponent conventions and approximate range of values is the same for D__floating as for F__floating. The precision of a D__floating datum is approximately one part in 2^{55}, typically 16 decimal digits.

G_floating

The G_floating data type need not be supported in a subset implementation. A G_floating datum is 8 contiguous bytes starting on an arbitrary byte boundary. The bits are labeled from the right ⟨0⟩ through ⟨63⟩, as shown in Figure 1.2. A G_floating datum is specified by its address A, the address of the byte containing bit ⟨0⟩. The form of a G_floating datum is sign magnitude with bit ⟨15⟩, the sign bit; bits ⟨14:4⟩, an excess 1024 binary exponent; and bits ⟨3:0⟩ and ⟨63:16⟩, a normalized 53-bit fraction with the redundant most-significant fraction bit not represented. Within the fraction, bits of increasing significance are from ⟨48⟩ through ⟨63⟩, ⟨32⟩ through ⟨47⟩, ⟨16⟩ through ⟨31⟩, and ⟨0⟩ through ⟨3⟩. The 11-bit exponent field encodes the values 0 through 2047. An exponent value of 0 together with a sign bit of 0 is taken to indicate that the G_floating datum has a value of 0. Exponent values of 1 through 2047 indicate true binary exponents of -1023 through $+1023$. An exponent value of 0 together with a sign bit of 1 is taken as reserved. Floating-point instructions processing a reserved operand take a reserved operand fault (see Chapters 3 and 5). The value of a G_floating datum is in the approximate range $.56*10^{-308}$ through $.9*10^{308}$. The precision of a G_floating datum is approximately one part in 2^{52}, typically 15 decimal digits.

H_floating

The H_floating data type need not be supported by a subset implementation. An H_floating datum is 16 contiguous bytes starting on an arbitrary byte boundary. The bits are labeled from the right ⟨0⟩ through ⟨127⟩, as shown in Figure 1.2. An H_floating datum is specified by its address A which is the address of the byte containing bit ⟨0⟩. The form of an H_floating datum is sign magnitude with bit ⟨15⟩, the sign bit; bits ⟨14:0⟩, an excess 16384 binary exponent; and bits ⟨127:16⟩, a normalized 113-bit fraction with the redundant most-significant fraction bit not represented. Within the fraction, bits of increasing significance are from ⟨112⟩ through ⟨127⟩, ⟨96⟩ through ⟨111⟩, ⟨80⟩ through ⟨95⟩, ⟨64⟩ through ⟨79⟩, ⟨48⟩ through ⟨63⟩, ⟨32⟩ through ⟨47⟩, and ⟨16⟩ through ⟨31⟩. The 15-bit exponent field encodes the values 0 through 32767. An exponent value of 0 together with a sign bit of 0 is taken to indicate that the H_floating datum has a value of 0. Exponent values of 1 through 32767 indicate true binary exponents of -16383 through $+16383$. An exponent value of 0 together with a sign bit of 1 is taken as reserved. Floating-point instructions processing a reserved operand take a reserved operand fault (see Chapters 3 and 5). The value of an H_floating datum is in the approximate range $.84*10^{-4932}$ through $.59*10^{4932}$. The precision of an H_floating datum is approximately one part in 2^{112}, typically 33 decimal digits.

Variable-Length Bit Field

A variable-length bit field is 0 to 32 contiguous bits located arbitrarily with respect to byte boundaries. A variable bit field is specified by three attributes: the address A of a byte, a bit position P which is the starting location of the field with respect to bit ⟨0⟩ of the byte at A, and a size S of the field, as shown in Figure 1.3.

For bit strings in memory, the position is in the range -2^{31} through $2^{31}-1$ and is conveniently viewed as a signed 29-bit byte offset and a 3-bit bit-within-byte field, as shown in Figure 1.3. The sign extended 29-bit byte offset is added to the address A, and the resulting address specifies the byte in which the field begins. The 3-bit bit-within-byte field encodes the starting position (0 through 7) of the field within that byte. The VAX field instructions provide direct support for the interpretation of a field as a signed or unsigned integer. When interpreted as a signed integer, it is two's complement with bits of increasing significance from 0 through S-2; bit S-1 is the sign bit. When interpreted as an unsigned integer, bits of increasing significance are from 0 to S-1. A field of size 0 has a value identically equal to 0. A variable bit field may be contained in 1 to 5 bytes. From a memory management point of view, only the minimum number of aligned longwords necessary to contain the field may be actually referenced. (See Chapter 4.)

For bit fields in registers, the position is in the range 0 through 31.

Variable-Length Bit Field Data Type in Memory

Bit Field Position

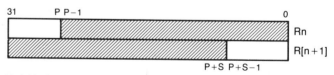

Variable-Length Bit Field Data Type across a Register Boundary

Figure 1.3
The Variable-Length Bit Field

The position operand specifies the starting position (0 through 31) of the field in the register. A variable bit field may be contained in two registers if the sum of position and size exceeds 32, as shown in Figure 1.3.

See Chapter 3 for further details on the specification of variable-length bit fields.

Absolute Queues

A queue is a circular, doubly linked list. A queue entry is specified by its address. Each queue entry is linked to the next via a pair of longwords. A queue is classified by the type of link it uses. Absolute queues use absolute addresses as links.

The first (lowest addressed) longword is the forward link; it specifies the address of the succeeding queue entry. The second (highest addressed) longword is the backward link; it specifies the address of the preceding queue entry.

A queue is specified by a queue header which is identical to a pair of queue linkage longwords. The forward link of the header is the address of the entry termed the head of the queue. The backward link of the header is the address of the entry termed the tail of the queue. The forward link of the tail points to the header.

An empty queue is specified by its header at address H, as shown in Figure 1.4. If an entry at address B is inserted into an empty queue (at either the head or tail), the second queue shown in Figure 1.4 results.

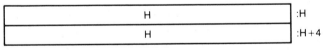

An Empty Absolute Queue

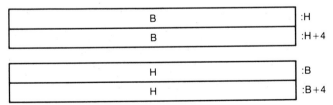

An Absolute Queue with One Entry

Figure 1.4
Absolute Queues

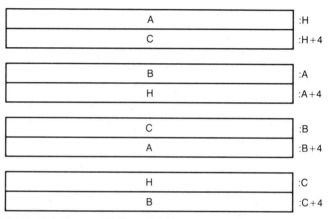

A	:H
B	:H+4

B	:A
H	:A+4

H	:B
A	:B+4

An Absolute Queue with Two Entries

A	:H
C	:H+4

B	:A
H	:A+4

C	:B
A	:B+4

H	:C
B	:C+4

An Absolute Queue with Three Entries

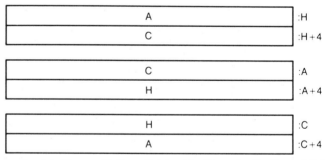

A	:H
C	:H+4

C	:A
H	:A+4

H	:C
A	:C+4

An Absolute Queue with Three Entries After Removing the Second Entry

Figure 1.4
Absolute Queues (*continued*)

The last three queues in Figure 1.4 illustrate the results of subsequent insertion of an entry at address A at the head, insertion of an entry at address C at the tail, and removal of the entry at address B.

Self-relative queues use displacements from queue entries as links. Queue entries are linked by a pair of longwords. The first longword (lowest addressed) is the forward link; it is a displacement of the succeeding queue entry from the present entry. The second longword (highest addressed) is the backward link; it is the displacement of the preceding queue entry from the present entry. A queue is specified by a queue header, which also consists of two longword links.

An empty queue is specified by its header at address H. Since the queue is empty, the self-relative links are zero, as shown in Figure 1.5. The remainder of the figure illustrates the results of subsequent insertion of an entry at address B at the head, insertion of an entry at address A at the tail, and insertion of an entry at address C at the tail.

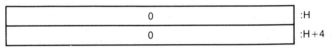

An Empty Self-Relative Queue

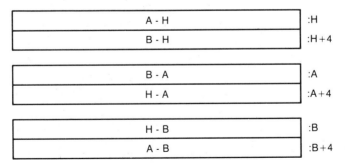

A Self-Relative Queue with One Entry

A Self-Relative Queue with Two Entries

Figure 1.5
Self-Relative Queues

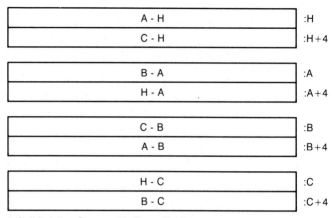

A Self-Relative Queue with Three Entries

Figure 1.5
Self-Relative Queues (*continued*)

Character String

A character string is a contiguous sequence of bytes in memory. A character string is specified by two attributes: the address A of the first byte of the string, and the length L of the string in bytes. The address of a string specifies the first character of a string. See Figure 1.6.

The length L of a string is in the range 0 through 65,535.

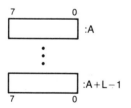

Character String "XYZ"

Character String Data Type (of Length L)

Figure 1.6
Two Attributes of the Character String

The trailing numeric string data type need not be supported in a subset implementation. A trailing numeric string is a contiguous sequence of bytes in memory. The string is specified by two attributes: the address A of the first byte (most significant digit) of the string, and the length L of the string in bytes.

All bytes of a trailing numeric string, except the least significant digit byte, must contain an ASCII decimal digit character (0 – 9). The highest addressed byte of a trailing numeric string represents an encoding of both the least significant digit and the sign of the numeric string.

The VAX numeric string instructions support any encoding. There are, however, three preferred encodings used by DIGITAL software: (1) unsigned numeric in which there is no sign and the least significant digit contains an ASCII decimal digit character, (2) zoned numeric, and (3) overpunched numeric. Because the overpunch format has been used by many compiler manufacturers over many years, and because various card encodings are used, several variations in overpunch format have evolved. Typically, these alternate forms are accepted on input; the normal form is generated as the output for all operations. The encoding of sign and digits in trailing numeric strings is shown in Table 1.1.

The length L of a trailing numeric string must be in the range 0 to 31 (0 to 31 digits). The value of a 0 length string is identically 0.

The address A of the string specifies the byte of the string containing the most significant digit. Digits of decreasing significance are assigned to increasing addresses. Figure 1.7 illustrates the representation of trailing numeric strings.

Table 1.1
Representation of Sign and Digits in Decimal String Data Types

	Zoned Trailing Numeric		Overpunch Trailing Numeric		Leading Separate Numeric		Packed Decimal
	Hex	ASCII	Hex	ASCII	Hex	ASCII	Hex
Sign							
positive					2B	+	A
positive*					20	⟨blank⟩	C E F
negative					2D	–	B
negative*							D

*These alternative representations of the sign are permitted. VAX instructions always produce the preferred representation, which is shown first.

Table 1.1

Representation of Sign and Digits in Decimal String Data Types (*continued*)

	Zoned Trailing Numeric		Overpunch Trailing Numeric		Leading Separate Numeric		Packed Decimal
	Hex	ASCII	Hex	ASCII	Hex	ASCII	Hex
Digit							
0	30	0	30	0	30	0	0
1	31	1	31	1	31	1	1
2	32	2	32	2	32	2	2
3	33	3	33	3	33	3	3
4	34	4	34	4	34	4	4
5	35	5	35	5	35	5	5
6	36	6	36	6	36	6	6
7	37	7	37	7	37	7	7
8	38	8	38	8	38	8	8
9	39	9	39	9	39	9	9
Combined Sign and Digit							
+0	30	0	7B	{			
+1	31	1	41	A			
+2	32	2	42	B			
+3	33	3	43	C			
+4	34	4	44	D			
+5	35	5	45	E			
+6	36	6	46	F			
+7	37	7	47	G			
+8	38	8	48	H			
+9	39	9	49	I			
−0	70	p	7D	}			
−1	71	g	4A	J			
−2	72	r	4B	K			
−3	73	s	4C	L			
−4	74	t	4D	M			
−5	75	u	4E	N			
−6	76	v	4F	O			
−7	77	w	50	P			
−8	78	x	51	Q			
−9	79	y	52	R			

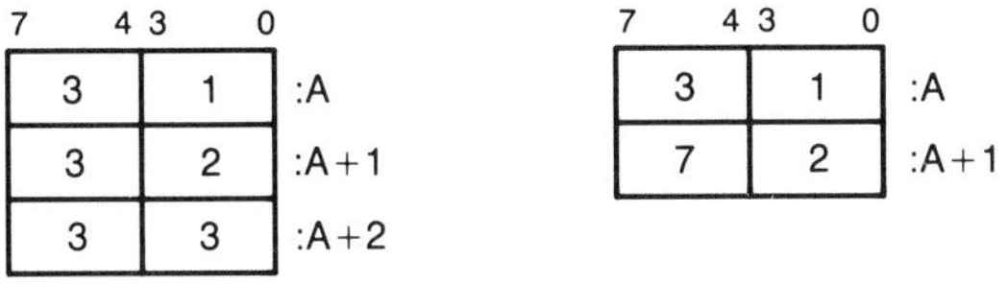

7	4 3	0	
3		1	:A
3		2	:A+1
3		3	:A+2

7	4 3	0	
3		1	:A
7		2	:A+1

Representation of "+123" and "-12" in Zoned Format

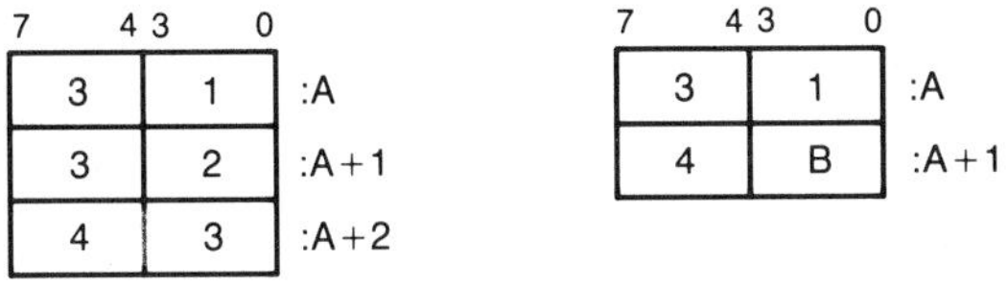

7	4 3	0	
3		1	:A
3		2	:A+1
4		3	:A+2

7	4 3	0	
3		1	:A
4		B	:A+1

Representation of "+123" and "-12" in Overpunch Format

Figure 1.7
Representations of Trailing Numeric Strings

Leading Separate Numeric String

The leading separate numeric string data type need not be supported in a subset implementation. A leading separate numeric string is a contiguous sequence of bytes in memory. A leading separate numeric string is specified by two attributes: the address A of the first byte (containing the sign character); and a length L, which is the length of the string in digits and not the length of the string in bytes. The number of bytes in a leading separate numeric string is L + 1.

The sign of a separate leading numeric string is stored in a separate byte. Each subsequent byte contains an ASCII digit character. The signs and digits of separate leading numeric strings are shown in Table 1.1.

The length L of a leading separate numeric string must be in the range 0 to 31 (0 to 31 digits). The value of a 0 length string is identically 0.

The address A of the string specifies the byte of the string containing the sign. Digits of decreasing significance are assigned to bytes of increasing addresses. Figure 1.8 illustrates leading separate numeric strings.

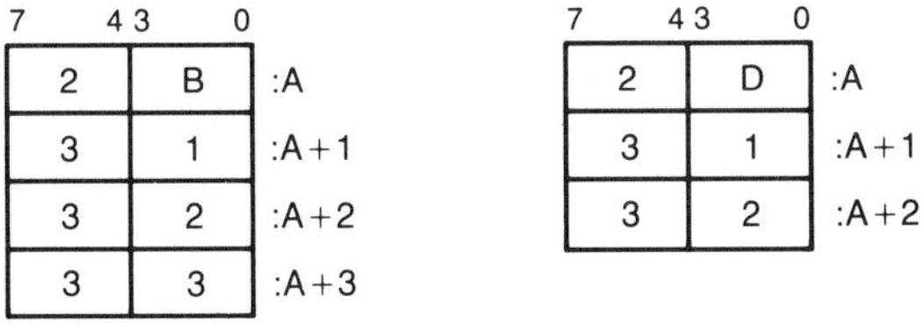

7	4 3	0	
2		B	:A
3		1	:A+1
3		2	:A+2
3		3	:A+3

7	4 3	0	
2		D	:A
3		1	:A+1
3		2	:A+2

Figure 1.8
Representation of "+123" and "-12" in Leading Separate Numeric String

Basic Architecture

17

```
7   4 3   0                    7   4 3   0
┌─────┬─────┐                  ┌─────┬─────┐
│  1  │  2  │ :A               │  0  │  1  │ :A
├─────┼─────┤                  ├─────┼─────┤
│  3  │ 12  │ :A+1             │  2  │ 13  │ :A+1
└─────┴─────┘                  └─────┴─────┘
```

Figure 1.9
Representation of "123" and "−12" in Packed Decimal String

Packed Decimal String

The packed decimal string data type need not be supported in a subset implementation. A packed decimal string is a contiguous sequence of bytes in memory. A packed decimal string is specified by two attributes: the address A of the first byte of the string; and a length L, which is the number of digits in the string and not the length of the string in bytes. The bytes of a packed decimal string are divided into two, 4-bit fields that must contain decimal digits, with the exception of the low nibble (bits $\langle 3:0 \rangle$) of the last (highest addressed) byte that must contain a sign.

The preferred sign representation is 12 for positive and 13 for negative, as shown in Table 1.1.

The length L is the number of digits in the packed decimal string (not counting the sign) and must be in the range 0 through 31. When the number of digits is odd, the digits and the sign fit in L/2 (integer part only) + 1 bytes. When the number of digits is even, it is required that an extra 0 digit appear in the high nibble (bits $\langle 7:4 \rangle$) of the first byte of the string. Again, the length in bytes of the string is L/2 + 1.

The address A of the string specifies the byte of the string containing the most significant digit in its high nibble. Digits of decreasing significance are assigned to increasing byte addresses and from high nibble to low nibble within a byte. Figure 1.9 illustrates packed decimal strings.

PROCESSOR STATE

The processor state consists of that portion of a process's state that, while the process is executing, is stored in processor registers rather than memory. The processor state includes

1. Sixteen 32-bit general-purpose registers denoted Rn or R[n], where n is in the range 0 through 15
2. A 32-bit processor status longword (PSL)
3. Privileged internal processor registers (IPR).

The general-purpose registers are used for temporary storage, accumulators, index registers, and base registers. A register containing an address is termed a base register. A register containing an address offset is termed an index register. (Regarding a register containing an address offset in multiples of operand size, see Chapter 2.) The bits of a register are numbered from the right ⟨0⟩ through ⟨31⟩, as shown in Figure 1.10.

Certain of the registers are assigned special meaning by the VAX architecture:

- R15 is the program counter (PC). PC contains the address of the next instruction byte of the program.

- R14 is the stack pointer (SP). SP contains the address of the top of the processor-defined stack.

- R13 is the current frame pointer (FP). The VAX procedure call convention builds a data structure on the stack called a stack frame. FP contains the address of the base of this data structure. (For more information about the VAX procedure call convention, see *VAX/VMS Run Time Library Reference Manual.*)

```
31                                                    0
┌──────────────────────────────────────────────────┐
│                                                    │ :Rn
└──────────────────────────────────────────────────┘
```
General-Purpose Register

```
31                                                    0
┌──────────────────────────────────────────────────┐
│                                                    │ :IPR n
└──────────────────────────────────────────────────┘
```
Internal Processor Register

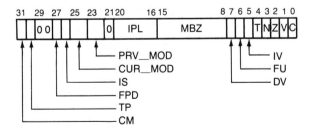

Processor Status Longword

Figure 1.10
The Processor State

- R12 is the argument pointer (AP). The VAX procedure call convention uses a data structure termed an argument list. AP contains the address of the base of this data structure.

Note that these registers are all used as base registers. The assignment of special meaning to these registers does not generally preclude their use for other purposes. As will be seen in Chapter 2, however, PC cannot be used as an accumulator, temporary, or index register. When a datum of type byte, word, longword, or F_floating is stored in a register, the bit numbering in the register corresponds to the numbering in memory. Hence a byte is stored in register bits ⟨7:0⟩, a word in register bits ⟨15:0⟩, and a longword or F_floating in register bits ⟨31:0⟩. A byte or word written to a register writes only bits ⟨7:0⟩ and ⟨15:0⟩, respectively; the other bits are unaffected. A byte or word read from a register reads only bits ⟨7:0⟩ and ⟨15:0⟩, respectively; the other bits are ignored.

When a quadword, D_floating, or G_floating datum is stored in a register R[n], it is actually stored in two adjacent registers R[n] and R[n+1]. Because of restrictions on the specification of PC (see Chapter 2), wraparound from PC to R0 and from SP to PC is UNPREDICTABLE. Bits ⟨31:0⟩ of the datum are stored in bits ⟨31:0⟩ of register R[n], and bits ⟨63:32⟩ of the datum are stored in bits ⟨31:0⟩ of register R[n+1].

When an octaword or H_floating datum is stored in register R[n], it is actually stored in adjacent registers R[n], R[n+1], R[n+2], and R[n+3]. Because of restrictions on the specification of PC (see Chapter 2), wraparound from PC to R0 and from AP, FP, and SP to PC is UNPREDICTABLE. Bits ⟨31:0⟩ of the datum are stored in bits ⟨31:0⟩ of register R[n], bits ⟨63:32⟩ in bits ⟨31:0⟩ of register R[n+1], bits ⟨95:64⟩ in bits ⟨31:0⟩ of register R[n+2], and bits ⟨127:96⟩ in bits ⟨31:0⟩ of register R[n+3].

A variable-length bit field may be specified in the registers with the restriction that the starting bit position P must be in the range 0 through 31. See Figure 1.3. As for quadword, D_floating, and G_floating, a pair of registers R[n] and R[n+1] is treated as a 64-bit register with bits ⟨31:0⟩ in register R[n] and bit ⟨63:32⟩ in register R[n+1].

None of the string data types stored in registers can be processed by the VAX string instructions. Therefore, there is no architectural specification of the representation of strings in registers.

Processor Status Longword

The processor status longword (PSL) is a longword consisting of a word of privileged processor status concatenated with the processor status word (PSW), as shown in Figure 1.10. The processor status word (PSW) contains the condition codes that give information on the results produced by previous instructions and the exception-enable bits which control the processor action on certain exception conditions (see Chapter 5). The condition codes are UNPREDICTABLE when they are affected by UNPREDICTABLE results. The VAX procedure call instructions conditionally set the IV and DV bits, clear the FU bit, and leave the T bit unchanged at procedure entry (see Chapter 3). See Table 1.2 for processor status longword descriptions.

Table 1.2
Processor Status Longword Fields

Extent	Name	Mnemonic	Meaning
31⟩	Compatibility Mode	CM	When set, the processor in in PDP-11 compatibility mode (see Chapter 9). When CM is clear, the processor is in native mode. Compatibility mode may be omitted from subset implementations of the VAX architecture. In a processor that does not implement compatibility mode, this bit is always clear.
30⟩	Trace Pending	TP	Forces a trace fault when set at the beginning of any instruction. Set by the processor if T is set at the beginning of an instruction.
29:28⟩	Reserved		Reserved to DIGITAL; must be 0.
27⟩	First Part Done	FPD	When set, execution of the instruction addressed by PC cannot simply be started at the beginning and must be restarted at some other implementation-dependent point in its operation. If FPD is set and the exception or interrupt service routine modifies FPD, the general registers, or the saved PSL (except for T or TP), the results of the restarted instruction's execution are UNPREDICTABLE. If a routine sets FPD, the results are also UNPREDICTABLE. However, if software is simulating unimplemented instructions, it may make free use of FPD in its simulation. If the hardware encounters a reserved instruction with FPD set, a reserved instruction fault is taken with the saved PSL⟨FPD⟩ set.
26⟩	Interrupt Stack	IS	When set, the processor is executing on the interrupt stack. Any mechanism that sets IS also clears current mode and raises IPL above 0. If an REI attempts to restore a PSL with IS = 1 and non-zero current mode or zero IPL, a reserved operand fault is taken. When clear, the processor is executing on the stack specified by current mode.
25:24⟩	Current Access Mode	CUR_MOD	The access mode of the currently executing process. 0 Kernel 1 Executive 2 Supervisor 3 User

Table 1.2

Processor Status Longword Fields (*continued*)

Extent	Name	Mnemonic	Meaning
⟨22:23⟩	Previous Access Mode	PRV_MOD	Loaded from current mode by exceptions and CHMx instructions, cleared by interrupts, and restored by REI (see Chapter 5).
⟨21⟩	Reserved		Reserved to DIGITAL; must be zero.
⟨20:16⟩	Interrupt Priority Level	IPL	The current processor priority, in the range 0 to 1F (hex). The processor will accept interrupts only on levels greater than the current level.
⟨15:8⟩	Reserved		Reserved to DIGITAL; must be 0.
⟨7⟩	Decimal Overflow enable	DV	When set, forces a decimal overflow trap after execution of an instruction that produced an overflowed decimal result (no room to store a non-zero digit) or had a conversion error. When DV is clear, no trap occurs. (However, the condition code V bit is still set.)
⟨6⟩	Floating Underflow enable	FU	When set, forces a floating underflow exception after execution of an instruction that produced an underflowed result. When FU is clear, no exception occurs.
⟨5⟩	Integer Overflow enable	IV	When set, forces an integer overflow trap after execution of an instruction that produced an integer result that overflowed or had a conversion error. When IV is clear, no integer overflow trap occurs. (However, the condition code V bit is still set.)
⟨4⟩	Trace enable	T	When set at the beginning of an instruction, causes TP to be set. Most programs should treat T as UNPREDICTABLE because it is set by debuggers and trace programs for tracing and for proceeding from a breakpoint. See Chapter 5 for how to use tracing.
⟨3⟩	Negative	N	When set, indicates that the last instruction that affected N produced a result that was negative. When N is clear, the result was positive or 0.
⟨2⟩	Zero	Z	When set, indicates that the last instruction that affected Z produced a result that was 0. When Z is clear, the result was non-zero.
⟨1⟩	Overflow	V	When set, indicates that the last instruction that affected V produced a result whose magnitude was too large to be represented properly in the operand that received the result or there was a conversion error. When V is clear, there was no overflow or conversion error.
⟨0⟩	Carry	C	When set, indicates that the last instruction that affected C had a carry out of the most significant bit of the result or a borrow into the most significant bit. When C is clear, there was no carry or borrow.

The PSL is automatically saved on the stack when an exception or
interrupt occurs and is saved in the process control block on a
process context switch (see Chapter 6). The PSL can also be read by
the MOVPSL instruction (see Chapter 3).

Bits ⟨31:16⟩ of the PSL can be changed explicitly only by executing a
return from exception or interrupt instruction (REI). Bits ⟨20:16⟩ can
also be changed by a move-to-processor-register instruction (MTPR)
to the IPL processor register. For more details, see Chapter 5.
Processor initialization sets the PSL to 041F0000, hex.

Internal Processor Registers

The privileged internal processor register space provides access to
many types of CPU control and status registers such as the memory
management base registers, parts of the PSL, and the multiple
stack pointers. These registers are explicitly accessible only by the
Move to Processor Register (MTPR) and Move from Processor
Register (MFPR) instructions which require kernel mode privileges.
Internal processor registers are longword size, as shown in Figure
1.10. For details, see Chapter 8.

Instruction Formats and Addressing Modes

2

The VAX architecture has a variable-length instruction format. An instruction specifies an operation and 0 to 6 operands. An operand specifier determines how an operand is accessed. An operand specifier consists of an addressing mode specifier and, if needed, a specifier extension, immediate data, or an address, as shown in Figure 2.1. The format of an instruction is:

opcode

adressing mode specifier 1

specifier extension, address, or immediate data 1 (if needed)

addressing mode specifier 2

.
.
.

addressing mode specifier n

specifier extension, address, or immediate data n (if needed)

```
            8 7               0
| specifier extension, if any | addressing |
|                             |    mode    |
```
Operand Specifier

```
        7          0
      |   opcode   |
```
Single-Byte Opcode

```
   15        8 7        0
  |  opcode  | FC - FF  |
```
Double-Byte Opcode

Figure 2.1
Opcodes and Operand Specifiers

OPCODE FORMATS

An instruction is specified by the byte address A of its opcode, as shown in Figure 2.1. The opcode may extend over 2 bytes; the length depends on the contents of the byte at address A. Only if the value of the byte is FC (hex) through FF (hex) is the opcode 2 bytes long, as shown in the last diagram in Figure 2.1.

OPERAND SPECIFIERS

Each instruction takes a specific sequence of operand specifier types. An operand specifier type conceptually has two attributes: the access type and the data type.

The access types include:

- Read—the specified operand is read only.
- Write—the specified operand is written only.
- Modify—the specified operand is read, potentially modified, and written. This is not done under a memory interlock.
- Address—the address of the specified operand in the form of a longword is the actual instruction operand. The specified operand is not accessed directly although the instruction may subsequently use the address to access that operand.
- Variable-length bit field base address—this is the same as address access type except for register mode. In register mode, the field is contained in register n designated by the operand specifier (or register n + 1 concatenated with register n). This access type is a special variant of the address access type.
- Branch—no operand is accessed. The operand specifier itself is a branch displacement.

The first five types are termed general mode addressing. The last type is termed branch mode addressing.

The data types include:

Byte

Word

Longword

F_floating

Quadword

D_floating

G_floating

Octaword

H_floating

For the address and branch access types that do not directly reference operands, the data type indicates:

- Address—the operand size to be used in the address calculation in autoincrement, autodecrement, and index modes
- Branch—the size of the branch displacement.

NOTATION

To describe the addressing modes, the following notation is used:

+	addition
−	subtraction
*	multiplication
←	is replaced by
=	is defined as
'	concatenation
Rn or R[n]	The contents of register n
PC or SP	the contents of register 15 or 14 respectively
(x)	the contents of memory location x
{ }	arithmetic parentheses for indicating precedence
SEXT(x)	x is sign extended to size of operand needed
ZEXT(x)	x is zero extended to size of operand needed
OA	operand address
!	comment delimiter

Each general mode addressing description includes the definition of the operand address and the specified operand. For operand specifiers of address access type, the operand address is the actual instruction operand; for other access types, the specified operand is the instruction operand. The branch mode addressing description includes the definition of the branch address.

GENERAL MODE ADDRESSING FORMATS

Except for literal mode, an operand specifier in the general mode addressing format consists of a register number in bits ⟨3:0⟩ and an addressing mode specifier in bits ⟨7:4⟩. The operand specifier could possibly be followed by a specifier extension, as shown in Figure 2.1.

For a summary of general register addressing, see Table 2.1.

Table 2.1
Summary of General Register Addressing

Addressing Mode	Assembler Notation	Decimal	Hexadecimal	r	m	w	a	v	PC	SP	AP & FP	Index-able
General Register Addressing Mode												
literal	S^#literal	0–3	0–3	y	f	f	f	f				f
indexed	base[Rx]	4	4	y	y	y	y	f		y	y	f
register	Rn	5	5	y	y	f	f	y	u	uq	uo	f
register deferred	(Rn)	6	6	y	y	y	y	y	u	y	y	y
autodecrement	–(Rn)	7	7	y	y	y	y	y	u	y	y	ux
autoincrement	(Rn)+	8	8	y	y	y	y	y	u	y	y	ux
autoincrement deferred	@(Rn)+	9	9	y	y	y	y	y	p	y	y	ux
byte displacement	B^displacement(Rn)	10	A	y	y	y	y	y	p	y	y	y
byte displacement deferred	@B^displacement(Rn)	11	B	y	y	y	y	y	p	y	y	y
word displacement	W^displacement(Rn)	12	C	y	y	y	y	y	p	y	y	y
word displacement deferred	@W^displacement(Rn)	13	D	y	y	y	y	y	p	y	y	y
longword displacement	L^displacement (Rn)	14	E	y	y	y	y	y	p	y	y	y
longword displacement deferred	@L^displacement(Rn)	15	F	y	y	y	y	y	p	y	y	y
Program Counter Addressing Mode												
immediate	I^#constant	8	8	y	u	u	y	y				u
absolute	@#address	9	9	y	y	y	y	y				y
byte relative	B^address	10	A	y	y	y	y	y				y

byte relative deferred	@B^address	11	B	y y y y y	y
word relative	W^address	12	C	y y y y y	y
word relative deferred	@W^address	13	D	y y y y y	y
longword relative	L^address	14	E	y y y y y	y
longword relative deferred	@L^address	15	F	y y y y y	y

Key:
base any indexable addressing mode
f reserved addressing mode fault
p Program Counter addressing
u UNPREDICTABLE
uq UNPREDICTABLE for quadword, octaword, D_floating, G_floating, and H_floating (and field if position + size greater than 32)
uo UNPREDICTABLE for octaword and H_floating
ux UNPREDICTABLE for index register same as base register
y yes, always valid addressing mode
r read access
m modify access
w write access
a address access
v field access

Register Mode The register mode operand specifier format is shown in Figure 2.2. No specifier extension follows. In register mode addressing, the operand is the contents of register n (or register n+1 concatenated with register n for quadword, D_floating, G_floating, and certain field operands). The format is as follows:

```
operand = Rn                          ! if one register

          or
          R[n+1]'Rn                   ! if two registers

          or
          R[n+3]'R[n+2]'R[n+1]'Rn   ! if four register
```

```
7    4 3   0
┌─────┬─────┐
│  5  │ reg │
└─────┴─────┘
```

Register

```
7    4 3   0
┌─────┬─────┐
│  6  │ reg │
└─────┴─────┘
```

Register Deferred

```
7    4 3   0
┌─────┬─────┐
│  7  │ reg │
└─────┴─────┘
```

Autodecrement

```
7    4 3   0
┌─────┬─────┐
│  8  │ reg │
└─────┴─────┘
```

Autoincrement

```
              8 7    4 3   0
┌──────────────────┬─────┬─────┐
│  immediate data  │  8  │  F  │
└──────────────────┴─────┴─────┘
```

Immediate Address Mode Specifier and Extension

```
7    4 3   0
┌─────┬─────┐
│  9  │ reg │
└─────┴─────┘
```

Autoincrement Deferred

```
39                                          8 7   4 3   0
+-------------------------------------------+-----+-----+
|          absolute address of data         |  9  |  F  |
+-------------------------------------------+-----+-----+
```
Absolute Address Mode Specifier and Extension


```
                    15          8 7   4 3   0
                    +-----------+-----+-----+
                    | byte displ|  A  | reg |
                    +-----------+-----+-----+
```
Byte Displacement Address Mode Specifier and Extension


```
             23                 8 7   4 3   0
             +------------------+-----+-----+
             | word displacement|  B  | reg |
             +------------------+-----+-----+
```
Word Displacement Address Mode Specifier and Extension


```
39                                    8 7   4 3   0
+-------------------------------------+-----+-----+
|        longword displacement        |  C  | reg |
+-------------------------------------+-----+-----+
```
Longword Displacement Address Mode Specifier and Extension


```
                    15          8 7   4 3   0
                    +-----------+-----+-----+
                    | byte displ|  D  | reg |
                    +-----------+-----+-----+
```
Byte Displacement Deferred Address Mode Specifier and Extension


```
             23                 8 7   4 3   0
             +------------------+-----+-----+
             | word displacement|  E  | reg |
             +------------------+-----+-----+
```
Word Displacement Deferred Address Mode Specifier and Extension


```
39                                    8 7   4 3   0
+-------------------------------------+-----+-----+
|        longword displacement        |  F  | reg |
+-------------------------------------+-----+-----+
```
Longword Displacement Deferred Address Mode Specifier and Extension

Figure 2.2
Addressing Mode Specifiers

Because registers do not have memory addresses, the operand address is not defined and register mode may not be used for operand specifiers of address access type (except in the case of the base address for variable bit field instructions, see Chapter 3). If register mode is so used, an illegal addressing mode fault results (see Chapter 5). PC may not be used in register mode addressing. If PC is read, the value read is UNPREDICTABLE. If PC is written, the next instruction executed or the next operand specified is UNPREDICTABLE. Likewise, SP may not be used in register mode addressing for an operand that takes two adjacent registers. Again, if it is used, the results are UNPREDICTABLE in the same fashion. If PC is used in register mode for a write access type operand that takes two adjacent registers, the contents of R0 are UNPREDICTABLE. If R12, R13, SP, or PC are used in register mode addressing for an operand that takes four adjacent registers, the results are UNPREDICTABLE. If PC is used in register mode for a write access type operand that requires four adjacent registers, the contents of R0, R1, and R2 are UNPREDICTABLE. Likewise, if R13 is used in register mode for a write access type operand that takes four adjacent registers, the contents of R0 are UNPREDICTABLE; and, if SP is used in register mode for a write access type operand which takes four adjacent registers, the contents of R0 and R1 are UNPREDICTABLE.

The assembler notation for register mode is Rn.

Register Deferred Mode

The register deferred mode operand specifier format is shown in Figure 2.2. No specifier extension follows. In register deferred mode addressing, the address of the operand is the contents of register n:

```
OA = Rn
operand = (OA)
```

PC should not be used in register deferred mode addressing. If PC is used, the address of the operand (and whether the operand is written if it is of modify or write access type) is UNPREDICTABLE.

The assembler notation for register deferred mode is (Rn).

Autoincrement Mode

The autoincrement mode operand specifier format is shown in Figure 2.2. No specifier extension follows. If Rn denotes PC, immediate data follows, and the mode is termed immediate mode, as the figure shows. In autoincrement mode addressing, the address of the operand is the contents of register n. After the operand address is determined, the size of the operand in bytes (1 for byte, 2 for word, 4 for longword and F__floating, 8 for quadword, G__floating and D__floating, and 16 for octaword and H__floating) is added to the

contents of register n. The contents of register n is then replaced by
the result:

```
OA = Rn
Rn ← Rn + size
operand = (OA)
```

Immediate mode may not be used for operands of modify or write
access type. If immediate mode is used for an operand of modify
access type, the value of the data read is UNPREDICTABLE. If
immediate mode is used for an operand of modify or write access
type, the address at which the operand is written (and whether it is
written) is UNPREDICTABLE.

The assembler notation for autoincrement mode is (Rn)+. For
immediate mode, the notation is I^#constant where constant is the
immediate data that follows.

Autoincrement Deferred Mode

The autoincrement deferred mode operand specifier format is shown
in Figure 2.2. No specifier extension follows. If Rn denotes PC, a
longword address follows, and the mode is termed absolute mode. In
autoincrement deferred mode addressing, the address of the operand
is the contents of a longword whose address is the contents of
register n. After the operand address is determined, 4 (the size in
bytes of a longword address) is added to the contents of register n
and the contents of register n is replaced by the result:

```
OA = (Rn)
Rn ← Rn + 4
operand = (OA)
```

The assembler notation autoincrement deferred mode is @(Rn)+.
The notation for absolute mode is @#address, where address is the
longword that follows.

Autodecrement Mode

The autodecrement mode operand specifier format is shown in Figure
2.2. No specifier extension follows. In autodecrement mode addressing, the size of the operand in bytes (1 for byte; 2 for word;
4 for longword or F_floating; 8 for quadword, G_floating, or
D_floating; and 16 for octaword or H_floating) is subtracted from the
contents of register n. The contents of register n are then replaced
by the result. The updated contents of register n is the address of the
operand:

```
Rn ← Rn − size
OA = Rn
operand = (OA)
```

PC should not be used in autodecrement mode. If it is used, the address of the operand (and whether the operand is written if it is of modify or write access type) is UNPREDICTABLE; the next instruction executed or the next operand specified is UNPREDICTABLE.

The assembler notation for autodecrement mode is $-(Rn)$.

Displacement Mode

There are three displacement mode operand specifier formats, all illustrated in Figure 2.2. They are termed byte displacement mode, word displacement mode, and longword displacement mode. In each, the specifier extension is a signed displacement.

In displacement mode addressing, the displacement (after being sign extended to 32 bits if it is byte or word) is added to the contents of register n. The result is the operand address:

```
OA = Rn + SEXT(displ)  ! if byte or word displacement
     or
     Rn + displ        ! if longword displacement
operand = (OA)
```

If Rn denotes PC, the mode is termed PC relative addressing mode. The updated contents of PC (the address of the first byte beyond the specifier extension) is used as the base address.

The assembler notation for byte, word, and longword displacement mode is B^D(Rn), W^D(Rn), and L^D(Rn) respectively, where D = displ.

Displacement Deferred Mode

The three displacement deferred mode operand specifier formats are termed byte displacement deferred mode, word displacement deferred mode, and longword displacement deferred mode. In each, the specifier extension is a signed displacement. See Figure 2.2.

In displacement deferred mode addressing, the displacement (after being sign extended to 32 bits if it is byte or word) is added to the contents of register n. The result is the address of a longword whose contents is the operand address:

```
OA = (Rn + SEXT(displ))  ! if byte or word displacement
     or
     (Rn + displ)        ! if longword displacement
operand = (OA)
```

If Rn notes PC, the mode is termed PC relative deferred addressing mode. The updated contents of PC (the address of the first byte beyond the specifier extension) is used as the base address.

The assembler notation for byte, word, and longword displacement deferred mode is @B^D(Rn), @W^D(Rn), and @L^D(Rn) respectively, where D = displ.

Literal Mode

The literal mode operand specifier format is shown in Figure 2.3. No specifier extension follows. For operands of data type byte, word, longword, quadword, and octaword, the operand is the zero extension of the 6-bit literal field:

operand = ZEXT(literal)

Thus for these data types, literal mode may be used for values in the range 0 through 63.

For operands of data type F_floating, D_floating, G_floating, and H_floating, the 6-bit literal field is composed of two 3-bit fields as shown in Figure 2.3. The exp and fra fields are used to form an F_floating, D_floating, G_floating, or H_floating operand as shown in Figure 2.4. The values that can be expressed by a floating-point literal are shown in Table 2.2.

Because there is no operand address, literal mode addressing may not be used for operand specifiers of address access type. Also, literal mode addressing may not be used for operand specifiers of write or modify access type. If literal mode is used for operand specifiers of either address, modify, or write access type, an illegal addressing mode fault results (see Chapter 5).

Literal mode addressing is a very efficient way of specifying integer values in the range 0 to 63 or the floating-point values shown in Table 2.2. Literal values outside the indicated range may be obtained by using immediate mode.

The assembler notation for literal mode is S^#literal.

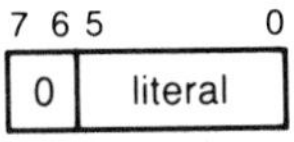

```
7 6 5          0
+--+-----------+
| 0|  literal  |
+--+-----------+
```

Literal Address Mode Specifier

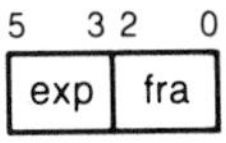

```
5    3 2   0
+-----+-----+
| exp | fra |
+-----+-----+
```

Representation of a Floating-Point Number as a Literal

Figure 2.3
Literal Address Mode Specifier and Representation of a
Floating-Point Number as a Literal

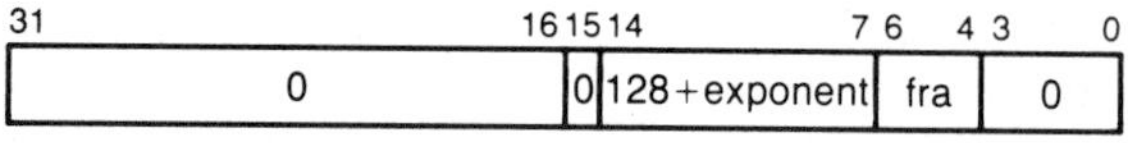

As an F__floating Number

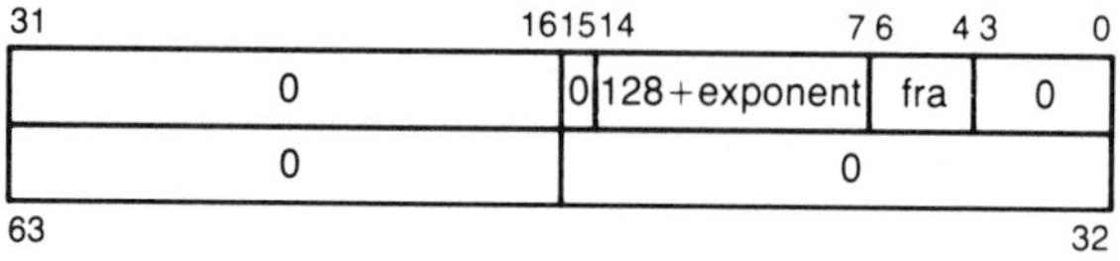

Bit positions: 31 ... 16 15 14 ... 7 6 4 3 0

| 0 | 0 | 128+exponent | fra | 0 |

As a D__floating Number

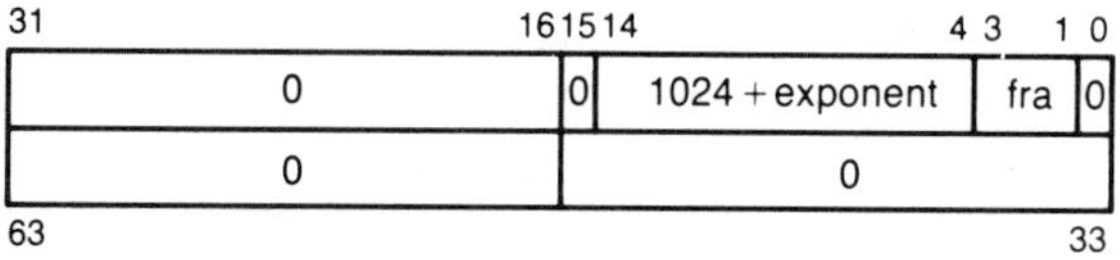

Bit positions: 31 ... 16 15 14 ... 7 6 4 3 0; second longword 63 ... 32

| 0 | 0 | 128+exponent | fra | 0 |
| 0 | | | | |

As a G__floating Number

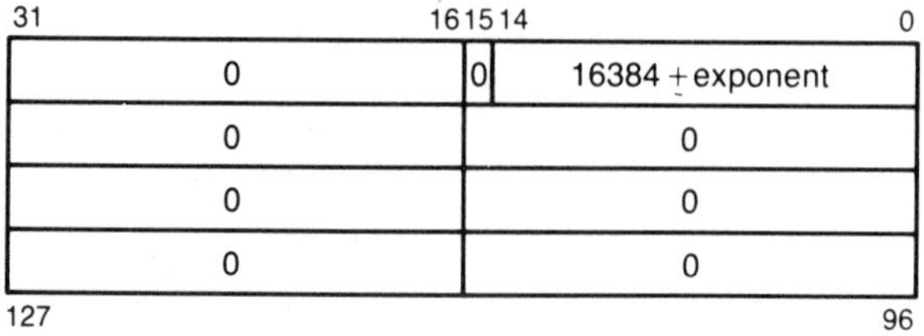

Bit positions: 31 ... 16 15 14 ... 4 3 1 0; second longword 63 ... 33

| 0 | 0 | 1024+exponent | fra | 0 |
| 0 | | | | |

As an H__floating Number

Bit positions: 31 ... 16 15 14 ... 0; last longword 127 ... 96

0	0	16384 ± exponent
0		0
0		0
0		0

Figure 2.4
Interpretation of a Literal

Table 2.2
Floating-Point Values Representable as Literals

Exponent	Fraction							
	0	1	2	3	4	5	6	7
0	$1/2$	$9/16$	$5/8$	$11/16$	$3/4$	$13/16$	$7/8$	$15/16$
1	1	$1 1/8$	$1 1/4$	$1 3/8$	$1 1/2$	$1 5/8$	$1 3/4$	$1 7/8$
2	2	$2 1/4$	$2 1/2$	$2 3/4$	3	$3 1/4$	$3 1/2$	$3 3/4$
3	4	$4 1/2$	5	$5 1/2$	6	$6 1/2$	7	$7 1/2$
4	8	9	10	11	12	13	14	15
5	16	18	20	22	24	26	28	30
6	32	36	40	44	48	52	56	60
7	64	72	80	88	96	104	112	120

Index Mode

The index mode operand specifier format is shown in Figure 2.5. Bits ⟨15:8⟩ contain a second operand specifier (termed the base operand specifier) for any of the addressing modes except register, literal, or index. The specification of register indexed, literal indexed, immediate indexed, or index indexed addressing mode results in an illegal addressing mode fault (see Chapter 5). If the base operand specifier requires a specifier extension, it immediately follows. The base operand specifier is subject to the same restrictions as would apply if it were used alone. If the use of some particular specifier is illegal (causes a fault or UNPREDICTABLE behavior) under some circumstances, then that specifier is similarly illegal as a base operand specifier in index mode under the same circumstances.

The operand to be specified by index mode addressing is termed the primary operand. The base operand specifier normally is used to determine an operand address. This address is termed the base operand address (BOA). The address of the primary operand specified is determined by multiplying the contents of the index register x by the size of the primary operand in bytes (1 for byte; 2 for word; 4 for longword or F_floating; 8 for quadword, D_floating or G_floating; and 16 for octaword and H_floating), adding BOA, and taking the result:

OA = BOA + {size * (Rx)}

operand = (OA)

If the base operand specifier is for autoincrement or autodecrement mode, the increment or decrement size is the size in bytes of the primary operand.

Indexed mode addressing permits very general and efficient accessing of arrays. The base address of the array is determined by the operand address calculation of the base operand specifier. The contents of the index register is taken as a logical index into the array. The logical index is converted into a real (byte) offset by multiplying the contents of the index register by the size of the primary operand in bytes.

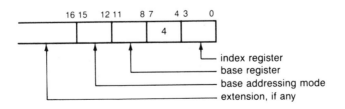

Figure 2.5
Indexed Address Mode Specifier and Extension

Certain restrictions are placed on the index register x. PC cannot be used as an index register. If PC is used, a reserved addressing mode fault occurs (see Chapter 5). If the base operand specifier is for an addressing mode that results in register modification (autoincrement mode, autodecrement mode, or autoincrement deferred mode), the same register cannot be the index register. If it is, the primary operand address is UNPREDICTABLE.

The names of the addressing modes resulting from indexed mode addressing are formed by appending the word "indexed" to the addressing mode of the base operand specifier. Following are the names and assembler notation. The index register is designated Rx to distinguish it from the register Rn in the base operand specifier.

- Register deferred indexed, (Rn)[Rx]
- Autoincrement indexed, (Rn)+[Rx]
- Autoincrement deferred indexed, @(Rn)+[Rx] or absolute indexed, @#address[Rx]
- Autodecrement indexed, −(Rn)[Rx]
- Byte, word, or longword displacement indexed, B^D(Rn)[Rx], W^D(Rn)[Rx], or L^D(Rn)[Rx]
- Byte, word, or longword displacement deferred indexed, @B^D(Rn)[Rx], @W^D(Rn)[Rx], or @L^D(Rn)[Rx]

BRANCH MODE ADDRESSING FORMATS

The two operand specifier formats are shown in Figure 2.6. In branch mode addressing, the byte or word displacement is sign extended to 32 bits and added to the updated contents of PC. The updated contents of PC is the address of the first byte beyond the operand specifier. The result is the branch address A:

```
A = PC + SEXT(displ)
```

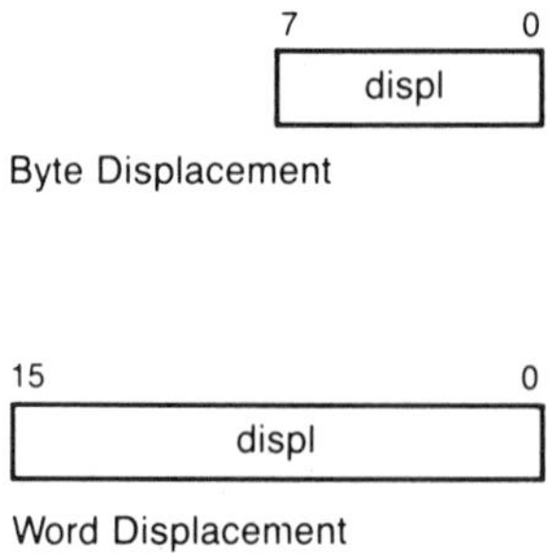

7   0
| displ |

Byte Displacement

15   0
| displ |

Word Displacement

Figure 2.6
Two Branch Mode Addressing Operand Specifier Formats

The assembler notation for byte and word branch mode addressing is A, where A is the branch address. Note that the branch address and not the displacement is used.

INSTRUCTION INTERPRE-TATION

The processor in interpreting an instruction performs the following three steps:

1. Reads and evaluates each operand specifier in order of instruction stream occurrence as follows:

   a. If access type is read: evaluates the operand address, reads the operand, and saves it.

   b. If access type is write: evaluates the operand address and saves it.

   c. If access type is modify: evaluates the operand address and saves it: reads the operand and saves it.

   d. If access type is address: evaluates the address and saves it.

   e. If access type is branch: saves the operand specifier.

2. Performs the operation indicated by the instruction.

3. Stores the result(s) using the saved addresses in the order indicated by the occurrence of operand specifiers in the instruction stream.

Note

The string instructions are an exception to this sequence performed by each instruction. Partial results are stored before the instruction operation is completed.

The variable-length bit field instructions treat the position, size, and base address operand specifiers as the specification of an implied field operand specifier.

If multiple exceptions occur, the order in which they are taken is UNPREDICTABLE. This can occur, for example, in a floating-point instruction whose destination operand specifier of write access type uses a reserved addressing mode and the operation results in an overflow fault.

The implications of this instruction interpretation process are:

1. Autoincrement and autodecrement operations occur as the operand specifiers are processed, and subsequent operand specifiers use the updated contents of registers modified by those operations.

2. Other than as indicated above, all input operands are read, and all addresses of output operands computed before any results of the instruction are stored.

3. An operand of modify access type is not read, modified, and written as an indivisible operation; therefore, modify access type operands cannot be used for synchronization. (For synchronization instructions, see Chapter 7.)

4. If an instruction references two operands of write or modify access type at the same address, the first will be overwritten by the second.

Instructions

3

This chapter describes the instructions generally used by all software, across all implementations of the VAX architecture. Certain instructions are specific to portions of the VAX architecture: memory management, interrupts and exceptions, process dispatching, and processor registers. These instructions are generally used by privileged software and are described in chapters devoted to those portions of the architecture. A concise list of opcode assignments appears in Appendix A.

Instruction Descriptions

The instruction set is divided into 12 major sections:

Integer arithmetic and logical

Address

Variable-length bit field

Control

Procedure call

Miscellaneous

Queue

Floating point

Character string

Cyclic redundancy check

Decimal string

Edit

Within each major section, closely related instructions are grouped and described together. The instruction group description is composed of the following:

1. The group name.
2. The format of each instruction in the group. The format presents the name and type of each instruction operand specifier and the order in which it appears in memory. Operand specifiers from left to right appear in increasing memory addresses.
3. The operation of the instruction.
4. The effect on condition codes.

5. Exceptions specific to the instruction. Exceptions generally possible for all instructions are not listed (for example, illegal or reserved addressing mode, trace, and memory management exceptions).

6. The opcodes, mnemonics, and names of each instruction in the group. The opcodes are given in hex.

7. A description in English of the instruction.

8. In many cases, notes on the instruction and programming examples.

Operand Specifier Notation

Operand specifiers are described in the following way:

⟨name⟩.⟨access type⟩⟨data type⟩

The name is suggestive of the operand in the context of the instruction. The name is often abbreviated.

The access type is represented by a letter denoting the operand specifier access type. These are:

a   Calculate the effective address of the specified operand. Address is returned in a longword that is the actual instruction operand. Context of address calculation (the size to be used in autoincrement, autodecrement, and indexing) is given by ⟨data type⟩.

b   No operand reference. The operand specifier is a branch displacement. The size of branch displacement is given by ⟨data type⟩.

m   Operand is read, potentially modified, and written. Note that this is not an indivisible memory operation. Also note that if the operand is not actually modified, it may not be written back. However, modify type operands are always checked for both read and write accessibility (see Chapter 4).

r   Operand is read only.

v   Calculate the effective address of the specified operand. If the effective address is in memory, the address is returned in a longword that is the actual instruction operand. The context of the address calculation is given by ⟨data type⟩. If the effective address is Rn, the operand is in Rn or R[n + 1]'Rn.

w   Operand is written only.

The data type in the operand specifier notation is a letter denoting the data type of the operand:

b   byte

d   D_floating

f   F_floating

g   G_floating

h	H_floating
l	longword
o	octaword
q	quadword
w	word
x	first data type specified by instruction
y	second data type specified by instruction

Operation Description Notation

The operation of each instruction is given as a sequence of control and assignment statements in an ALGOL-like syntax. No attempt is made to define the syntax formally; it is assumed to be familiar to the reader. The notation used is an extension of that introduced in Chapter 2.

+	addition
−	subtraction, unary minus
*	multiplication
/	division (quotient only)
'	concatenation
←	is replaced by
=	is defined as
Rn or R[n]	contents of register Rn
PC, SP, FP, or AP	the contents of register R15, R14, R13, or R12 respectively
PSW	the contents of the processor status word
PSL	the contents of the processor status longword
(x)	contents of memory location whose address is x
(x)+	contents of memory location whose address is x; x incremented by the size of operand referenced at x
−(x)	x decremented by size of operand to be referenced at x; contents of memory location whose address is new value of x
⟨x:y⟩	a modifier that delimits an extent from bit position x to bit position y inclusive
⟨x1,x2, . . . ,xn⟩	a modifier that enumerates bits x1,x2,...,xn
{ }	arithmetic parentheses used to indicate precede
AND	logical AND

OR	logical OR
XOR	logical XOR
NOT	logical (one's) complement
LSS	less than signed
LSSU	less than unsigned
LEQ	less than or equal signed
LEQU	less than or equal unsigned
EQL	equal signed
EQLU	equal unsigned
NEQ	not equal signed
NEQU	not equal unsigned
GEQ	greater than or equal signed
GEQU	greater than or equal unsigned
GTR	greater than signed
GTRU	greater than unsigned
SEXT(x)	x is sign extended to size of operand needed
ZEXT(x)	x is zero extended to size of operand needed
REM(x,y)	remainder of x divided by y, such that x/y and REM(x,y) have the same sign
MINU(x,y)	minimum unsigned of x and y
MAXU(x,y)	maximum unsigned of x and y

The following conventions are used:

1. Other than that caused by ( )+, or −( ), and the advancement of PC, only operands or portions of operands appearing on the left side of assignment statements are affected.

2. No operator precedence is assumed, other than that replacement (←) has the lowest precedence. Precedence is indicated explicitly by { }.

3. All arithmetic, logical, and relational operators are defined in the context of their operands. For example, " + " applied to floating operands means a floating add; whereas " + " applied to byte operands is an integer byte add. Similarly, "LSS" is a floating comparison when applied to floating operands; whereas "LSS" is an integer byte comparison when applied to byte operands.

4. Instruction operands are evaluated according to the operand specifier conventions (see Chapter 2). The order in which operands appear in the instruction description has no effect on the order of evaluation.

5. Condition codes are in general affected on the value of actual stored results, not on "true" results (which might be generated

internally to greater precision). Thus, for example, two positive
integers can be added together and the sum stored, because of
overflow, as a negative value. The condition codes will indicate a
negative value even though the "true" result is clearly positive.

ADAWI   Add Aligned Word Interlocked

Format:

```
opcode add.rw, sum.mw
```

Operation:

```
tmp ← add;
{set interlock};
sum ← sum + tmp;
{release interlock};
```

Condition Codes:

```
N ← sum LSS 0;
Z ← sum EQL 0;
V ← {integer overflow};
C ← {carry from most significant bit};
```

Exceptions:
reserved operand fault
integer overflow

Opcode:

```
58   ADAWI
```

Description:
The addend operand is added to the sum operand, and the sum
operand is replaced by the result. The operation is interlocked against
similar operations on other processors in a multiprocessor system.
The destination must be aligned on a word boundary (bit 0 of the
address of the sum operand must be zero). If it is not, a reserved
operand fault is taken.

Notes:

1. Integer overflow occurs if the input operands to the add have the same sign and the result has the opposite sign. On overflow, the sum operand is replaced by the low order bits of the true result.

2. If the addend and the sum operands overlap, the result and the condition codes are UNPREDICTABLE.

ADD

Add

Format:

```
opcode add.rx, sum.mx                    2 operand
opcode addl.rx, add2.rx, sum.wx          3 operand
```

Operation:

```
sum ← sum + add;        !2 operand
sum ← addl + add2;      !3 operand
```

Condition Codes:

```
N ← sum LSS 0;
Z ← sum EQL 0;
V ← {integer overflow};
C ← {carry from most significant bit};
```

Exception:

```
integer overflow
```

Opcodes:

```
80   ADDB2   Add Byte 2 Operand
81   ADDB3   Add Byte 3 Operand
A0   ADDW2   Add Word 2 Operand
A1   ADDW3   Add Word 3 Operand
C0   ADDL2   Add Long 2 Operand
C1   ADDL3   Add Long 3 Operand
```

Description:

In 2 operand format, the addend operand is added to the sum operand and the sum operand is replaced by the result. In 3 operand format, the addend 1 operand is added to the addend 2 operand and the sum operand is replaced by the result.

Notes:
Integer overflow occurs if the input operands to the add have the same sign and the result has the opposite sign. On overflow, the sum operand is replaced by the low order bits of the true result.

DWC

Add With Carry

Format:

```
opcode add.rl, sum.ml
```

Operation:

```
sum ← sum + add + C;
```

Condition Codes:

```
N ← sum LSS 0;
Z ← sum EQL 0;
V ← {integer overflow};
C ← {carry from most significant bit};
```

Exceptions:

```
integer overflow
```

Opcodes:

```
D8   ADWC   Add With Carry
```

Description:
The contents of the condition code C bit and the addend operand are added to the sum operand, and the sum operand is replaced by the result.

Notes:
1. On overflow, the sum operand is replaced by the low order bits of the true result.
2. The two additions in the operation are performed simultaneously.

ASH

Arithmetic Shift

Format:

```
opcode cnt.rb, src.rx, dst.wx
```

Operation:

```
dst ← src shifted cnt bits;
```

Condition Codes:

```
N ← dst LSS 0;
Z ← dst EQL 0;
V ← {integer overflow};
C ← 0;
```

Exception:

```
integer overflow
```

Opcodes:

```
78  ASHL  Arithmetic Shift Long
79  ASHQ  Arithmetic Shift Quad
```

Description:

The source operand is arithmetically shifted by the number of bits specified by the count operand, and the destination operand is replaced by the result. The source operand is unaffected. A positive count operand shifts to the left bringing zeros into the least significant bit. A negative count operand shifts to the right bringing copies of the most significant (sign) bit into the most significant bit. A 0 count operand replaces the destination operand with the unshifted source operand.

Notes:

1. Integer overflow occurs on a left shift if any bit shifted into the sign bit position differs from the sign bit of the source operand.

2. If cnt GTR 32 (ASHL) or cnt GTR 64 (ASHQ), the destination operand is replaced by 0.

3. If cnt LEQ −31 (ASHL) or cnt LEQ −63 (ASHQ), all the bits of the destination operand are copies of the sign bit of the source operand.

BIC   Bit Clear

Format:

```
opcode mask.rx, dst.mx           2 operand
opcode mask.rx, src.rx, dst.wx   3 operand
```

Operation:

```
dst ← dst AND {NOT mask};      !2 operand
dst ← src AND {NOT mask};      !3 operand
```

Condition Codes:

```
N ← dst LSS 0;
Z ← dst EQL 0;
V ← 0;
C ← C;
```

Exceptions:
none

Opcodes:

```
8A  BICB2  Bit Clear Byte
8B  BICB3  Bit Clear Byte
AA  BICW2  Bit Clear Word
AB  BICW3  Bit Clear Word
CA  BICL2  Bit Clear Long
CB  BICL3  Bit Clear Long
```

Description:
In 2 operand format, the destination operand is ANDed with the one's complement of the mask operand, and the destination operand is replaced by the result. In 3 operand format, the source operand is ANDed with the one's complement of the mask operand and the destination operand is replaced by the result.

BIS   Bit Set

Format:

```
opcode mask.rx, dst.mx          2 operand
opcode mask.rx, src.rx, dst.wx  3 operand
```

Operation:

```
dst ← dst OR mask;             !2 operand
dst ← src OR mask;             !3 operand
```

Condition Codes:

```
N ← dst LSS 0;
Z ← dst EQL 0;
V ← 0;
C ← C;
```

Exceptions:
none

Opcodes:

```
88  BISB2  Bit Set Byte 2 Operand
89  BISB3  Bit Set Byte 3 Operand
A8  BISW2  Bit Set Word 2 Operand
A9  BISW3  Bit Set Word 3 Operand
C8  BISL2  Bit Set Long 2 Operand
C9  BISL3  Bit Set Long 3 Operand
```

Description:
In 2 operand format, the mask operand is ORed with the destination operand and the destination operand is replaced by the result. In 3 operand format, the mask operand is ORed with the source operand and the destination operand is replaced by the result.

BIT

Bit Test

Format:

```
opcode mask.rx, src.rx
```

Operation:

```
tmp ← src AND mask;
```

Condition Codes:

```
N ← tmp LSS 0;
Z ← tmp EQL 0;
V ← 0;
C ← C;
```

Exceptions:

Opcodes:

```
93  BITB  Bit Test Byte
B3  BITW  Bit Test Word
D3  BITL  Bit Test Long
```

Description:
The mask operand is ANDed with the source operand. Both operands are unaffected. The only action is to affect condition codes.

CLR

Clear

Format:

```
opcode dst.wx
```

Operation:

```
dst ← 0;
```

Condition Codes:

```
N ← 0;
Z ← 1;
V ← 0;
C ← C;
```

Exceptions:
none

Opcodes:

```
94    CLRB  Clear Byte
B4    CLRW  Clear Word
D4    CLRL  Clear Long
7C    CLRQ  Clear Quad
7CFD  CLRO  Clear Octa
```

Description:
The destination operand is replaced by 0.

Notes:
CLRx dst is equivalent to MOVx S$^\wedge$#0, dst, but is 1 byte shorter.

Compare

Format:

opcode srcl.rx, src2.rx

Operation:

srcl - src2;

Condition Codes:

N ← srcl LSS src2;
Z ← srcl EQL src2;
V ← 0;
C ← srcl LSSU src2;

Exceptions:
none

Opcodes:

91 CMPB Compare Byte
B1 CMPW Compare Word
D1 CMPL Compare Long

Description:
The source 1 operand is compared with the source 2 operand. The only action is to affect the condition codes.

Convert

Format:

opcode src.rx, dst.wy

Operation:

dst ← conversion of src;

Condition Codes:

N ← dst LSS 0;
Z ← dst EQL 0;
V ← {integer overflow};
C ← 0;

Exception:

```
integer overflow
```

Opcodes:

```
99  CVTBW  Convert Byte to Word
98  CVTBL  Convert Byte to Long
33  CVTWB  Convert Word to Byte
32  CVTWL  Convert Word to Long
F6  CVTLB  Convert Long to Byte
F7  CVTLW  Convert Long to Word
```

Description:
The source operand is converted to the data type of the destination operand, and the destination operand is replaced by the result. Conversion of a shorter data type to a longer one is done by sign extension; conversion from longer to shorter is done by truncation of the higher numbered (most significant) bits.

Notes:
Integer overflow occurs if any truncated bits of the source operand are not equal to the sign bit of the destination operand.

DEC   Decrement

Format:

```
opcode dif.mx
```

Operation:

```
dif ← dif - 1;
```

Condition Codes:

```
N ← dif LSS 0;
Z ← dif EQL 0;
V ← {integer overflow};
C ← {borrow into most significant bit};
```

Exception:

```
integer overflow
```

Opcodes:

```
97  DECB  Decrement Byte
B7  DECW  Decrement Word
D7  DECL  Decrement Long
```

Description:
One is subtracted from the difference operand, and the difference operand is replaced by the result.

Notes:
1. Integer overflow occurs if the largest negative integer is decremented. On overflow, the difference operand is replaced by the largest positive integer.
2. DECx dif is equivalent to SUBx S^#1, dif, but is 1 byte shorter.

DIV

Divide

Format:

```
opcode divr.rx, quo.mx                    2 operand
opcode divr.rx, divd.rx, quo.wx           3 operand
```

Operation:

```
quo ← quo / divr;        !2 operand
quo ← divd / divr;       !3 operand
```

Condition Codes:

```
N ← quo LSS 0;
Z ← quo EQL 0;
V ← {integer overflow} OR {divr EQL 0};
C ← 0;
```

Exceptions:

```
integer overflow
divide by zero
```

Opcodes:

```
86  DIVB2  Divide Byte 2 Operand
87  DIVB3  Divide Byte 3 Operand
A6  DIVW2  Divide Word 2 Operand
A7  DIVW3  Divide Word 3 Operand
```

```
C6   DIVL2   Divide Long 2 Operand
C7   DIVL3   Divide Long 3 Operand
```

Description:
In 2 operand format, the quotient operand is divided by the divisor operand and the quotient operand is replaced by the result. In 3 operand format, the dividend operand is divided by the divisor operand and the quotient operand is replaced by the result.

Notes:
1. The remainder, if any, is lost.
2. Division is performed such that the remainder (unless it is 0) has the same sign as the dividend; that is, the result is truncated toward 0.
3. Integer overflow occurs if and only if the largest negative integer is divided by −1.   On overflow, operands are affected as in item 3 below.
4. If the divisor operand is 0, then in 2 operand format the quotient operand is not affected; in 3 operand format the quotient operand is replaced by the dividend operand.

DIV

Extended Divide

Format:

```
opcode divr.rl, divd.rq, quo.wl, rem.wl
```

Operation:

```
quo ← divd / divr;
rem ← REM(divd, divr);
```

Condition Codes:

```
N ← quo LSS 0;
Z ← quo EQL 0;
V ← {integer overflow} OR {divr EQL 0};
C ← 0;
```

Exceptions:

```
integer overflow
divide by zero
```

Opcodes:

```
7B   EDIV   Extended Divide
```

Description:
The dividend operand is divided by the divisor operand; the quotient operand is replaced by the quotient; and the remainder operand is replaced by the remainder.

Notes:
1. The division is performed such that the remainder operand (unless it is 0) has the same sign as the dividend operand.
2. On overflow, the operands are affected as in item 3 below.
3. If the divisor operand is 0, then the quotient operand is replaced by bits ⟨31:0⟩ of the dividend operand; the remainder operand is replaced by 0.

EMUL

Extended Multiply

Format:

```
opcode mulr.rl, muld.rl, add.rl, prod.wq
```

Operation:

```
prod ← {muld * mulr} + SEXT(add);
```

Condition Codes:

```
N ← prod LSS 0;
Z ← prod EQL 0;
V ← 0;
C ← 0;
```

Exceptions:
none

Opcode:

```
7A   EMUL   Extended Multiply
```

Description:
The multiplicand operand is multiplied by the multiplier operand, giving a double-length result. The addend operand is sign-extended to double length and added to the result. The product operand is replaced by the final result.

INC

Increment

Format:

```
opcode sum.mx
```

Operation:

```
sum ← sum + 1;
```

Condition Codes:

```
N ← sum LSS 0;
Z ← sum EQL 0;
V ← {integer overflow};
C ← {carry from most significant bit};
```

Exception:

```
integer overflow
```

Opcodes:

```
96  INCB  Increment Byte
B6  INCW  Increment Word
D6  INCL  Increment Long
```

Description:
One is added to the sum operand, and the sum operand is replaced by the result.

Notes:
1. Arithmetic overflow occurs if the largest positive integer is incremented. On overflow, the sum operand is replaced by the largest negative integer.
2. INCx sum is equivalent to ADDx S^#1, sum, but is 1 byte shorter.

MCOM   Move Complemented

Format:

```
opcode src.rx, dst.wx
```

Operation:

```
dst ← NOT src;
```

Condition Codes:

```
N ← dst LSS 0;
Z ← dst EQL 0;
V ← 0;
C ← C;
```

Exceptions:

Opcodes:

```
92  MCOMB  Move Complemented Byte
B2  MCOMW  Move Complemented Word
D2  MCOML  Move Complemented Long
```

Description:

The destination operand is replaced by the one's complement of the source operand.

MNEG

Move Negated

Format:

```
opcode src.rx, dst.wx
```

Operation:

```
dst ← −src;
```

Condition Codes:

```
N ← dst LSS 0;
Z ← dst EQL 0;
V ← {integer overflow};
C ← dst NEQ 0;
```

Exception:

```
integer overflow
```

Opcodes:

```
8E  MNEGB  Move Negated Byte
AE  MNEGW  Move Negated Word
CE  MNEGL  Move Negated Long
```

Description:

The destination operand is replaced by the negative of the source operand.

Notes:

Integer overflow occurs if the source operand is the largest negative integer (which has no positive counterpart). On overflow, the destination operand is replaced by the source operand.

Move

Format:

opcode src.rx, dst.wx

Operation:

dst ← src;

Condition Codes:

N ← dst LSS 0;
Z ← dst EQL 0;
V ← 0;
C ← C;

Exceptions:
none

Opcodes:

90	MOVB	Move	Byte
B0	MOVW	Move	Word
D0	MOVL	Move	Long
7D	MOVQ	Move	Quad
7DFD	MOVO	Move	Octa

Description:
The destination operand is replaced by the source operand.

MOVZ

Move Zero-Extended

Format:

opcode src.rx, dst.wy

Operation:

dst ← ZEXT(src);

Condition Codes:

N ← 0;
Z ← dst EQL 0;
V ← 0;
C ← C;

Exceptions:

Opcodes:

9B MOVZBW Move Zero-Extended Byte to Word

9A MOVZBL Move Zero-Extended Byte to Long

3C MOVZWL Move Zero-Extended Word to Long

Description:

For MOVZBW, bits ⟨7:0⟩ of the destination operand are replaced by
the source operand; bits ⟨15:8⟩ are replaced by 0. For MOVZBL, bits
⟨7:0⟩ of the destination operand are replaced by the source operand;
bits ⟨31:8⟩ are replaced by 0. For MOVZWL, bits ⟨15:0⟩ of the
destination operand are replaced by the source operand; bits ⟨31:16⟩
are replaced by 0.

MUL   Multiply

Format:

opcode mulr.rx, prod.mx   2 operand

opcode mulr.rx, muld.rx, prod.wx   3 operand

Operation:

prod ← prod * mulr;   !2 operand

prod ← muld * mulr;   !3 operand

Condition Codes:

N ← prod LSS 0;

Z ← prod EQL 0;

V ← {integer overflow};

C ← 0;

Exception:

integer overflow

Opcodes:

84 MULB2 Multiply Byte 2 Operand

85 MULB3 Multiply Byte 3 Operand

A4 MULW2 Multiply Word 2 Operand

A5 MULW3 Multiply Word 3 Operand

C4 MULL2 Multiply Long 2 Operand

C5 MULL3 Multiply Long 3 Operand

Description:
In 2 operand format, the product operand is multiplied by the multiplier operand and the product operand is replaced by the low half of the double-length result. In 3 operand format, the multiplicand operand is multiplied by the multiplier operand and the product operand is replaced by the low half of the double-length result.

Notes:
Integer overflow occurs if the high half of the double-length result is not equal to the sign extension of the low half.

PUSHL   Push Long

Format:
```
opcode src.rl
```

Operation:
```
-(SP) ← src;
```

Condition Codes:
```
N ← src LSS 0;
Z ← src EQL 0;
V ← 0;
C ← C;
```

Exceptions:
none

Opcode:
```
DD   PUSHL   Push Long
```

Description:
The longword source operand is pushed on the stack.

Notes:
PUSHL is equivalent to MOVL src, -(SP), but is 1 byte shorter.

ROTL   Rotate Long

Format:
```
opcode cnt.rb, src.rl, dst.wl
```

Operation:

```
dst ← src rotated cnt bits;
```

Condition Codes:

```
N ← dst LSS 0;
Z ← dst EQL 0;
V ← 0;
C ← C;
```

Exceptions:
none

Opcode:

```
9C  ROTL  Rotate Long
```

Description:
The source operand is rotated logically by the number of bits specified by the count operand, and the destination operand is replaced by the result. The source operand is unaffected. A positive count operand rotates to the left. A negative count operand rotates to the right. A zero count operand replaces the destination operand with the source operand.

SBWC   Subtract With Carry

Format:

```
opcode sub.rl, dif.ml
```

Operation:

```
dif ← dif - sub - C;
```

Condition Codes:

```
N ← dif LSS 0;
Z ← dif EQL 0;
V ← {integer overflow};
C ← {borrow into most significant bit};
```

Exception:

```
integer overflow
```

Opcode:

D9 SBWC   Subtract With Carry

Description:

The subtrahend operand and the contents of the condition code C bit are subtracted from the difference operand, and the difference operand is replaced by the result.

Notes:

1. On overflow, the difference operand is replaced by the low order bits of the true result.

2. The 2 subtractions in the operation are performed simultaneously.

SUB   Subtract

Format:

```
opcode sub.rx, dif.mx              2 operand
opcode sub.rx, min.rx, dif.wx      3 operand
```

Operation:

```
dif ← dif - sub;        !2 operand
dif ← min - sub;        !3 operand
```

Condition Codes:

```
N ← dif LSS 0;
Z ← dif EQL 0;
V ← {integer overflow};
C ← {borrow into most significant bit};
```

Exceptions:

integer overflow

Opcodes:

```
82   SUBB2   Subtract Byte 2 Operand
83   SUBB3   Subtract Byte 3 Operand
A2   SUBW2   Subtract Word 2 Operand
A3   SUBW3   Subtract Word 3 Operand
C2   SUBL2   Subtract Long 2 Operand
C3   SUBL3   Subtract Long 3 Operand
```

Description:
In 2 operand format, the subtrahend operand is subtracted from the difference operand and the difference operand is replaced by the result. In 3 operand format, the subtrahend operand is subtracted from the minuend operand and the difference operand is replaced by the result.

Notes:
Integer overflow occurs if the input operands to the subtract are of different signs and the sign of the result is the sign of the subtrahend. On overflow, the difference operand is replaced by the low order bits of the true result.

TST

Test

Format:

opcode src.rx

Operation:

src - 0;

Condition Codes:

N ← src LSS 0;
Z ← src EQL 0;
V ← 0;
C ← 0;

Exceptions:
none

Opcodes:

```
95   TSTB   Test Byte
D5   TSTL   Test Long
B5   TSTW   Test Word
```

Description:
The condition codes are affected according to the value of the source operand.

Notes:
TSTx src is equivalent to CMPx src, S^#0, but is 1 byte shorter.

Exclusive-OR

Format:

```
opcode mask.rx, dst.mx          2 operand
opcode mask.rx, src.rx, dst.wx   3 operand
```

Operation:

```
dst ← dst XOR mask;     !2 operand
dst ← src XOR mask;     !3 operand
```

Condition Codes:

```
N ← dst LSS 0;
Z ← dst EQL 0;
V ← 0;
C ← C;
```

Exceptions:
none

Opcodes:

```
8C  XORB2  Exclusive-OR Byte 2 Operand
8D  XORB3  Exclusive-OR Byte 3 Operand
AC  XORW2  Exclusive-OR Word 2 Operand
AD  XORW3  Exclusive-OR Word 3 Operand
CC  XORL2  Exclusive-OR Long 2 Operand
CD  XORL3  Exclusive-OR Long 3 Operand
```

Description:
In 2 operand format, the mask operand is XORed with the destination operand and the destination operand is replaced by the result. In 3 operand format, the mask operand is XORed with the source operand and the destination operand is replaced by the result.

MOVA

Move Address

Format:

opcode src.ax, dst.wl

Operation:

dst ← src;

Condition Codes:

N ← dst LSS 0;
Z ← dst EQL 0;
V ← 0;
C ← C;

Exceptions:
none

Opcodes:

9E	MOVAB	Move Address Byte
3E	MOVAW	Move Address Word
DE	MOVAL	Move Address Long,
	MOVAF	Move Address F_floating
7E	MOVAQ	Move Address Quad,
	MOVAD	Move Address D_floating,
	MOVAG	Move Address G_floating
7EFD	MOVAH	Move Address H_floating,
	MOVAO	Move Address Octa

Description:
The destination operand is replaced by the source operand. The
context in which the source operand is evaluated is given by the data
type of the instruction. The operand whose address replaces the
destination operand is not referenced.

Notes:
The source operand is of address access type which causes the
address of the specified operand to be moved.

Push Address

Format:

opcode src.ax

Operation:

−(SP) ← src;

Condition Codes:

N ← src LSS 0;

Z ← src EQL 0;

V ← 0;

C ← C;

Exceptions:

Opcodes:

9F	PUSHAB	Push Address Byte	
3F	PUSHAW	Push Address Word	
DF	PUSHAL	Push Address Long,	
	PUSHAF	Push Address F_floating	
7F	PUSHAQ	Push Address Quad,	
	PUSHAD	Push Address D_floating,	
	PUSHAG	Push Address G_floating	
7FFD	PUSHAH	Push Address H_floating	
	PUSHAO	Push Address Octa	

Description:
The source operand is pushed on the stack. The context in which the source operand is evaluated is given by the data type of the instruction. The operand whose address is pushed is not referenced.

Notes:
1. PUSHAx src is equivalent to MOVAx src, −(SP), but is 1 byte shorter.
2. The source operand is of address access type which causes the address of the specified operand to be pushed.

VARIABLE-LENGTH BIT FIELD INSTRUCTIONS

A variable-length bit field is specified by three operands:

1. A longword position operand.
2. A byte field size operand that must be in the range 0 through 32 or a reserved operand fault occurs.
3. A base address (relative to which the position is used to locate the bit field). The address is obtained from an operand of address access type. Unlike other instances of operand specifiers of address access type, however, register mode may be designated in the operand specifier. In this case, the field is contained in the register n designated by the operand specifier (or register n + 1 concatenated with register n; see Chapter 1). If the field is contained in a register and size is not zero, the position operand must have a value in the range 0 through 31 or a reserved operand fault occurs.

In order to simplify the description of the variable-length bit field instructions, a macro FIELD(pos, size, address) is introduced with the following expansion (if size NEQ 0):

```
FIELD(pos, size, address)

=(address + SEXT(pos⟨31:3⟩))⟨⟨size − 1} + pos⟨2:0⟩:pos⟨2:0⟩⟩
        !if address not specified by register mode
= {R[n+1]'Rn}⟨⟨size − 1} + pos:pos⟩ 0 059
        !if address specified by register mode and pos +
        !size GTRU 32
= Rn⟨⟨size − 1} + pos:pos⟩
        !if address specified by register mode and pos +
        !size LEQU 32
```

The number of bytes referenced by the contents ( ) operator above is:

```
1 + {{{size − 1} + pos⟨2:0⟩} / 8}
```

Zero bytes are referenced if the field size is 0.

CMP

Compare Field

Format:

```
opcode pos.rl, size.rb, base.vb, src.rl
```

Operation:

```
tmp ← if size NEQU 0 then SEXT(FIELD (pos, size, base))
                else 0;              !CMPV
```

```
tmp ← if size NEQU 0 then ZEXT(FIELD (pos, size, base))
                    else 0;          !CMPZV
tmp - src;
```

Condition Codes:

```
N ← tmp LSS src;
Z ← tmp EQL src;
V ← 0;
C ← tmp LSSU src;
```

Exception:
reserved operand

Opcodes:

```
EC  CMPV   Compare Field
ED  CMPZV  Compare Zero-Extended Field
```

Description:
The field specified by the position, size, and base operands is compared with the source operand. For CMPV, the source operand is compared with the sign-extended field. For CMPZV, the source operand is compared with the zero-extended field. The only action is to affect the condition codes.

Notes:
1. A reserved operand fault occurs if:
   - size GTRU 32
   - pos GTRU 31, size NEQ 0, and the field is contained in the registers.
2. On a reserved operand fault, the condition codes are UNPREDICTABLE.

EXT

Extract Field

Format:

```
opcode pos.rl, size.rb, base.vb, dst.wl
```

Operation:

```
dst ← if size NEQU 0 then SEXT(FIELD(pos, size, base))
                    else 0;          !EXTV
```

```
dst ← if size NEQU 0 then ZEXT(FIELD(pos, size, base))
              else 0;          !EXTZV
```

Condition Codes:

```
N ← dst LSS 0;
Z ← dst EQL 0;
V ← 0;
C ← C;
```

Exception:
reserved operand

Opcodes:

```
EE   EXTV    Extract Field
EF   EXTZV   Extract Zero-Extended Field
```

Description:
For EXTV, the destination operand is replaced by the sign-extended field specified by the position, size, and base operands. For EXTZV, the destination operand is replaced by the zero-extended field specified by the position, size, and base operands. If the size operand is 0, the only actions are to replace the destination operand with 0 and to affect the condition codes.

Notes:
1. A reserved operand fault occurs if:
   - size GTRU 32
   - pos GTRU 31, size NEQ 0, and the field is contained in the registers.
2. On a reserved operand fault, the destination operand is unaffected and the condition codes are UNPREDICTABLE.

FF   Find First

Format:

```
opcode startpos.rl, size.rb, base.vb, findpos.wl
```

Operation:

```
state = if {FFS} then 1 else 0;
if size NEQU 0 then
        begin
```

```
              tmpl ← FIELD(startpos, size, base);
              tmp2 ← 0;
              while {tmpl⟨tmp2⟩ NEQ state} AND
                      {tmp2 LEQU {size - 1}} do
                      tmp2 ← tmp2 + 1;
              findpos ← startpos + tmp2;
              end
else
              findpos ← startpos;
```

Condition Codes:

```
N ← 0;
Z ← {bit not found};
V ← 0;
C ← 0;
```

Exception:
reserved operand

Opcodes:

```
EB   FFC   Find First Clear
EA   FFS   Find First Set
```

Description:
A field specified by the start position, size, and base operands is
extracted. The field is tested for a bit in the state indicated by the
instruction, starting at bit 0 and extending to the highest bit in the field.
If a bit in the indicated state is found, the find position operand is
replaced by the position of the bit and the Z condition code bit
is cleared. If no bit in the indicated state is found, the find position
operand is replaced by the position (relative to the base) of a bit one
position to the left of the specified field and the Z condition code bit is
set. If the size operand is 0, the find position operand is replaced by
the start position operand and the Z condition code bit is set.

Notes:
1. A reserved operand fault occurs if:
   - size GTRU 32
   - startpos GTRU 31, size NEQ 0, and the field is contained in the
     registers.
2. On a reserved operand fault, the find position operand is unaffected
   and the condition codes are UNPREDICTABLE.

Insert Field

Format:

opcode src.rl, pos.rl, size.rb, base.vb

Operation:

if size NEQU 0 then FIELD(pos, size, base) ← src⟨{size−1}:0⟩;

Condition Codes:

N ← N;
Z ← Z;
V ← V;
C ← C;

Exception:
reserved operand

Opcode:

F0 INSV Insert Field

Description:
The field specified by the position, size, and base operands is replaced by bits ⟨size − 1:0⟩ of the source operand. If the size operand is 0, the instruction has no effect.

Notes:
1. A reserved operand fault occurs if:
   - size GTRU 32
   - pos GTRU 31, size NEQ 0, and the field is contained in the registers.
2. On a reserved operand fault, the field is unaffected and the condition codes are UNPREDICTABLE.

CONTROL INSTRUCTIONS

ACB

Add Compare and Branch

Format:

opcode limit.rx, add.rx, index.mx, displ.bw

Operation:

```
index ← index + add;
if {{add GEQ 0} AND {index LEQ limit}} OR
        {{add LSS 0} AND {index GEQ limit}} then
        PC ← PC + SEXT(displ);
```

Condition Codes:

```
N ← index LSS 0;
Z ← index EQL 0;
V ← {integer overflow};
C ← C;
```

Exceptions:

integer overflow

floating overflow

floating underflow

reserved operand

Opcodes:

9D	ACBB	Add Compare and Branch Byte
3D	ACBW	Add Compare and Branch Word
Fl	ACBL	Add Compare and Branch Long
4F	ACBF	Add Compare and Branch F_floating
6F	ACBD	Add Compare and Branch D_floating
4FFD	ACBG	Add Compare and Branch G_floating
6FFD	ACBH	Add Compare and Branch H_floating

Description:

The addend operand is added to the index operand, and the index operand is replaced by the result. The index operand is compared with the limit operand. If the addend operand is positive (or 0) and the comparison is less than or equal, or if the addend is negative and the comparison is greater than or equal, the sign-extended branch displacement is added to PC. PC is then replaced by the result.

Notes:

1. ACB efficiently implements the general FOR or DO loops in high-level languages since the sense of the comparison between index and limit is dependent on the sign of the addend.

2. On integer overflow, the index operand is replaced by the low order bits of the true result. Comparison and branch determination proceed normally on the updated index operand.

3. On floating underflow, if FU is clear, the index operand is replaced by 0 and comparison and branch determination proceed normally. A fault occurs if FU is set and the index operand is unaffected.

4. On floating overflow, the instruction takes a floating overflow fault and the index operand is unaffected.

5. On a reserved operand fault, the index operand is unaffected and the condition codes are UNPREDICTABLE.

AOBLEQ

Add One and Branch Less Than or Equal

Format:

```
opcode limit.rl, index.ml, displ.bb
```

Operation:

```
index ← index + 1;
if index LEQ limit then PC ← PC + SEXT(displ);
```

Condition Codes:

```
N ← index LSS 0;
Z ← index EQL 0;
V ← {integer overflow};
C ← C;
```

Exception:
integer overflow

Opcode:

```
F3   AOBLEQ   Add One and Branch Less Than or Equal
```

Description:
One is added to the index operand and the index operand is replaced by the result. The index operand is compared with the limit operand. If it is less than or equal, the sign-extended branch displacement is added to PC. PC is then replaced by the result.

Notes:
1. Integer overflow occurs if the index operand before addition is the largest positive integer. On overflow, the index operand is replaced by the largest negative integer and the branch is taken.

2. The C-bit is unaffected.

AOBLSS

Add One and Branch Less Than

Format:

```
opcode limit.rl, index.ml, displ.bb
```

Operation:

```
index ← index + 1;
if index LSS limit then PC ← PC + SEXT(displ);
```

Condition Codes:

```
N ← index LSS 0;
Z ← index EQL 0;
V ← {integer overflow};
C ← C;
```

Exception:
integer overflow

Opcode:

```
F2  AOBLSS  Add One and Branch Less Than
```

Description:
One is added to the index operand, and the index operand is replaced
by the result. The index operand is compared with the limit operand.
If it is less than, the sign-extended branch displacement is added
to the PC and PC is replaced by the result.

Notes:
1. Integer overflow occurs if the index operand before addition is the
   largest positive integer. On overflow, the index operand is replaced
   by the largest negative integer; thus the branch is taken (unless
   the limit operand is the largest negative integer).
2. The C-bit is unaffected.

Branch on (condition)

Format:

```
opcode displ.bb
```

Operation:

```
if condition then PC ← PC + SEXT(displ);
```

Condition Codes:

N ← N;
Z ← Z;
V ← V;
C ← C;

Exceptions:
none

Opcodes: Condition

14	{N OR Z} EQL 0	BGTR	Branch on Greater Than (signed)
15	{N OR Z} EQL 1	BLEQ	Branch on Less Than or Equal (signed)
12	Z EQL 0	BNEQ,	Branch on Not Equal (signed)
		BNEQU	Branch on Not Equal Unsigned
13	Z EQL 1	BEQL	Branch on Equal (signed)
		BEQLU	Branch on Equal Unsigned
18	N EQL 0	BGEQ	Branch on Greater Than or Equal (signed)
19	N EQL 1	BLSS	Branch on Less Than (signed)
1A	{C OR Z} EQL 0	BGTRU	Branch on Greater Than Unsigned
1B	{C OR Z} EQL 1	BLEQU	Branch Less Than or Equal Unsigned
1C	V EQL 0	BVC	Branch on Overflow Clear
1D	V EQL 1	BVS	Branch on Overflow Set
1E	C EQL 0	BGEQU	Branch on Greater Than or Equal Unsigned
		BCC	Branch on Carry Clear
1F	C EQL 1	BLSSU	Branch on Less Than Unsigned
		BCS	Branch on Carry Set

Description:
The condition codes are tested and, if the condition indicated by the instruction is met, the sign-extended branch displacement is added to the PC. PC is then replaced by the result.

Notes:

The VAX conditional branch instructions permit considerable flexibility in branching but require care in choosing the correct branch instruction. The conditional branch instructions are best seen as three overlapping groups:

1. Overflow and Carry Group

```
BVS      V EQL 1
BVC      V EQL 0
BCS      C EQL 1
BCC      C EQL 0
```

These instructions are typically used to check for overflow (when overflow traps are not enabled), for multiprecision arithmetic, and for other special purposes.

2. Unsigned Group

```
BLSSU    C EQL 1
BLEQU    {C OR Z} EQL 1
BEQLU    Z EQL 1
BNEQU    Z EQL 0
BGEQU    C EQL 0
BGTRU    {C OR Z} EQL 0
```

These instructions typically follow integer and field instructions where the operands are treated as unsigned integers, address instructions, and character-string instructions.

3. Signed Group

```
BLSS     N EQL 1
BLEQ     {N OR Z} EQL 1
BEQL     Z EQL 1
BNEQ     Z EQL 0
BGEQ     N EQL 0
BGTR     {N OR Z} EQL 0
```

These instructions typically follow integer and field instructions where the operands are being treated as signed integers, floating-point instructions, and decimal-string instructions.

BB   Branch on Bit

Format:

```
opcode pos.rl, base.vb, displ.bb
```

Operation:

```
teststate = if {BBS} then 1 else 0;
if FIELD(pos, 1, base) EQL teststate then
        PC ← PC + SEXT(displ);
```

Condition Codes:

```
N ← N;
Z ← Z;
V ← V;
C ← C;
```

Exception:
reserved operand

Opcodes:

```
E0   BBS   Branch on Bit Set
E1   BBC   Branch on Bit Clear
```

Description:
The single-bit field specified by the position and base operands is tested. If it is in the test state indicated by the instruction, the sign-extended branch displacement is added to PC and PC is replaced by the result.

Notes:
1. See the section "Variable-Length Bit Field Instructions" earlier in this chapter for a definition of FIELD.
2. A reserved operand fault occurs if pos GTRU 31 and the bit is contained in a register.
3. On a reserved operand fault, the condition codes are UNPREDICTABLE.

BB

Branch on Bit (and modify without interlock)

Format:

```
opcode pos.rl, base.vb, displ.bb
```

Operation:

```
teststate = if {BBSS or BBSC} then 1 else 0;
newstate = if {BBSS or BBCS} then 1 else 0;
tmp ← FIELD(pos, 1, base);
```

```
FIELD(pos, l, base) ← newstate;
if tmp EQL teststate then
        PC ← PC + SEXT(displ);
```

Condition Codes:

```
N ← N;
Z ← Z;
V ← V;
C ← C;
```

Exception:
reserved operand

Opcodes:

```
E2  BBSS  Branch on Bit Set and Set
E3  BBCS  Branch on Bit Clear and Set
E4  BBSC  Branch on Bit Set and Clear
E5  BBCC  Branch on Bit Clear and Clear
```

Description:
The single-bit field specified by the position and base operands is tested. If it is in the test state indicated by the instruction, the sign-extended branch displacement is added to PC and PC is replaced by the result. Regardless of whether the branch is taken or not, the tested bit is put in the new state as indicated by the instruction.

Notes:
1. See the section "Variable-Length Bit Field Instructions" earlier in this chapter for a definition of FIELD.
2. A reserved operand fault occurs if pos GTRU 31 and the bit is contained in a register.
3. On a reserved operand fault, the field is unaffected and the condition codes are UNPREDICTABLE.
4. The modification of the bit is not an interlocked operation. See BBSSI and BBCCI for interlocking instructions.

BB Branch on Bit Interlocked

Format:

```
opcode pos.rl, base.vb, displ.bb
```

Operation:

```
teststate = if {BBSSI} then 1 else 0;
newstate = teststate;
{set interlock};
tmp ← FIELD(pos, 1, base);
FIELD(pos, 1, base) ← newstate;
{release interlock};
if tmp EQL teststate then PC ← PC + SEXT(displ);
```

Condition Codes:

```
N ← N;
Z ← Z;
V ← V;
C ← C;
```

Exception:
reserved operand

Opcodes:

E6 BBSSI Branch on Bit Set and Set Interlocked

E7 BBCCI Branch on Bit Clear and Clear Interlocked

Description:
The single-bit field specified by the position and base operands is tested. If it is in the test state indicated by the instruction, the sign-extended branch displacement is added to the PC and PC is replaced by the result. Regardless of whether the branch is taken or not, the tested bit is put in the new state as indicated by the instruction. If the bit is contained in memory, the reading of the state of the bit and the setting of it to the new state is an interlocked operation. No other processor or I/O device can do an interlocked access on the bit during the interlocked operation.

Notes:
1. See the section "Variable-Length Bit Field Instructions" earlier in this chapter for a definition of FIELD.
2. A reserved operand fault occurs if pos GTRU 31 and the bit is contained in registers.
3. On a reserved operand fault, the field is unaffected and the condition codes are UNPREDICTABLE.
4. Except for memory interlocking, BBSSI is equivalent to BBSS and BBCCI is equivalent to BBCC.

5. This instruction is designed to modify interlocks with other processors or devices. For example, to implement "busy waiting":

```
1$:  BBSSI    bit,base,1$
```

BLB

Branch on Low Bit

Format:

```
opcode src.rl, displ.bb
```

Operation:

```
teststate = if {BLBS} then 1 else 0;
if src<0> EQL teststate then PC ← PC + SEXT(displ);
```

Condition Codes:

```
N ← N;
Z ← Z;
V ← V;
C ← C;
```

Exceptions:
none

Opcodes:

```
E8   BLBS   Branch on Low Bit Set
E9   BLBC   Branch on Low Bit Clear
```

Description:
The low bit (bit 0) of the source operand is tested and, if it is equal to the test state indicated by the instruction, the sign-extended branch displacement is added to PC. PC is then replaced by the result.

BR

Branch

Format:

```
opcode displ.bx
```

Operation:

```
PC ← PC + SEXT(displ);
```

Condition Codes:

```
N ← N;
Z ← Z;
V ← V;
C ← C;
```

Exceptions:
none

Opcodes:

```
11  BRB  Branch With Byte Displacement
31  BRW  Branch With Word Displacement
```

Description:
The sign-extended branch displacement is added to PC, and PC is replaced by the result.

BSB   Branch to Subroutine

Format:

```
opcode displ.bx
```

Operation:

```
-(SP) ← PC;
PC ← PC + SEXT(displ);
```

Condition Codes:

```
N ← N;
Z ← Z;
V ← V;
C ← C;
```

Exceptions:
none

Opcodes:

```
10  BSBB  Branch to Subroutine With Byte Displacement
30  BSBW  Branch to Subroutine With Word Displacement
```

Description:

PC is pushed on the stack as a longword. The sign-extended branch displacement is added to PC, and PC is replaced by the result.

Case

Format:

```
opcode selector.rx, base.rx, limit.rx,
        displ[0].bw,..., displ[limit].bw
```

Operation:

```
tmp ← selector - base;
PC ← PC + if tmp LEQU limit then
            SEXT(displ[tmp]) else {2 + 2 * ZEXT(limit)};
```

Condition Codes:

```
N ← tmp LSS limit;
Z ← tmp EQL limit;
V ← 0;
C ← tmp LSSU limit;
```

Exceptions:

Opcodes:

```
8F   CASEB   Case Byte
AF   CASEW   Case Word
CF   CASEL   Case Long
```

Description:

The base operand is subtracted from the selector operand, and a temporary is replaced by the result. The temporary is compared with the limit operand; if it is less than or equal unsigned, a branch displacement selected by the temporary value is added to PC. PC is then replaced by the result. Otherwise, two times the sum of the limit operand and 1 is added to PC, and PC is replaced by the result. This causes PC to be moved past the array of branch displacements. Regardless of the branch taken, the condition codes are affected by the comparison of the temporary operand with the limit operand.

Notes:
1. After operand evaluation, PC is pointing at displ[0], not at the next instruction. The branch displacements are relative to the address of displ[0].
2. The selector and base operands can both be considered either as signed or unsigned integers.
3. The Pascal statement:

```
case i of
      32:                    x := sin(x);
      33:                    x := cos(x);
      34:                    x := exp(x);
      35:                    x := ln(x);
      36, 37:                x := arctanh(x);
      otherwise              x := reserved
end
```

is translated by the VAX Pascal compiler to:

```
        casel  i, #32, #⟨37 – 32⟩
1$:     .word  sin – 1$          ; Selector is 32.
        .word  cos – 1$          ; Selector is 33.
        .word  exp – 1$          ; Selector is 34.
        .word  ln – 1$           ; Selector is 35.
        .word  arctanh – 1$      ; Selector is 36.
        .word  arctanh – 1$      ; Selector is 37.
otherwise:
        movl   reserved, x       ; Selector is less than
                                 ; 32 or greater than 37.
```

JMP   Jump

Format:

opcode dst.ab

Operation:

PC ← dst;

Condition Codes:

N ← N;
Z ← Z;

```
V ← V;
C ← C;
```

Exceptions:
none

Opcode:

```
17   JMP   Jump
```

Description:
PC is replaced by the destination operand.

Jump to Subroutine

Format:

```
opcode dst.ab
```

Operation:

```
-(SP) ← PC;
PC ← dst;
```

Condition Codes:

```
N ← N;
Z ← Z;
V ← V;
C ← C;
```

Exceptions:
none

Opcodes:

```
16   JSB   Jump to Subroutine
```

Description:
PC is pushed on the stack as a longword. PC is replaced by the destination operand.

Notes:
Since the operand specifier conventions cause the evaluation of the destination operand before saving PC, JSB can be used for coroutine calls with the stack used for linkage. The form of such a call is JSB @(SP)+.

Return from Subroutine

Format:

opcode

Operation:

PC ← (SP)+;

Condition Codes:

N ← N;
Z ← Z;
V ← V;
C ← C;

Exceptions:
none

Opcodes:

05   RSB   Return From Subroutine

Description:
PC is replaced by a longword popped from the stack.

Notes:
1. RSB is used to return from subroutines called by the BSBB, BSBW
   and JSB instructions.
2. RSB is equivalent to JMP @(SP)+, but is 1 byte shorter.

SOBGEQ

Subtract One and Branch Greater Than or Equal

Format:

opcode index.ml, displ.bb

Operation:

index ← index - 1;
if index GEQ 0 then PC ← PC + SEXT(displ);

Condition Codes:

N ← index LSS 0;

```
Z ← index EQL 0;
V ← {integer overflow};
C ← C;
```

Exception:
integer overflow

Opcode:

```
F4  SOBGEQ  Subtract One and Branch Greater Than or Equal
```

Description:
One is subtracted from the index operand, and the index operand is
replaced by the result. If the index operand is greater than or equal to
0, the sign-extended branch displacement is added to PC. PC is
then replaced by the result.

Notes:
1. Integer overflow occurs if the index operand before subtraction is
   the largest negative integer. On overflow, the index operand is
   replaced by the largest positive integer, and thus the branch
   is taken.
2. The C-bit is unaffected.

OBGTR

Subtract One and Branch Greater Than

Format:

```
opcode index.ml, displ.bb
```

Operation:

```
index ← index - 1;
if index GTR 0 then PC ← PC + SEXT(displ);
```

Condition Codes:

```
N ← index LSS 0;
Z ← index EQL 0;
V ← {integer overflow};
C ← C;
```

Exception:
integer overflow

Opcode:

F5 SOBGTR   Subtract One and Branch Greater Than

Description:

One is subtracted from the index operand, and the index operand is replaced by the result. If the index operand is greater than 0, the sign-extended branch displacement is added to PC. PC is then replaced by the result.

Notes:

1. Integer overflow occurs if the index operand before subtraction is the largest negative integer. On overflow, the index operand is replaced by the largest positive integer, and thus the branch is taken.

2. The C-bit is unaffected.

PROCEDURE CALL INSTRUCTIONS

Three instructions are used to implement a standard procedure-calling interface.* Two instructions implement the call to the procedure, the third implements the matching return. The CALLG instruction calls a procedure with the argument list in an arbitrary location. The CALLS instruction calls a procedure with the argument list on the stack. Upon return after a CALLS, this list is automatically removed from the stack. Both call instructions specify the address of the entry point of the procedure being called. The entry point is assumed to consist of a word termed the entry mask followed by the procedure's instructions. The procedure terminates by executing a RET instruction.

The entry mask specifies the subprocedure's register use and overflow enables, as shown in Figure 3.1. On CALL, the stack is aligned to a longword boundary and the trap enables in the PSW are set to a known state to ensure consistent behavior of the called procedure. Integer overflow-enable and decimal overflow-enable are affected according to bits ⟨14⟩ and ⟨15⟩ of the entry mask respectively. Floating underflow-enable is cleared. The registers R11 through R0 specified by bits ⟨11⟩ through ⟨0⟩, respectively, are saved on the stack and are restored by the RET instruction. In addition, PC, SP, FP, and AP are always preserved by the CALL instructions and restored by the RET instruction.

All external procedure calls generated by standard DIGITAL language processors and all intermodule calls to major VAX software subsystems comply with the procedure-calling software standard. The procedure-calling standard requires that all registers in the range R2 through R11 used in the procedure must appear in the mask. R0 and

*Refer to *VAX/VMS Introduction to System Routines* for the procedure-calling standard.

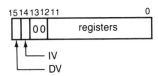

Figure 3.1
Procedure Entry Mask

R1 are not preserved by any called procedure that complies with the procedure-calling standard.

In order to preserve the state, the CALL instructions form a structure on the stack termed a call frame or stack frame, shown in Figure 3.2. This structure contains the saved registers, the saved PSW, the register save mask, and several control bits. The frame also includes a longword that the CALL instructions clear; this is used to implement the VAX/VMS condition-handling facility. Refer to the *VAX/VMS Run Time Library Reference Manual*. At the end of execution of the CALL instruction, FP contains the address of the stack frame. The RET instruction uses the contents of FP to find the stack frame and restore state. The condition-handling facility assumes that FP always points to the stack frame. Note that the saved condition codes and the saved trace enable (PSW⟨T⟩) are cleared.

The contents of the frame PSW⟨3:0⟩ at the time RET is executed will become the condition codes resulting from the execution of the procedure. Similarly, the content of the frame PSW⟨4⟩ at the time the RET is executed will become the PSW⟨T⟩ bit.

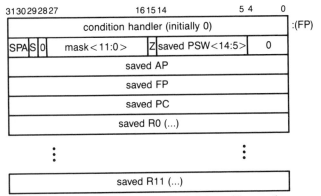

(0 to 3 bytes specified by SPA, Stack Pointer Alignment)

S = Set if CALLS; clear if CALLG.
Z = Always cleared by CALL. Can be set by software to force a reserved operand fault on a RET.

Figure 3.2
Procedure Call Stack Frame

CALLG Call Procedure with General Argument List

Format:

opcode arglist.ab, dst.ab

Operation:

{align stack};
{create stack frame};
{set arithmetic exception enables};
{set new values of AP,FP,PC};

Condition Codes:

N ← 0;
Z ← 0;
V ← 0;
C ← 0;

Exception:
reserved operand

Opcodes:

FA CALLG Call Procedure with General Argument List

Description:
SP is saved in a temporary, and then bits ⟨1:0⟩ are replaced by 0 so that the stack is longword aligned. The procedure entry mask is scanned from bits ⟨11⟩ to ⟨0⟩, and the contents of registers whose number corresponds to set bits in the mask are pushed on the stack as longwords. PC, FP, and AP are pushed on the stack as longwords. The condition codes are cleared. A longword containing the following is pushed on the stack: the saved two low bits of SP in bits ⟨31:30⟩, a 0 in bit ⟨29⟩ and bit ⟨28⟩, the low 12 bits of the procedure entry mask in bits ⟨27:16⟩, a 0 in bit ⟨15⟩ and PSW⟨14:0⟩ in bits ⟨14:0⟩ with T cleared. A longword 0 is pushed on the stack. FP is replaced by SP. AP is replaced by the arglist operand. The trap-enables in the PSW are set to a known state. Integer overflow and decimal overflow are affected according to bits ⟨14⟩ and ⟨15⟩, respectively, of the entry mask; floating underflow is cleared. The T-bit is unaffected. PC is replaced by the sum of destination operand plus 2, which transfers control to the called procedure at the byte beyond the entry mask.

Notes:
1. If bits ⟨13:12⟩ of the entry mask are not 0, a reserved operand fault occurs.

2. On a reserved operand fault, condition codes are UNPREDICTABLE.

3. The procedure-calling standard and the condition-handling facility require the following register-saving conventions. R0 and R1 are always available for function return values and are never saved in the entry mask. All registers R2 through R11 that are modified in the called procedure must be preserved in the mask.

4. The alignment bytes left on the stack are UNPREDICTABLE. They may, for example, be written with zeros when the stack is aligned.

Call Procedure with Stack Argument List

Format:

```
opcode numarg.rl, dst.ab
```

Operation:

```
{push arg count};
{align stack};
{create stack frame};
{set arithmetic exception enables};
{set new values of AP,FP,PC};
```

Condition Codes:

```
N ← 0;
Z ← 0;
V ← 0;
C ← 0;
```

Exception:
reserved operand

Opcode:

```
FB   CALLS   Call Procedure with Stack Argument List
```

Description:
The numarg operand is pushed on the stack as a longword. (Byte 0 contains the number of arguments; high-order 24 bits are used by DIGITAL software.) SP is saved in a temporary, and then bits ⟨1:0⟩ of SP are replaced by 0 so that the stack is longword aligned. The procedure entry mask is scanned from bit ⟨11⟩ to bit ⟨0⟩, and the

contents of registers whose number corresponds to set bits in the mask are pushed on the stack. PC, FP, and AP are pushed on the stack as longwords. The condition codes are cleared. A longword containing the following is pushed on the stack: saved two low bits of SP in bits ⟨31:30⟩, a 1 in bit ⟨29⟩, a 0 in bit ⟨28⟩, the low 12 bits of the procedure entry mask in bits ⟨27:16⟩, a 0 in bit ⟨15⟩ and PSW⟨14:0⟩ in bits ⟨14:0⟩ with T cleared. A longword 0 is pushed on the stack. FP is replaced by SP. AP is set to the value of the stack pointer after the numarg operand was pushed on the stack. The trap-enables in the PSW are set to a known state. Integer overflow and decimal overflow are affected according to bits ⟨14⟩ and ⟨15⟩, respectively, of the entry mask; floating underflow is cleared. T-bit is unaffected. PC is replaced by the sum of destination operand plus 2, which transfers control to the called procedure at the byte beyond the entry mask. The appearance of the stack after CALLS is executed is shown in Figure 3.2.

Notes:

1. If bits ⟨13:12⟩ of the entry mask are not 0, a reserved operand fault occurs.

2. On a reserved operand fault, the condition codes are UNPREDICTABLE.

3. Normal use is to push the arglist onto the stack in reverse order prior to the CALLS. On return, the arglist is removed from the stack automatically.

4. The procedure-calling standard and the condition-handling facility require the following register-saving conventions. R0 and R1 are always available for function return values and are never saved in the entry mask. All registers R2 through R11 that are modified in the called procedure must be preserved in the entry mask.

5. The alignment bytes left on the stack are UNPREDICTABLE. They may, for example, be written with zeros when the stack is aligned.

RET Return from Procedure

Format:

opcode

Operation:

{restore SP from FP};
{restore registers};
{drop stack alignment};

```
{if CALLS then remove arglist};
{restore PSW};
```

Condition Codes:

```
N ← tmpl⟨3⟩;
Z ← tmpl⟨2⟩;
V ← tmpl⟨1⟩;
C ← tmpl⟨0⟩;
```

Exception:
reserved operand

Opcode:

```
04  RET  Return from Procedure
```

Description:
SP is replaced by FP plus 4. A longword containing the following is popped from the stack and saved in a temporary: stack alignment bits in bits ⟨31:30⟩, a flag distinguishing CALLS from CALLG in bit ⟨29⟩, the low 12 bits of the procedure entry mask in bits ⟨27:16⟩, and a saved PSW in bits ⟨15:0⟩. PC, FP, and AP are replaced by longwords popped from the stack. A register restore mask is formed from bits ⟨27:16⟩ of the temporary. Scanning from bit ⟨0⟩ to bit ⟨11⟩ of the restore mask, the contents of registers whose number is indicated by set bits in the mask are replaced by longwords popped from the stack. SP is incremented by ⟨31:30⟩ of the temporary. PSW is replaced by bits ⟨15:0⟩ of the temporary. If bit ⟨29⟩ in the temporary is 1 (indicating that the procedure was called by CALLS), a longword containing the number of arguments is popped from the stack. Four times the unsigned value of the low byte of this longword is added to SP, and SP is replaced by the result.

Notes:
1. A reserved operand fault occurs if tmp1⟨15:8⟩ NEQ 0.
2. On a reserved operand fault, the condition codes are UNPREDICTABLE.
3. The value of tmp1⟨28⟩ is ignored.
4. The procedure-calling standard and condition-handling facility assume that procedures returning a function value or a status code do so in R0 or R0 and R1.
5. If FP⟨1:0⟩ is not zero, or if the stack frame is ill-formed, the results are UNPREDICTABLE.

BICPSW

Bit Clear PSW

Format:

opcode mask.rw

Operation:

PSW ← PSW AND {NOT mask};

Condition Codes:

N ← N AND {NOT mask⟨3⟩};
Z ← Z AND {NOT mask⟨2⟩};
V ← V AND {NOT mask⟨1⟩};
C ← C AND {NOT mask⟨0⟩};

Exception:
reserved operand

Opcode:

B9 BICPSW Bit Clear PSW

Description:
PSW is ANDed with the one's complement of the mask operand, and PSW is replaced by the result.

Notes:
A reserved operand fault occurs if mask ⟨15:8⟩ is not zero. On a reserved operand fault, the PSW is not affected.

BISPSW

Bit Set PSW

Format:

opcode mask.rw

Operation:

PSW ← PSW OR mask;

Condition Codes:

N ← N OR mask⟨3⟩;

```
Z ← Z OR mask⟨2⟩;
V ← V OR mask⟨1⟩;
C ← C OR mask⟨0⟩;
```

Exception:

reserved operand

Opcode:

```
B8  BISPSW  Bit Set PSW
```

Description:

PSW is ORed with the mask operand, and PSW is replaced by the result.

Notes:

A reserved operand fault occurs if mask⟨15:8⟩ is not zero. On a reserved operand fault, the PSW is not affected.

PT   Breakpoint

Format:

```
opcode
```

Operation:

```
PSL⟨TP⟩ ← 0;
{initiate breakpoint fault};      !push current PSL on stack
```

Condition Codes:

```
N ← 0; !condition codes cleared after BPT fault
Z ← 0;
V ← 0;
C ← 0;
```

Exception:

Opcode:

```
03  BPT  Breakpoint
```

Description:

In order to understand the operation of this instruction, read Chapter 5, Exceptions and Interrupts. This instruction is used, together with PSL⟨T⟩, to implement debugging facilities.

BUG Bugcheck

Format:

```
opcode message.bx
```

Operation:

```
{fault to report error}
```

Condition Codes:

```
N ← N;
Z ← Z;
V ← V;
C ← C;
```

Exception:
reserved instruction

Opcode:

```
FEFF  BUGW  Bugcheck with Word Message Identifier
FDFF  BUGL  Bugcheck with Longword Message Identifier
```

Description:
The hardware treats these opcodes as reserved to DIGITAL and faults. The VAX/VMS operating system treats these as requests to report software detected errors. The in-line message identifier is zero-extended to a longword (BUGW) and interpreted as a condition value. If the process is privileged to report bugs, a log entry is made. If the process is not privileged, a reserved instruction is signaled.

HALT Halt

Format:

```
opcode
```

Operation:

```
If PSL(CUR_MOD) NEQU kernel then
        {privileged instruction fault}
else
        {halt the processor};
```

Condition Codes:

```
N ← 0;  !If privileged instruction fault
Z ← 0;  !condition codes are cleared after
V ← 0;  !the fault. PSL saved on stack
C ← 0;  !contains condition codes prior to HALT.
N ← N;  !If processor halt
Z ← Z;
V ← V;
C ← C;
```

Exception:
privileged instruction

Opcode:

```
00  HALT  Halt
```

Description:
In order to understand the operation of this instruction, read Chapter 5, Exceptions and Interrupts. If the process is running in kernel mode, the processor is halted. Otherwise, a privileged instruction fault occurs.

Notes:
This opcode is 0 to trap many branches to data.

Compute Index

Format:

```
opcode subscript.rl, low.rl, high.rl, size.rl,
       indexin.rl, indexout.wl
```

Operation:

```
indexout ← {indexin + subscript} *size;
if {subscript LSS low} or {subscript GTR high} then
       {subscript range trap};
```

Condition Codes:

```
N ← indexout LSS 0;
Z ← indexout EQL 0;
V ← 0;
C ← 0;
```

Exception:

subscript range

Opcode:

OA INDEX Compute Index

Description:

The indexin operand is added to the subscript operand, and the sum multiplied by the size operand. The indexout operand is replaced by the result. If the subscript operand is less than the low operand or greater than the high operand, a subscript range trap is taken.

Notes:

1. No arithmetic exception other than subscript range can result from this instruction. Thus no indication is given if overflow occurs in either the add or multiply steps. If overflow occurs on the add step, the sum is the low order 32 bits of the true result. If overflow occurs on the multiply step, the indexout operand is replaced by the low order 32 bits of the true product of the sum and the subscript operand. In the normal use of this instruction, overflow cannot occur without a subscript range trap occurring.

2. The index instruction is useful in index calculations for arrays of the fixed-length data types (integer and floating) and for index calculations for arrays of bit fields, character strings, and decimal strings. The indexin operand permits cascading INDEX instructions for multidimensional arrays. For one-dimensional bit field arrays, it also permits introduction of the constant portion of an index calculation which is not readily absorbed by address arithmetic. The following notes show some of the uses of INDEX.

3. The COBOL statements:

```
01  A-ARRAY.
    02 A PIC X(25) OCCURS 15 TIMES INDEXED BY I.
01  B PIC X(25).
MOVE A(I) TO B.
```

can be translated by a VAX COBOL compiler to:

```
INDEX  I(R11), #^X01, #^X0F, #^X19, #^X00, R0
MOVC3  #^X19, A-25(R11)[R0], B(R11)
```

4. The FORTRAN statements:

```
INTEGER*4    A(11:24), I
A(I) = 1
```

can be translated by a VAX FORTRAN compiler to:

```
INDEX  I(R11), #11, #24, #1, #0, R0
```

```
        MOVL    #1, A-44(R11)[R0]
```

5. The Pascal statements:

```
var
    i : integer;
    a : array[11..24] of integer;
    a[i] := 1
```

can be translated by a VAX Pascal compiler to:

```
INDEX    I,#11,#24,#1,#0,R0
MOVZBL   #1,A-44[R0]
```

MOVPSL

Move from PSL

Format:

opcode dst.wl

Operation:

dst ← PSL;

Condition Codes:

N ← N;
Z ← Z;
V ← V;
C ← C;

Exceptions:
none

Opcode:

DC MOVPSL   Move from PSL

Description:
The destination operand is replaced by PSL (see Chapter 5).

NOP

No Operation

Format:
opcode

Operation:

Condition Codes:

```
N ← N;
Z ← Z;
V ← V;
C ← C;
```

Exceptions:
none

Opcode:

```
01  NOP  No Operation
```

Description:
No operation is performed.

POPR

Pop Registers

Format:

```
opcode mask.rw
```

Operation:

```
tmp1 ← mask
for tmp2 ← 0 step 1 until 14 do
        if tmp1⟨tmp2⟩ EQL 1 then R[tmp2] ← (SP)+;
```

Condition Codes:

```
N ← N;
Z ← Z;
V ← V;
C ← C;
```

Exceptions:
none

Opcode:

```
BA  POPR  Pop Registers
```

Description:
The contents of registers whose number corresponds to set bits in the mask operand are replaced by longwords popped from the stack. R[n] is replaced if mask⟨n⟩ is set. The mask is scanned from bit ⟨0⟩ to bit ⟨14⟩. Bit ⟨15⟩ is ignored.

Push Registers

Format:

opcode mask.rw

Operation:

tmp1 ← mask;
for tmp2 ← 14 step −1 until 0 do
        if tmp1⟨tmp2⟩ EQL 1 then −(SP) ← R[tmp2];

Condition Codes:

N ← N;
Z ← Z;
V ← V;
C ← C;

Exceptions:
none

Opcode:

BB   PUSHR   Push Registers

Description:
The contents of registers whose number corresponds to set bits in the mask operand are pushed on the stack as longwords. R[n] is pushed if mask⟨n⟩ is set. The mask is scanned from bit ⟨14⟩ to bit ⟨0⟩. Bit ⟨15⟩ is ignored.

Notes:
The order of pushing is specified so that the contents of higher numbered registers are stored at higher memory addresses. This results in, for example, a quadword datum stored in adjacent registers being stored by PUSHR in memory in the correct order.

XFC

Extended Function Call

Format:
opcode

Operation:

{XFC fault};

Condition Codes:

N ← 0 ;

Z ← 0 ;

V ← 0 ;

C ← 0 ;

Exceptions:

Opcode:

FC XFC Extended Function Call

Description:

In order to understand the operation of this instruction, read Chapter 5. This instruction provides for user-defined extensions to the instruction set.

QUEUE INSTRUCTIONS

A queue is a circular, doubly linked list. A queue entry is specified by its address. The VAX architecture supports two distinct types of links: absolute and self-relative. An absolute link contains the absolute address of the entry to which it points. A self-relative link contains a displacement from the present queue entry. A queue is classified by the type of link it uses.

Because a queue contains redundant links, it is possible to create ill-formed queues. The VAX instructions produce UNPREDICTABLE results when used on ill-formed queues or on queues with overlapping entries.

Absolute Queues

Absolute queues use absolute addresses as links. Queue entries are linked by a pair of longwords.

The first (lowest addressed) longword is the forward link; it specifies the address of the succeeding queue entry. The second (highest addressed) longword is the backward link; it specifies the address of the preceding queue entry. A queue is specified by a queue header that is identical to a pair of queue linkage longwords. The forward link of the header is the address of the entry termed the head of the queue. The backward link of the header is the address of the entry termed the tail of the queue. The forward link of the tail points to the header.

Two general operations can be performed on queues: insertion of entries and removal of entries. Operations at the head or tail are always valid because the queue header is always present. Operations elsewhere in the queue depend on specific entries being present and may become invalid if another process is simultaneously performing operations on the queue. Therefore, if more than one process can perform operations on a queue simultaneously, insertions and removals should only be done at the head or tail of the queue. If only one process (or one process at a time) can perform operations on a queue, insertions and removals can be made at other than the head or tail of the queue.

Two instructions are provided for manipulating absolute queues: INSQUE and REMQUE. INSQUE inserts an entry specified by an entry operand into the queue following the entry specified by the predecessor operand. REMQUE removes the entry specified by the entry operand. Queue entries can be on arbitrary byte boundaries. Both INSQUE and REMQUE are implemented as non-interruptible instructions.

Self-Relative Queues

Self-relative queues use displacements from queue entries as links. Queue entries are linked by a pair of longwords. The first longword (lowest addressed) is the forward link; it specifies displacement of the succeeding queue entry from the present entry. The second longword (highest addressed) is the backward link; it specifies the displacement of the preceding queue entry from the present entry. A queue is specified by a queue header, which also consists of two longword links.

Four operations can be performed on self-relative queues: insert at head, insert at tail, remove from head, and remove from tail. Furthermore, these operations are interlocked to allow cooperating processes in a multiprocessor system to access a shared list without additional synchronization. Queue entries must be quadword aligned. A hardware-supported, interlocked memory access mechanism is used to read the queue header. Bit $\langle 0 \rangle$ of the queue header is used as a secondary interlock and is set when the queue is being accessed. If an interlocked queue instruction encounters the secondary interlock set, it terminates after setting the condition codes to indicate failure to gain access to the queue. If the secondary interlock bit is not set, then the interlocked queue instruction sets it during its operation and clears it at instruction completion. This prevents other interlocked queue instructions from operating on the same queue.

INSQHI

Insert Entry into Queue at Head, Interlocked

Format:

```
opcode entry.ab, header.aq
```

Operation:

```
! Must have write access to header.
! Header must be quadword aligned.
! Header cannot be equal to entry.
tmp1 ← (header){interlocked}; ! Acquire hardware interlock.
                              ! tmp1(2:1) must be zero.
if tmp1(0) EQLU 1 then
        begin
        (header){interlocked} ← tmp1;
                              ! Release hardware lock.
        {set condition codes and terminate instruction};
        end;
(header){interlocked} ← tmp1 v 1;
                              ! Release hardware lock,
                              ! and set secondary interlock.
If {all memory accesses can be completed} then
                ! Check if following addresses can be written
                ! without causing a memory management exception
                !       entry
                !       header + tmp1
                ! Also, check for quadword alignment.
        begin
        {insert entry into queue};
        {release secondary interlock};
        end;
else
        begin
        {release secondary interlock};
        {backup instruction};
        {initiate fault};
        end;
```

Condition Codes:

```
if {secondary interlock was clear} then
        begin
```

```
        N ← 0;
        Z ← (entry) EQL (entry+4);   ! First entry in queue.
        V ← 0;
        C ← 0;
        end;
else
        begin
        N ← 0;
        Z ← 0;
        V ← 0;
        C ← 1;                       ! Secondary interlock failed.
        end;
```

Exception:
reserved operand

Opcode:

5C INSQHI   Insert Entry into Queue at Head, Interlocked

Description:
The entry specified by the entry operand is inserted into the queue
following the header. If the entry inserted was the first one in the
queue, the condition code Z-bit is set; otherwise, the Z-bit is cleared.
The insertion is a non-interruptible operation. The insertion is
interlocked to prevent concurrent interlocked insertions or removals at
the head or tail of the same queue by another process, even in a
multiprocessor environment. Before performing any part of the
operation, the processor validates that the entire operation can be
completed. This ensures that if a memory management exception
occurs, the queue is left in a consistent state (see Chapters 4 and 5).
If the instruction fails to acquire the secondary interlock, the instruction
sets condition codes and terminates.

Notes:
1. Because the insertion is non-interruptible, processes running in
   kernel mode can share queues with interrupt service routines (see
   Chapters 4, 5, and 6).
2. The INSQHI, INSQTI, REMQHI, and REMQTI instructions are
   implemented such that cooperating software processes in a
   multiprocessor may access a shared list without additional
   synchronization.
3. To set a software interlock realized with a queue, the following can
   be used:

```
INSERT: INSQHI ...          ; Attempt to insert entry.
```

```
                        BEQL    1$          ; If queue was empty, branch.
                        BCS     INSERT      ; If queue was locked, try agai
                        CALL    WAIT(...)   ; If the entry was queued, wait
              1$:
```

4. During access validation, any access that cannot be completed results in a memory management exception even though the queue insertion is not started.

5. A reserved operand fault occurs if entry or header is an address that is not quadword aligned (if its address bits⟨2:0⟩ NEQU 0) or if (header)⟨2:1⟩ is not zero. A reserved operand fault also occurs if header equals entry. In this case, the queue is not altered.

INSQTI   Insert Entry into Queue at Tail, Interlocked

Format:

opcode entry.ab, header.aq

Operation:

```
!must have write access to header.
!header must be quadword aligned.
!header cannot be equal to entry.
tmp1 ← (header){interlocked};       !acquire hardware interlock.
                                    !tmp1(2:1) must be zero.
if tmp1(0) EQLU 1 then
begin
(header){interlocked} ← tmp1;       !release hardware interlock
{set condition codes and terminate instruction};
end;
else
begin
(header){interlocked} ← tmp1 v 1; !set secondary interlock
                                  !release hardware interlock
If {all memory accesses can be completed} then
        !check if the following addresses can be written
        !without causing a memory management exception:
        !       entry
        !       header + (header + 4)
        !Also, check for quadword alignment
        begin
        {insert entry into queue};
        {release secondary interlock};
        end;
```

```
        else
                begin
                {release secondary interlock};
                {backup instruction};
                {initiate fault};
                end;
        end;
```

Condition Codes:

```
if {secondary interlock was clear} then
        begin
        N ← 0;
        Z ← (entry) EQL (entry+4);      !first entry in queue
        V ← 0;
        C ← 0;
        end;
else
        begin
        N ← 0;
        Z ← 0;
        V ← 0;
        C ← 1;                          !secondary interlock failed
        end;
```

Exception:
reserved operand

Opcode:

5D INSQTI Insert Entry into Queue at Tail, Interlocked

Description:
The entry specified by the entry operand is inserted into the queue preceding the header. If the entry inserted was the first one in the queue, the condition code Z-bit is set; otherwise, the Z-bit is cleared. The insertion is a non-interruptible operation. The insertion is interlocked to prevent concurrent interlocked insertions or removals at the head or tail of the same queue by another process, even in a multiprocessor environment. Before performing any part of the operation, the processor validates that the entire operation can be completed. This ensures that if a memory management exception occurs, the queue is left in a consistent state (see Chapters 4 and 5). If the instruction fails to acquire the secondary interlock, the instruction sets condition codes and terminates.

Notes:

1. Because the insertion is non-interruptible, processes running in kernel mode can share queues with interrupt service routines (see Chapters 4, 5, and 6).

2. The INSQHI, INSQTI, REMQHI, and REMQTI instructions are implemented such that cooperating software processes in a multiprocessor may access a shared list without additional synchronization.

3. To set a software interlock realized with a queue, the following can be used:

```
INSERT: INSQHI ...        ; Attempt to insert entry.
        BEQL    1$        ; If queue was empty, branch.
        BCS     INSERT    ; If queue was locked, try aga
        CALL    WAIT(...) ; If the entry was queued, wai
        1$:
```

4. During access validation, any access that cannot be completed results in a memory management exception even though the queue insertion is not started.

5. A reserved operand fault occurs if entry, header, or (header + 4) is an address that is not quadword aligned (if its address bits⟨2:0⟩ NEQU 0) or if (header)⟨2:1⟩ is not zero. A reserved operand fault also occurs if header equals entry. In this case, the queue is not altered.

INSQUE

Insert Entry in Queue

Format:

```
opcode entry.ab, pred.ab
```

Operation:

```
If {all memory accesses can be completed} then
        begin
        (entry) ← (pred);           !forward link of entry
        (entry + 4) ← pred;         !backward link of entry
        ((pred) + 4) ← entry;       !backward link of successor
        (pred) ← entry;             !forward link of predecessor
        end;
else
        begin
        {backup instruction};
        {initiate fault};
        end;
```

Condition Codes:

N ← (entry) LSS (entry+4);

Z ← (entry) EQL (entry+4);   !first entry in queue

V ← 0;

C ← (entry) LSSU (entry+4);

Exceptions:

Opcode:

OE INSQUE Insert Entry in Queue

Description:

The entry specified by the entry operand is inserted into the queue following the entry specified by the predecessor operand. If the entry inserted was the first one in the queue, the condition code Z-bit is set; otherwise, the Z-bit is cleared. The insertion is a non-interruptible operation. Before performing any part of the operation, the processor validates that the entire operation can be completed. This ensures that if a memory management exception occurs, the queue is left in a consistent state (see Chapters 4 and 5).

Notes:

1. Three types of insertion can be performed by appropriate choice of predecessor operand:

   • Insert at head

     INSQUE entry,h   ;h is queue head

   • Insert at tail

     INSQUE   ;h is queue head
     entry,@h+4
     (Note "@" in this case only)

   • Insert after arbitrary predecessor

     INSQUE entry,p   ;p is predecessor

2. Because the insertion is non-interruptible, processes running in kernel mode can share queues with interrupt service routines (see Chapters 4, 5, and 6).

3. The INSQUE and REMQUE instructions are implemented such that cooperating software processes in a single processor may access a shared list without additional synchronization if the insertions and removals are only at the head or tail of the queue.

4. To set a software interlock realized with a queue, the following can be used:

```
      INSQUE   ...              ;was queue empty?
      BEQL     1$               ;yes
      CALL     WAIT(...)        ;no, wait
   1$:
```

5. During access validation, any access that cannot be completed
   results in a memory management exception, even though the
   queue insertion is not started.

REMQHI

Remove Entry from Queue at Head, Interlocked

Format:

opcode header.aq, addr.wl

Operation:

```
!must have write access to header.
!header must be quadword aligned.
!header cannot equal address of addr.
tmpl ← (header){interlocked};    !acquire hardware interlock.
                                 !tmpl⟨2:1⟩ must be zero.
if tmpl⟨0⟩ EQLU 1 then
      begin
      (header){interlocked} ← tmpl;
             !release hardware interlock
      {set condition codes and terminate instruction};
      end;
(header){interlocked} ← tmpl v 1;!set secondary interlock
                                 !release hardware interlock
If {all memory accesses can be completed} then
      !check if the following can be done without
      !causing a memory management exception:
      !write addr operand
      !read contents of header + tmpl {if tmpl NEQU 0}
      !write into header + tmpl + (header + tmpl)
      !                            !{if tmpl NEQU 0}
      !Also, check for quadword alignment
      begin
      {remove entry from queue};
      {release secondary interlock};
      end
```

```
else
        begin
        {release secondary interlock};
        {backup instruction};
        {initiate fault};
        end;
```

Condition Codes:

```
if {secondary interlock was clear} then
        begin
        N ← 0;
        Z ← (header) EQL 0;    !queue empty after removal
        V ← {queue empty before this instruction};
        C ← 0;
        end;
else
        begin
        N ← 0;
        Z ← 0;
        V ← 1;               !did not remove anything
        C ← 1;               !secondary interlock failed
        end;
```

Exception:
reserved operand

Opcode:

5E   REMQHI   Remove Entry from Queue at Head, Interlocked

Description:
If the secondary interlock is clear, the queue entry following the
header is removed from the queue and the address operand is
replaced by the address of the entry removed. If the queue was
empty prior to this instruction or if the secondary interlock failed, the
condition code V-bit is set; otherwise, it is cleared.

If the interlock succeeded and the queue is empty at the end of this
instruction, the condition code Z-bit is set; otherwise, the Z-bit is
cleared. The removal is interlocked to prevent concurrent interlocked
insertions or removals at the head or tail of the same queue by
another process, even in a multiprocessor environment. The removal
is a non-interruptible operation. Before performing any part of the
operation, the processor validates that the entire operation can be
completed. This ensures that if a memory management exception

Instructions   **111**

occurs, the queue is left in a consistent state (see Chapters 4 and 5)
If the instruction fails to acquire the secondary interlock, the instructio
sets condition codes and terminates without altering the queue.

Notes:

1. Because the removal is non-interruptible, processes running in
   kernel mode can share queues with interrupt service routines (see
   Chapters 4, 5, and 6).

2. The INSQHI, INSQTI, REMQHI, and REMQTI instructions are
   implemented such that cooperating software processes in a
   multiprocessor may access a shared list without additional
   synchronization.

3. To release a software interlock realized with a queue, the following
   can be used:

```
1$:        REMQHI  ...           ;removed last?
   BEQL    2$                    ;yes
   BCS     1$                    ;try removing again
   CALL    ACTIVATE( ... )       ;Activate other waiters
2$:
```

4. To remove entries until the queue is empty, the following can be
   used:

```
1$:        REMQHI  ...           ;anything removed?
   BVS     2$                    ;no

   .
   process removed entry
   .

   BR      1$                    ;

   .

2$:        BCS     1$            ;try removing again
   queue empty
```

5. During access validation, any access that cannot be completed
   results in a memory management exception even though the
   queue removal is not started.

6. A reserved operand fault occurs if header or (header + (header))
   is an address that is not quadword aligned (if its address bits $\langle 2:0 \rangle$
   NEQU 0) or if (header)$\langle 2:1 \rangle$ is not zero. A reserved operand fault
   also occurs if the header address operand equals the address
   of the addr operand. In this case, the queue is not altered.

Remove Entry from Queue at Tail, Interlocked

Format:

```
opcode header.aq, addr.wl
```

Operation:

```
!must have write access to header.
!header must be quadword aligned.
!header cannot equal address of addr.
tmpl ← (header){interlocked};    !acquire hardware interlock.
                                 !tmpl(2:1) must be zero.
if tmpl(0) EQLU 1 then
        begin
        (header){interlocked} ← tmpl;
                !release hardware interlock
        {set condition codes and terminate instruction};
        end;
(header){interlocked} ← tmpl v 1;!set secondary interlock
                                 !release hardware interlock
If {all memory accesses can be completed} then
        !check if the following can be done without
        !causing a memory management exception:
        !write addr operand
        !read contents of header + (header + 4)
        !                          {if tmpl NEQU 0}
        !write into header + (header + 4)
        ! + (header + 4 + (header + 4)) {if tmpl NEQU 0}
        !Also, check for quadword alignment
        begin
        {remove entry from queue};
        {release secondary interlock};
        end;
    else
        begin
        {release secondary interlock};
        {backup instruction};
        {initiate fault};
        end;
```

Condition Codes:

```
if {secondary interlock was clear} then
        begin
        N ← 0;
        Z ← (header + 4) EQL 0;!queue empty after removal
        V ← {queue empty before this instruction};
        C ← 0;
        end;
else
        begin
        N ← 0;
        Z ← 0;
        V ← 1;              !did not remove anything
        C ← 1;              !secondary interlock failed
        end;
```

Exception:
reserved operand

Opcode:

5F REMQTI Remove Entry from Queue at Tail, Interlocked

Description:
If the secondary interlock is clear, the queue entry preceding the header is removed from the queue and the address operand is replaced by the address of the entry removed. If the queue was empty prior to this instruction or if the secondary interlock failed, the condition code V-bit is set; otherwise, it is cleared.

If the interlock succeeded and the queue is empty at the end of this instruction, the condition code Z-bit is set; otherwise, the Z-bit is cleared. The removal is interlocked to prevent concurrent interlocked insertions or removals at the head or tail of the same queue by another process, even in a multiprocessor environment. The removal is a non-interruptible operation. Before performing any part of the operation, the processor validates that the entire operation can be completed. This ensures that if a memory management exception occurs, the queue is left in a consistent state (see Chapters 4 and 5). If the instruction fails to acquire the secondary interlock, the instruction sets condition codes and terminates without altering the queue.

Notes:
1. Because the removal is non-interruptible, processes running in kernel mode can share queues with interrupt service routines (see Chapters 4, 5, and 6).

2. The INSQHI, INSQTI, REMQHI, and REMQTI instructions are implemented such that cooperating software processes in a multiprocessor may access a shared list without additional synchronization.

3. To release a software interlock realized with a queue, the following can be used:

```
1$:     REMQTI...            ;removed last?
  BEQL  2$                   ;yes
  BCS   1$                   ;try removing again
  CALL  ACTIVATE(...)        ;Activate other waiters
2$:
```

4. To remove entries until the queue is empty, the following can be used:

```
1$:     REMQTI ...           ;anything removed?
  BVS   2$                   ;no

  .
  process removed entry
  .

  BR    1$                   ;

2$:     BCS   1$             ;try removing again
  queue empty
```

5. During access validation, any access that cannot be completed results in a memory management exception even though the queue removal is not started.

6. A reserved operand fault occurs if header, (header + 4), or (header + (header + 4) + 4) is an address that is not quadword aligned (if its address bits⟨2:0⟩ NEQU 0) or if (header)⟨2:1⟩ is not zero. A reserved operand fault also occurs if the header address operand equals the address of the addr operand. In this case, the queue is not altered.

REMQUE

Remove Entry from Queue

Format:

```
opcode entry.ab,addr.wl
```

Operation:

```
if {all memory accesses can be completed} then
        begin
        ((entry+4)) ← (entry);    !forward link of predecessor
        ((entry)+4) ← (entry +4);!backward link of successor
        addr ← entry;
        end;
else
        begin
        {backup instruction};
        {initiate fault};
        end;
```

Condition Codes:

```
N ← (entry) LSS (entry+4);
Z ← (entry) EQL (entry+4);          !queue empty
V ← entry EQL (entry+4);            !no entry to remove
C ← (entry) LSSU (entry+4);
```

Exceptions:
none

Opcode:

```
OF   REMQUE   Remove Entry from Queue
```

Description:
The queue entry specified by the entry operand is removed from the queue. The address operand is replaced by the address of the entry removed. If there was no entry in the queue to be removed, the condition code V-bit is set; otherwise, it is cleared. If the queue is empty at the end of this instruction, the condition code Z-bit is set; otherwise, the Z-bit is cleared. The removal is a non-interruptible operation. Before performing any part of the operation, the processor validates that the entire operation can be completed. This ensures that if a memory management exception occurs, the queue is left in a consistent state (see Chapters 4 and 5).

Notes:
1. Three types of removal can be performed by suitable choice of entry operand:
    • Remove at head

    ```
    REMQUE @h,addr       ;h is queue header
    ```

    • Remove at tail

```
REMQUE @h+4,addr        ;h is queue header
```

- Remove arbitrary entry

```
REMQUE entry,addr       ;
```

2. Because the removal is non-interruptible, processes running in kernel mode can share queues with interrupt service routines (see Chapters 4, 5, and 6).

3. The INSQUE and REMQUE instructions are implemented such that cooperating software processes in a single processor may access a shared list without additional synchronization if the insertions and removals are only at the head or tail of the queue.

4. To release a software interlock realized with a queue, the following can be used:

```
REMQUE  . . .              ;queue empty?

BEQL    1$                 ;yes

CALL    ACTIVATE( . . . )  ;Activate other waiters

1$:
```

5. To remove entries until the queue is empty, the following can be used:

```
1$:        REMQUE   . . .     ;anything removed?

BVS        EMPTY             ;no

.

.

.

BR         1$                ;
```

6. During access validation, any access that cannot be completed results in a memory management exception even though the queue removal is not started.

The floating-point instructions operate on four data types, termed F__floating, D__floating, G__floating, and H__floating. Subset implementations of the VAX architecture may not include all four data types. Operating system software may emulate omitted instructions and may use user-mode stack space during emulation. For more detail about subsetting and emulation, see Chapter 11.

epresentation
Mathematically, a floating-point number may be defined as having the form

$$(+ \text{ or } -) \ (2^K) * f$$

where K is an integer and f is a non-negative fraction. For a non-vanishing number, K and f are uniquely determined by imposing the condition

```
1/2 LEQ f LSS 1
```

The fractional factor, f, of the number is then said to be binary normalized. For the number zero, f must be assigned the value 0, and the value of K is indeterminate.

The VAX floating-point data formats are derived from this mathematic representation for floating-point numbers. Four types of floating-point data are provided: the two standard PDP-11 formats (F_floating and D_floating), and two extended range formats (G_floating and H_floating). Single-precision, or floating, data is 32 bits long. Double precision, or D_floating, data is 64 bits long. Extended range double-precision, or G_floating, data is 64 bits long. Extended range quadruple-precision, or H_floating, data is 128 bits long. Sign magnitude notation is used.

The most significant bit of the floating-point data is the sign bit: 0 for positive and 1 for negative.

The fractional factor f is assumed normalized, so that its most significant bit must be 1. This 1 is the "hidden" bit: it is not stored in the data word, but of course the hardware restores it before carrying out arithmetic operations. The F_floating and D_floating data types use 23 and 55 bits, respectively, for f, which with the hidden bit imply effective significance of 24 bits and 56 bits for arithmetic operations. The extended range data types, G_floating and H_floating, use 52 and 112 bits, respectively, for f, which with the hidden bit, imply effective significance of 53 and 113 bits for arithmetic operations.

In the F_floating and D_floating data types, 8 bits are reserved for the storage of the exponent K in excess 128 notation. Thus exponent from −128 to +127 could be represented, in biased form, by 0 to 255. For reasons given below, a biased EXP of 0 (true exponent of −128), is reserved for floating-point zero. Thus, for the F_floating and D_floating data types, exponents are restricted to the range −127 to +127 inclusive, or in excess 128 notation, 1 to 255.

In the G_floating data type, 11 bits are reserved for the storage of the exponent in excess 1024 notation. Thus, exponents are restricted to −1023 to +1023 inclusive (in excess notation, 1 to 2047). In the H_floating data type 15 bits are reserved for the storage of the exponent in excess 16384 notation. Thus, exponents are restricted to −16383 to +16383 inclusive (in excess notation, 1 to 32767). A biased exponent of 0 is reserved for floating-point zero.

Floating-Point Zero—Because of the hidden bit, the fractional factor is not available to distinguish between zero and non-zero numbers whose fractional factor is exactly 1/2. Therefore, VAX architecture reserves a sign-exponent field of 0 for this purpose. Any positive, floating-point number with biased exponent of 0 is treated as if it were an exact 0 by the floating-point instruction set. In particular, a floating-point operand, whose bits are all zeros, is treated as zero; this is the format generated by all floating-point instructions for which the result is zero.

Reserved Operands—A reserved operand is defined to be any bit pattern with a sign bit of 1 and a biased exponent of 0. In VAX architecture, all floating-point instructions generate a fault if a reserved operand is encountered. A reserved operand is never generated as a result of a floating-point instruction.

Overview of the Instruction Set

VAX architecture has the standard arithmetic operations ADD, SUB, MUL, and DIV implemented for all four floating data types. The results of these operations are always rounded, as described in the following section on accuracy. The architecture has, in addition, two composite operations, EMOD and POLY, also implemented for all four floating-point data types. EMOD generates a product of two operands and then separates the product into its integer and fractional terms. POLY evaluates a polynomial, given the degree, the argument, and pointer to a table of coefficients. Details on the operation of EMOD and POLY are given in their respective descriptions. All of these instructions are subject to the rounding errors associated with floating-point operations as well as to exponent overflow and underflow. Accuracy is discussed in the next section, and exceptions are discussed in Chapter 6.

VAX architecture also has a complete set of instructions for conversion from integer arithmetic types (byte, word, longword) to all floating types (F_floating, D_floating, G_floating, H_floating), and also for floating types to integer arithmetic types. VAX also has a set of instructions for conversion between all of the floating types except between D_floating and G_floating. Many of these instructions are exact, in the sense defined in the section on accuracy to follow. A few instructions, however, may generate rounding error, floating overflow, or floating underflow, or may induce integer overflow. Details are given in the description of the CVT instructions.

There is a class of move-type instructions that is always exact: MOV, NEG, CLR, CMP, and TST. And, finally, there is the ACB (add, compare, and branch) instruction, that is subject to rounding errors, overflow, and underflow.

All of the VAX floating-point instructions fault if a reserved operand is encountered. Floating-point instructions also fault on the occurrence of floating overflow or divide by zero. The FU bit, in the PSW, is available to enable or disable an exception on underflow. If the FU bit is clear, no exception occurs on underflow and zero is returned as the result. If the FU bit is set, a fault occurs on underflow. Further details on the actions taken if any of these exceptions occurs are included in the descriptions of the instructions and are completely discussed in Chapter 5.

Accuracy

General comments on the accuracy of the VAX floating-point instruction set are presented here. The descriptions of the individual instructions may include additional details on the accuracy at which they operate.

An instruction is defined to be exact if its result, extended on the right by an infinite sequence of zeros, is identical to that of an infinite precision calculation involving the same operands. The a priori accuracy of the operands is thus ignored. For all arithmetic operations except DIV, a zero operand implies that the instruction is exact. The same statement holds for DIV if the zero operand is the dividend. But if the zero operand is the divisor, division is undefined and the instruction faults.

For non-zero, floating-point operands, the fractional factor is binary normalized with 24 or 56 bits for single precision (F_floating) or double precision (D_floating), respectively; and the fractional factor is binary normalized with 53 or 113 bits for extended range double precision (G_floating), and extended range quadruple precision (H_floating), respectively.

Note that an arithmetic result is exact if no non-zero bits are lost in chopping the infinite precision result to the data length to be stored. Chopping means that the 24 (F_floating), 56 (D_floating), 53 (G_floating), or 113 (H_floating) high-order bits of the normalized fractional factor of a result are stored; the rest of the bits are discarded. The first bit lost in chopping is referred to as the "rounding" bit. The value of a rounded result is related to the chopped result as follows:

1. If the rounding bit is 1, the rounded result is the chopped result incremented by an LSB (least significant bit).

2. If the rounding bit is 0, the rounded and chopped results are identical.

All VAX processors implement rounding so as to produce results identical to the results produced by the following algorithm. Add a 1 to the rounding bit and propagate the carry if it occurs. Note that a renormalization may be required after rounding takes place. If this happens, the new rounding bit will be 0. Therefore, renormalization can happen only once. The following statements summarize the relations among chopped, rounded, and true (infinite precision) results:

1. If a stored result is exact

   ```
   rounded value = chopped value = true value
   ```

2. If a stored result is not exact, its magnitude

   - Is always less than that of the true result for chopping

   - Is always less than that of the true result for rounding if the rounding bit is zero

   - Is greater than that of the true result for rounding if the rounding bit is one.

rogramming onsiderations

In order to be consistent with the floating-point instruction set which faults on reserved operands, software-implemented floating-point functions (the absolute function, for example) should verify that the input operand(s) is (are) not reserved. An easy way to do this is a floating move or test of the input operand(s).

In order to facilitate high-speed implementations of the floating-point instruction set, certain restrictions are placed on the addressing mode combinations usable within a single floating-point instruction. These combinations involve the logically inconsistent simultaneous use of a value as both a floating-point operand and an address. Specifically, if within the same instruction the content of register Rn is used as both a part of a floating-point input operand (operand type .rf, .rd, .rg, .rh, .mf, .md, .mg, or .mh) and as an address in an addressing mode that modifies Rn (autoincrement, autodecrement, or autoincrement deferred), the value of the floating-point operand is UNPREDICTABLE.

.DD

Add

Format:

```
opcode add.rx, sum.mx              2 operand
opcode addl.rx, add2.rx, sum.wx    3 operand
```

Operation:

```
sum ← sum + add;        !2 operand
sum ← addl + add2;      !3 operand
```

Condition Codes:

```
N ← sum LSS 0;
Z ← sum EQL 0;
V ← 0;
C ← 0;
```

Exceptions:
floating overflow

floating underflow

reserved operand

Opcodes:

40	ADDF2	Add F_floating 2 Operand
41	ADDF3	Add F_floating 3 Operand
60	ADDD2	Add D_floating 2 Operand
61	ADDD3	Add D_floating 3 Operand
40FD	ADDG2	ADD G_floating 2 Operand
41FD	ADDG3	ADD G_floating 3 Operand
60FD	ADDH2	ADD H_floating 2 Operand
61FD	ADDH3	ADD H_floating 3 Operand

Description:
In 2 operand format, the addend operand is added to the sum operand and the sum operand is replaced by the rounded result. In 3 operand format, the addend 1 operand is added to the addend 2 operand and the sum operand is replaced by the rounded result.

Notes:
1. On a reserved operand fault, the sum operand is unaffected and the condition codes are UNPREDICTABLE.
2. On floating underflow, a fault occurs if FU is set. Zero is stored as the result of floating underflow only if FU is clear. On a floating underflow fault, the sum operand is unaffected. If FU is clear, the sum operand is replaced by 0 and no exception occurs.
3. On floating overflow, the instruction faults. The sum operand is unaffected, and the condition codes are UNPREDICTABLE.

CLR   Clear

Format:

```
opcode dst.wx
```

Operation:

dst ← 0;

Condition Codes:

N ← 0;
Z ← 1;
V ← 0;
C ← C;

Exceptions:
none

Opcodes:

D4   CLRF   Clear F_floating
7C   CLRG   Clear G_floating,
       CLRD   Clear D_floating
7CFD   CLRH   Clear H_floating

Description:
The destination operand is replaced by 0.

Notes:
CLRx dst is equivalent to MOVx #0, dst, but is 5 (F__floating), or 9 (D__floating or G__floating), or 17 (H__floating) bytes shorter.

CMP   Compare

Format:

opcode src1.rx, src2.rx

Operation:

src1-src2;

Condition Codes:

N ← src1 LSS src2;
Z ← src1 EQL src2;
V ← 0;
C ← 0;

Exception:
reserved operand

Opcodes:

```
51    CMPF   Compare F_floating
71    CMPD   Compare D_floating
51FD  CMPG   Compare G_floating
71FD  CMPH   Compare H_floating
```

Description:
The source 1 operand is compared with the source 2 operand. The only action is to affect the condition codes.

Notes:
On a reserved operand fault, the condition codes are UNPREDICTABLE.

CVT   Convert

Format:
opcode src.rx, dst.wy

Operation:
dst ← conversion of src;

Condition Codes:
```
N ← dst LSS 0;
Z ← dst EQL 0;
V ← {integer overflow};
C ← 0;
```

Exceptions:
integer overflow

floating overflow

floating underflow

reserved operand

Opcodes:

```
4C    CVTBF   Convert Byte to F_floating
4D    CVTWF   Convert Word to F_floating
4E    CVTLF   Convert Long to F_floating
6C    CVTBD   Convert Byte to D_floating
6D    CVTWD   Convert Word to D_floating
```

6E	CVTLD	Convert Long to D_floating
4CFD	CVTBG	Convert Byte to G_floating
4DFD	CVTWG	Convert Word to G_floating
4EFD	CVTLG	Convert Long to G_floating
6CFD	CVTBH	Convert Byte to H_floating
6DFD	CVTWH	Convert Word to H_floating
6EFD	CVTLH	Convert Long to H_floating
48	CVTFB	Convert F_floating to Byte
49	CVTFW	Convert F_floating to Word
4A	CVTFL	Convert F_floating to Long
4B	CVTRFL	Convert Rounded F_floating to Long
68	CVTDB	Convert D_floating to Byte
69	CVTDW	Convert D_floating to Word
6A	CVTDL	Convert D_floating to Long
6B	CVTRDL	Convert Rounded D_floating to Long
48FD	CVTGB	Convert G_floating to Byte
49FD	CVTGW	Convert G_floating to Word
4AFD	CVTGL	Convert G_floating to Long
4BFD	CVTRGL	Convert Rounded G_floating to Long
68FD	CVTHB	Convert H_floating to Byte
69FD	CVTHW	Convert H_floating to Word
6AFD	CVTHL	Convert H_floating to Long
6BFD	CVTRHL	Convert Rounded H_floating to Long
56	CVTFD	Convert F_floating to D_floating
99FD	CVTFG	Convert F_floating to G_floating
98FD	CVTFH	Convert F_floating to H_floating
76	CVTDF	Convert D_floating to F_floating
32FD	CVTDH	Convert D_floating to H_floating
33FD	CVTGF	Convert G_floating to F_floating
56FD	CVTGH	Convert G_floating to H_floating
F6FD	CVTHF	Convert H_floating to F_floating
F7FD	CVTHD	Convert H_floating to D_floating
76FD	CVTHG	Convert H_floating to G_floating

Description:
The source operand is converted to the data type of the destination operand, and the destination operand is replaced by the result. The form of the conversion is as follows:

```
CVTBF    exact
CVTBD    exact
CVTBG    exact
CVTBH    exact
CVTWF    exact
CVTWD    exact
CVTWG    exact
CVTWH    exact
CVTLF    rounded
CVTLD    exact
CVTLG    exact
CVTLH    exact
CVTFB    truncated
CVTDB    truncated
CVTGB    truncated
CVTHB    truncated
CVTFW    truncated
CVTDW    truncated
CVTGW    truncated
CVTHW    truncated
CVTFL    truncated
CVTRFL   rounded
CVTDL    truncated
CVTRDL   rounded
CVTGL    truncated
CVTRGL   rounded
CVTHL    truncated
CVTRHL   rounded
CVTFD    exact
CVTFG    exact
CVTFH    exact
CVTDF    rounded
CVTDH    exact
CVTGF    rounded
CVTGH    exact
CVTHF    rounded
CVTHD    rounded
CVTHG    rounded
```

Notes:

1. Only CVTDF, CVTGF, CVTHF, CVTHD, and CVTHG can result in floating overflow fault. The destination operand is unaffected, and the condition codes are UNPREDICTABLE.

2. Only conversions with a floating-point source operand can result in a reserved operand fault. On a reserved operand fault, the destination operand is unaffected and the condition codes are UNPREDICTABLE.

3. Only conversions with an integer destination operand can result in integer overflow. On integer overflow, the destination operand is replaced by the low-order bits of the true result.

4. Only CVTGF, CVTHF, CVTHD, and CVTHG can result in floating underflow. If FU is set, a fault occurs. Zero is stored as the result of floating underflow only if FU is clear. On a floating underflow fault, the destination operand is unaffected. If FU is clear, the destination operand is replaced by 0 and no exception occurs.

5. When CVTRFL, CVTRDL, CVTRGL, and CVTRHL round, the rounding is done in sign magnitude, before conversion to two's complement.

Divide

Format:

```
opcode divr.rx, quo.mx          2 operand
opcode divr.rx, divd.rx, quo.wx 3 operand
```

Operation:

```
quo ← quo / divr;      !2 operand
quo ← divd / divr;     !3 operand
```

Condition Codes:

```
N ← quo LSS 0;
Z ← quo EQL 0;
V ← 0;
C ← 0;
```

Exceptions:
floating overflow
floating underflow
divide by zero
reserved operand

Opcodes:

46	DIVF2	Divide F_floating 2 Operand
47	DIVF3	Divide F_floating 3 Operand
66	DIVD2	Divide D_floating 2 Operand
67	DIVD3	Divide D_floating 3 Operand
46FD	DIVG2	Divide G_floating 2 Operand
47FD	DIVG3	Divide G_floating 3 Operand
66FD	DIVH2	Divide H_floating 2 Operand
67FD	DIVH3	Divide H_floating 3 Operand

Description:

In 2 operand format, the quotient operand is divided by the divisor operand and the quotient operand is replaced by the rounded result. In 3 operand format, the dividend operand is divided by the divisor operand and the quotient operand is replaced by the rounded result.

Notes:

1. On a reserved operand fault, the quotient operand is unaffected and the condition codes are UNPREDICTABLE.

2. On floating underflow, a fault occurs if FU is set. Zero is stored as the result of floating underflow only if FU is clear. On a floating underflow fault, the quotient operand is unaffected. If FU is clear, the quotient operand is replaced by 0 and no exception occurs.

3. On floating overflow, the instruction faults. The quotient operand is unaffected, and the condition codes are UNPREDICTABLE.

4. On divide by zero, the quotient operand and condition codes are affected as in item 3 above.

EMOD

Extended Multiply and Integerize

Format:

```
opcode mulr.rx, mulrx.rb, muld.rx, int.wl, fract.wx
```

EMODG and EMODH:

```
opcode mulr.rx, mulrx.rw, muld.rx, int.wl, fract.wx
```

Operation:

```
int ← integer part of muld * {mulr'mulrx};
fract ← fractional part of muld * {mulr'mulrx};
```

Condition Codes:

N ← fract LSS 0 ;
Z ← fract EQL 0 ;
V ← {integer overflow};
C ← 0 ;

Exceptions:

integer overflow

floating underflow

reserved operand

Opcodes:

54   EMODF   Extended Multiply and Integerize F_floating

74   EMODD   Extended Multiply and Integerize D_floating

54FD EMODG   Extended Multiply and Integerize G_floating

74FD EMODH   Extended Multiply and Integerize H_floating

Description:

The multiplier extension operand is concatenated with the multiplier operand to gain 8 (EMODD and EMODF), 11 (EMODG), or 15 (EMODH) additional low-order fraction bits. The low-order 5 or 1 bits of the 16-bit multiplier extension operand are ignored by the EMODG and EMODH instructions, respectively. The multiplicand operand is multiplied by the extended multiplier operand. The multiplication is such that the result is equivalent to the exact product truncated (before normalization) to a fraction field of 32 bits in F_floating, 64 bits in D_floating and G_floating, and 128 in H_floating. Regarding the result as the sum of an integer and fraction of the same sign, the integer operand is replaced by the integer part of the result; the fraction operand is replaced by the rounded fractional part of the result.

Notes:

1. On a reserved operand fault, the integer operand and the fraction operand are unaffected. The condition codes are UNPREDICTABLE.

2. On floating underflow, a fault occurs if FU is set. The integer and fraction parts are replaced by 0 on the occurrence of floating underflow only if FU is clear. On a floating underflow fault, the integer and fraction parts are unaffected. If FU is clear, the integer and fraction parts are replaced by 0 and no exception occurs.

3. On integer overflow, the integer operand is replaced by the low-order bits of the true result.

4. Floating overflow is indicated by integer overflow. Integer overflow is possible, however, in the absence of floating overflow.

5. The signs of the integer and fraction are the same unless integer overflow results.

6. Because the fraction part is rounded after separation of the intege part, it is possible that the value of the fraction operand is 1.

7. Rounding is performed before conversion to two's complement.

MNEG

Move Negated

Format:

```
opcode src.rx, dst.wx
```

Operation:

```
dst ← -src;
```

Condition Codes:

```
N ← dst LSS 0;
Z ← dst EQL 0;
V ← 0;
C ← 0;
```

Exception:
reserved operand

Opcodes:

52	MNEGF	Move Negated F_floating
72	MNEGD	Move Negated D_floating
52FD	MNEGG	Move Negated G_floating
72FD	MNEGH	Move Negated H_floating

Description:
The destination operand is replaced by the negative of the source operand.

Notes:
On a reserved operand fault, the destination operand is unaffected and the condition codes are UNPREDICTABLE.

MOV

Move

Format:

```
opcode src.rx, dst.wx
```

Operation:

```
dst ← src;
```

Condition Codes:

```
N ← dst LSS 0;
Z ← dst EQL 0;
V ← 0;
C ← C;
```

Exception:
reserved operand

Opcodes:

```
50    MOVF  Move F_floating
70    MOVD  Move D_floating
50FD  MOVG  Move G_floating
70FD  MOVH  Move H_floating
```

Description:
The destination operand is replaced by the source operand.

Notes:
On a reserved operand fault, the destination operand is unaffected and the condition codes are UNPREDICTABLE.

MUL   Multiply

Format:

```
opcode mulr.rx, prod.mx            2 operand
opcode mulr.rx, muld.rx, prod.wx   3 operand
```

Operation:

```
prod ← prod * mulr;    !2 operand
prod ← muld * mulr;    !3 operand
```

Condition Codes:

```
N ← prod LSS 0;
Z ← prod EQL 0;
```

```
V ← 0 ;
C ← 0 ;
```

Exceptions:

floating overflow

floating underflow

reserved operand

Opcodes:

44	MULF2	Multiply F_floating 2 Operand
45	MULF3	Multiply F_floating 3 Operand
64	MULD2	Multiply D_floating 2 Operand
65	MULD3	Multiply D_floating 3 Operand
44FD	MULG2	Multiply G_floating 2 Operand
45FD	MULG3	Multiply G_floating 3 Operand
64FD	MULH2	Multiply H_floating 2 Operand
65FD	MULH3	Multiply H_floating 3 Operand

Description:

In 2 operand format, the product operand is multiplied by the multiplier operand and the product operand is replaced by the rounded result. In 3 operand format, the multiplicand operand is multiplied by the multiplier operand and the product operand is replaced by the rounded result.

Notes:

1. On a reserved operand fault, the product operand is unaffected and the condition codes are UNPREDICTABLE.

2. On floating underflow, a fault occurs if FU is set. Zero is stored as the result of floating underflow only if FU is clear. On a floating underflow fault, the product operand is unaffected. If FU is clear, the product operand is replaced by 0 and no exception occurs.

3. On floating overflow, the instruction faults. The product operand is unaffected, and the condition codes are UNPREDICTABLE.

▬▬▬▬▬▬

POLY   Polynomial Evaluation

Format:

```
opcode arg.rx, degree.rw, tbladdr.ab
```

Operation:

```
tmp1 ← degree;
if tmp1 GTRU 31 then {initiate reserved operand fault};
tmp2 ← tbladdr;
tmp3 ← {(tmp2)+};        !tmp3 accumulates the partial result
                        !tmp3 is of type x
if POLYH then −(SP) ← arg;
while tmp1 GTRU 0 do
begin            !computation loop
tmp4 ← {arg * tmp3};     !tmp4 accumulates new partial result.
                        !tmp3 has old partial result.
        !Perform multiply, and retain the 31 (POLYF), ⁄
        !63 (POLYD, POLYG), or 127 (POLYH) most significant
        !bits of the fraction by truncating the unnormalized
        !product. (The most significant bit of the 31, 63,
        !or 127 bits in the product magnitude will be zero
        !if the product magnitude is LSS 1/2 and GEQ 1/4.)
        !Use the result in the following add operation.
tmp4 ← tmp4 + (tmp2);
        !Align fractions, perform add, and retain the
        !31 (POLYF), 63 (POLYD, POLYG), or 127 (POLYH)
        !most significant bits of the fraction by truncating
        !the unnormalized result.
        !normalize, and round to type x.
        !Check for overflow and underflow only after the
combined
        !multiply, add, normalize, round sequence.
if OVERFLOW then FLOATING OVERFLOW FAULT
if UNDERFLOW then
        begin
        if FU EQL 1 then FLOATING UNDERFLOW FAULT;
        tmp4 ← 0; !force result to 0;
        end;
tmp1 ← tmp1 − 1;
tmp2 ← tmp2 + {size of data type};
tmp3 ← tmp4;
        !update partial result in tmp3
end;
if POLYF then
        begin
        R0 ← tmp3;
```

Instructions   **133**

```
                    R1 ← 0;
                    R2 ← 0;
                    R3 ← tmp2;
                    end;
        if POLYD or POLYG then
                    begin
                    R1'R0 ← tmp3;
                    R2 ← 0;
                    R3 ← tmp2;
                    R4 ← 0;
                    R5 ← 0;
                    end;
        if POLYH then
                    begin
                    SP ← SP + 16;
                    R3'R2'R1'R0 ← tmp3;
                    R4 ← 0;
                    R5 ← tmp2;
                    end;
```

Condition Codes:

```
N ← R0 LSS 0;
Z ← R0 EQL 0;
V ← 0;
C ← 0;
```

Exceptions:
floating overflow
floating underflow
reserved operand

Opcodes:

```
55      POLYF   Polynomial Evaluation F_floating
75      POLYD   Polynomial Evaluation D_floating
55FD    POLYG   Polynomial Evaluation G_floating
75FD    POLYH   Polynomial Evaluation H_floating
```

Description:
The table address operand points to a table of polynomial coefficients.
The coefficient of the highest order term of the polynomial is pointed
to by the table address operand. The table is specified with lower
order coefficients stored at increasing addresses. The data type of the

coefficients is the same as the data type of the argument operand. The evaluation is carried out by Horner's method, and the contents of R0 (R1'R0 for POLYD and POLYG, R3'R2'R1'R0 for POLYH) are replaced by the result. The result computed is

```
result = C[0]*x⁰ + x*(C[1] + x*(C[2] + ... x*C[d]))
```

where x is the argument and d is the degree. The unsigned-word degree operand specifies the highest numbered coefficient to participate in the evaluation. POLYH requires four longwords on the stack to store arg in case the instruction is interrupted.

Notes:

1. After execution, the registers are as shown in Figure 3.3 through 3.6.

2. On a floating fault:
   - If PSL⟨FPD⟩ = 0, the instruction faults and all relevant side effects are restored to their original state.
   - If PSL⟨FPD⟩ = 1, the instruction is suspended and state is saved in the general registers as follows:

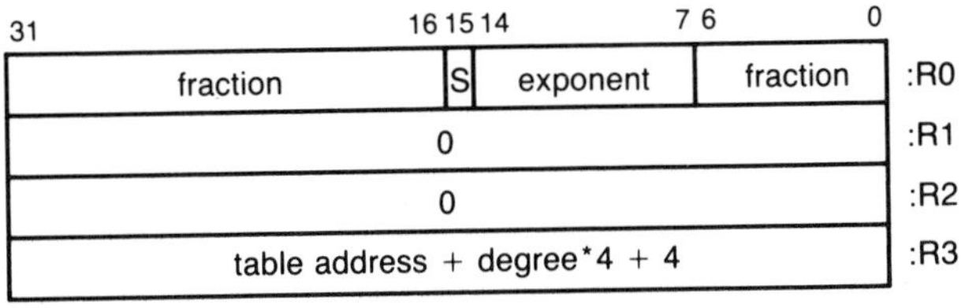

31	16 15 14		7 6		0	
fraction	S	exponent		fraction		:R0
0						:R1
0						:R2
table address + degree*4 + 4						:R3

POLYF

Figure 3.3
POLYF Result Register

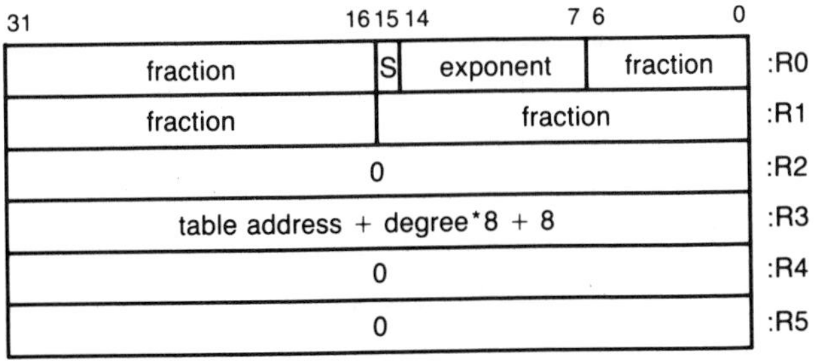

31	16 15 14		7 6		0	
fraction	S	exponent		fraction		:R0
fraction			fraction			:R1
0						:R2
table address + degree*8 + 8						:R3
0						:R4
0						:R5

POLYD

Figure 3.4
POLYD Result Register

```
POLYF

RO = tmp3            !partial result after iteration prior to the
                     !one causing the overflow or underflow

R1 = arg

R2⟨7:0⟩ = tmp1       !number of iterations remaining

R2⟨31:8⟩ = implementation dependent

R3 = tmp2            !points to table entry causing exception

POLYD and POLYG

R1'RO = tmp3         !partial result after iteration prior to the
                     !one causing the overflow or underflow

R2⟨7:0⟩ = tmp1       !number of iterations remaining

R2⟨31:8⟩ = implementation dependent

R3 = tmp2            !points to table entry causing exception

R5'R4 = arg

POLYH

R3'R2'R1'RO = tmp3   !partial result after iteration prior to the
                     !one causing the overflow or underflow

R4⟨7:0⟩ = tmp1       !number of iterations remaining

R4⟨31:8⟩ = implementation dependent

R5 = tmp2            !points to table entry causing exception
```

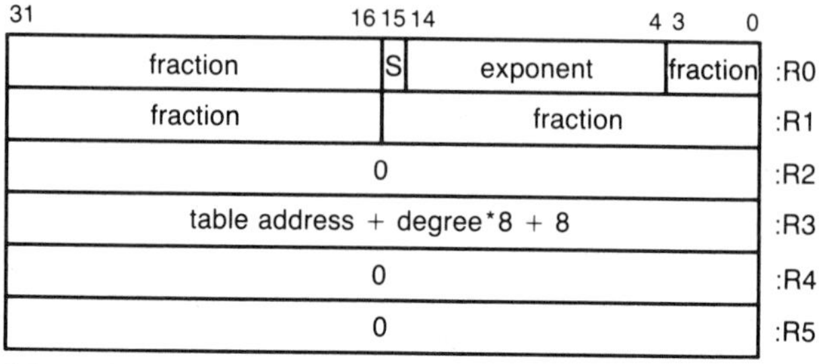

POLYG

Figure 3.5
POLYG Result Register

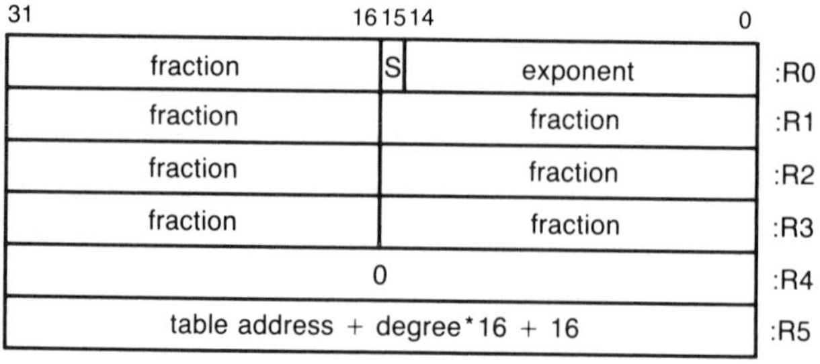

POLYH

Figure 3.6
POLYH Result Register

arg is saved on the stack in use during the faulting instruction. Implementation dependent information is saved to allow the instruction to continue after possible scaling of the coefficients and partial result by a fault handler.

3. If the unsigned-word degree operand is 0 and the argument is not a reserved operand, the result is C[0]. If the degree is 0 and either the argument or C[0] is a reserved operand, a reserved operand fault occurs.

4. If the unsigned-word degree operand is greater than 31, a reserved operand fault occurs.

5. On a reserved operand fault:

   - If PSL⟨FPD⟩ = 0, the reserved operand is either the degree operand (greater than 31), or the argument operand, or some coefficient.

   - If PSL⟨FPD⟩ = 1, the reserved operand is a coefficient, and R3 (except for POLYH) or R5 (for POLYH) is pointing at the value that caused the exception.

   - The state of the saved condition codes and the other registers is UNPREDICTABLE. If the reserved operand is changed and the contents of the condition codes and all registers are preserved, the fault is continuable.

6. On floating underflow after the rounding operation at any iteration of the computation loop, a fault occurs if FU is set. If FU is clear, the temporary result (tmp3) is replaced by 0 and the operation continues. In this case, the final result may be non-zero if underflow occurred before the last iteration.

7. On floating overflow after the rounding operation at any iteration of the computation loop, the instruction terminates with a fault.

8. If the argument is zero, the result is C[0]. Additionally, if one of the coefficients in the table (other than C[0]) is a reserved operand, whether a reserved operand fault occurs is UNPREDICTABLE.

9. For POLYH, some implementations may not save arg on the stack until after an interrupt or fault occurs. However, arg will always be on the stack if an interrupt or floating fault occurs after FPD is set. If the four longwords on the stack overlap any of the source operands, the results are UNPREDICTABLE.

Example:
To compute $P(x) = C0 + C1*x + C2*x^2$
where C0 = 1.0, C1 = .5, and C2 = .25

```
POLYF    X,#2,PTABLE
    .
    .
    .
```

```
PTABLE:            .FLOAT  0.25      ;C2
                   .FLOAT  0.5       ;C1
                   .FLOAT  1.0       ;C0
```

Subtract

Format:

```
opcode sub.rx, dif.mx           2 operand
opcode sub.rx, min.rx, dif.wx   3 operand
```

Operation:

```
dif ← dif - sub;      !2 operand
dif ← min - sub;      !3 operand
```

Condition Codes:

```
N ← dif LSS 0;
Z ← dif EQL 0;
V ← 0;
C ← 0;
```

Exceptions:

floating overflow

floating underflow

reserved operand

Opcodes:

```
42     SUBF2 Subtract F_floating 2 Operand
43     SUBF3 Subtract F_floating 3 Operand
62     SUBD2 Subtract D_floating 2 Operand
63     SUBD3 Subtract D_floating 3 Operand
42FD   SUBG2 Subtract G_floating 2 Operand
43FD   SUBG3 Subtract G_floating 3 Operand
62FD   SUBH2 Subtract H_floating 2 Operand
63FD   SUBH3 Subtract H_floating 3 Operand
```

Description:

In 2 operand format, the subtrahend operand is subtracted from the difference operand and the difference is replaced by the rounded result. In 3 operand format, the subtrahend operand is subtracted from the minuend operand and the difference operand is replaced by the rounded result.

Notes:

1. On a reserved operand fault, the difference operand is unaffected and the condition codes are UNPREDICTABLE.

2. On floating underflow, a fault occurs if FU is set. Zero is stored as the result of floating underflow only if FU is clear. On a floating underflow fault, the difference operand is unaffected. If FU is clear, the difference operand is replaced by 0 and no exception occurs.

3. On floating overflow, the instruction faults. The difference operand is unaffected, and the condition codes are UNPREDICTABLE.

ST   Test

Format:

opcode src.rx

Operation:

src - 0;

Condition Codes:

N ← src LSS 0;
Z ← src EQL 0;
V ← 0;
C ← 0;

Exception:

reserved operand

Opcodes:

53	TSTF	Test F_floating
73	TSTD	Test D_floating
53FD	TSTG	Test G_floating
73FD	TSTH	Test H_floating

Description:

The condition codes are affected according to the value of the source operand.

Notes:

1. TSTx src is equivalent to CMPx src, #0, but is 5 (F_floating) or 9 (D_floating or G_floating) or 17 (H_floating) bytes shorter.

2. On a reserved operand fault, the condition codes are UNPREDICTABLE.

CHARACTER-STRING INSTRUCTIONS

The character-string instructions, except for MOVC3 and MOVC5, may be omitted from subset implementations of the VAX architecture. Execution of an omitted instruction results in an emulated instruction exception. Omitted instructions may be emulated by operating system software and may use user-mode stack space during emulation. For more detail, refer to Chapter 11.

A character string is specified by two operands:

- An unsigned word operand that specifies the length of the character string in bytes

- The address of the lowest addressed byte of the character string. This is specified by a byte operand of address access type.

Each of the character-string instructions uses general registers R0 through R1, R0 through R3, or R0 through R5 to contain a control block that maintains updated addresses and state during the execution of the instruction. When instruction execution is completed, these registers are available to software to use as string specification operands for a subsequent instruction on a contiguous character string. During the execution of the instructions, pending interrupt conditions are tested. If any is found, the control block is updated, a first-part-done bit is set in the PSL, and the instruction interrupted (see Chapter 5). After the interruption, the instruction resumes transparently.

The format of the control block is shown in Figure 3.7. The fields length 1, length 2 (if required), and length 3 (if required) contain the number of bytes remaining to be processed in the first, second, and third string operands respectively. The fields address 1, address 2 (if required), and address 3 (if required) contain the address of the next byte to be processed in the first, second, and third string operands respectively.

Memory access faults will not occur when a zero-length string is specified because no memory reference occurs.

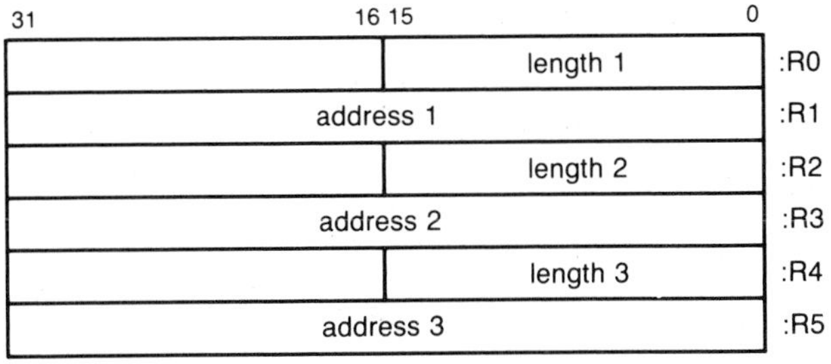

Figure 3.7
Character-String Instruction Control Block

Compare Characters

Format:

```
opcode len.rw, srcladdr.ab, src2addr.ab    3 operand
opcode srcllen.rw, srcladdr.ab, fill.rb,
       src2len.rw, src2addr.ab             5 operand
```

Operation:

```
tmpl ← len;                                !3 operand
tmp2 ← srcladdr;
tmp3 ← src2addr;
if tmpl EQL 0 then; !Condition Codes affected on tmpl EQL 0
if tmpl GTRU 0 then
        begin
        while {tmpl NEQU 0} do
                if (tmp2) EQL (tmp3) then
                !Condition Codes affected
                !on ((tmp2) EQL (tmp3))
                        begin
                        tmpl ← tmpl - l;
                        tmp2 ← tmp2 + l;
                        tmp3 ← tmp3 + l;
                        end;
                else exit while loop;
        end;
R0 ← tmpl;
R1 ← tmp2;
R2 ← R0;
R3 ← tmp3;
```

```
tmp1 ← src1len;                              !5 operand
tmp2 ← src1addr;
tmp3 ← src2len;
tmp4 ← src2addr;
if {tmp1 EQL 0} AND {tmp3 EQL 0} then; !Condition codes affected on
                                       !{tmp1 EQL 0} AND {tmp3 EQL 0}
       while {tmp1 NEQU 0} AND {tmp3 NEQU 0} do
              if (tmp2) EQL (tmp4) then !Condition Codes affecte
                                        !on ((tmp2) EQL (tmp4))
                       begin
                       tmp1 ← tmp1 - 1;
                       tmp2 ← tmp2 + 1;
                       tmp3 ← tmp3 - 1;
                       tmp4 ← tmp4 + 1;
                       end;
              else exit while loop;
if NOT{tmp1 NEQU 0} AND {tmp3 NEQU 0} then
       begin
       while {tmp1 NEQU 0} AND {(tmp2) EQL fill} do !Condition Code
                                      !affected on ((tmp2) EQL fil
                       begin
                       tmp1 ← tmp1 - 1;
                       tmp2 ← tmp2 + 1;
                       end;
       while {tmp3 NEQU 0} AND {fill EQL (tmp4)} do !Condition Code
                                      !affected on (fill EQL (tmp4
                       begin
                       tmp3 ← tmp3 - 1;
                       tmp4 ← tmp4 + 1;
                       end;
       end;
R0 ← tmp1;
R1 ← tmp2;
R2 ← tmp3;
R3 ← tmp4;
```

Condition Codes:

```
!Final Condition Codes reflect last affecting
!of Condition Codes in Operation above.
N ← {first byte} LSS {second byte};
Z ← {first byte} EQL {second byte};
```

V ← 0;

C ← {first byte} LSSU {second byte};

Exceptions:
none

Opcodes:

29 CMPC3 Compare Characters 3 Operand

2D CMPC5 Compare Characters 5 Operand

Description:
In 3 operand format, the bytes of string 1 specified by the length and address 1 operands are compared with the bytes of string 2 specified by the length and address 2 operands. Comparison proceeds until inequality is detected or all the bytes of the strings have been examined. Condition codes are affected by the result of the last byte comparison. In 5 operand format, the bytes of the string 1 specified by the length 1 and address 1 operands are compared with the bytes of the string 2 specified by the length 2 and address 2 operands. If one string is longer than the other, the shorter string is conceptually extended to the length of the longer by appending (at higher addresses) bytes equal to the fill operand. Comparison proceeds until inequality is detected or all the bytes of the strings have been examined. Condition codes are affected by the result of the last byte comparison. For either CMPC3 or CMPC5, two zero-length strings compare equal (Z is set and N, V, and C are cleared).

Notes:
1. After execution of CMPC3:

    R0 = number of bytes remaining in string 1 (including byte that terminated comparison); R0 is zero only if strings are equal

    R1 = address of the byte in string 1 that terminated comparison; if strings are equal, address of one byte beyond string 1

    R2 = R0

    R3 = address of the byte in string 2 that terminated comparison; if strings are equal, address of one byte beyond string 2.

2. After execution of CMPC5:

    R0 = number of bytes remaining in string 1 (including byte that terminated comparison); R0 is zero only if string 1 and string 2 are of equal length and equal or string 1 was exhausted before comparison terminated

R1 = address of the byte in string 1 that terminated comparison; if comparison did not terminate before string 1 exhausted, address of one byte beyond string 1

R2 = number of bytes remaining in string 2 (including byte that terminated comparison); R2 is zero only if string 2 and string 1 are of equal length or string 2 was exhausted before comparison terminated

R3 = address of the byte in string 2 that terminated comparison; if comparison did not terminate before string 2 was exhausted, address of one byte beyond string 2.

3. If both strings have zero length, condition code Z is set and N, V, and C are cleared just as in the case of two equal strings.

LOCC

Locate Character

Format:

opcode char.rb, len.rw, addr.ab

Operation:

```
tmp1 ← len;
tmp2 ← addr;
if tmp1 GTRU 0 then
        begin
        while {tmp1 NEQ 0} AND {(tmp2) NEQ char} do
                begin
                tmp1 ← tmp1 - 1;
                tmp2 ← tmp2 + 1;
                end;
        end;
R0 ← tmp1;
R1 ← tmp2;
```

Condition Codes:

```
N ← 0;
Z ← R0 EQL 0;
V ← 0;
C ← 0;
```

Exceptions:
none

Opcode:
3A LOCC Locate Character

Description:
The character operand is compared with the bytes of the string specified by the length and address operands. Comparison continues until equality is detected or all bytes of the string have been compared. If equality is detected, the condition code Z-bit is cleared; otherwise, the Z-bit is set.

Notes:
1. After execution:

    R0 = number of bytes remaining in the string (including located one) if byte located; otherwise 0

    R1 = address of the byte located if byte located; otherwise address of one byte beyond the string.

2. If the string has zero length, condition code Z is set just as though each byte of the entire string were unequal to character.

MATCHC   Match Characters

Format:
opcode objlen.rw, objaddr.ab, srclen.rw, srcaddr.ab

Operation:
```
tmpl ← objlen;
tmp2 ← objaddr;
tmp3 ← srclen;
tmp4 ← srcaddr;
tmp5 ← tmpl;
while {tmpl NEQU 0} AND {tmp3 GEQU tmpl} do
        begin
        if (tmp2) EQL (tmp4) then
                begin
                tmpl ← tmpl - 1;
                tmp2 ← tmp2 + 1;
                tmp3 ← tmp3 - 1;
```

```
                        tmp4 ← tmp4 + l;
                        end
            else
                        begin
                        tmp2 ← tmp2 - ZEXT (tmp5-tmpl);
                        tmp3 ← {tmp3 - l} + {tmp5-tmpl};
                        tmp4 ← {tmp4 + l} - ZEXT (tmp5-tmpl);
                        tmpl ← tmp5;
                        end;
            end;
if {tmp3 LSSU tmpl} then
            begin
            tmp4 ← tmp4 + tmp3;
            tmp3 ← 0;
            end;
R0 ← tmpl;
R1 ← tmp2;
R2 ← tmp3;
R3 ← tmp4;
```

Condition Codes:

```
N ← 0;
Z ← R0 EQL 0; !match found
V ← 0;
C ← 0;
```

Exceptions:
none

Opcode:

39   MATCHC   Match Characters

Description:
The source string specified by the source length and source address operands is searched for a substring that matches the object string specified by the object length and object address operands. If the substring is found, the condition code Z-bit is set; otherwise, it is cleared.

Notes:

1. After execution:

   R0 = if a match occurred 0; otherwise, the number ofbytes in the object string

   R1 = if a match occurred, the address of one byte beyond the object string (that is, objaddr + objlen); otherwise, the address of the object string

   R2 = if a match occurred, the number of bytes remaining in the source string; otherwise 0

   R3 = if a match occurred, the address of one byte beyond the last byte matched; otherwise, the address of one byte beyond the source string (that is, srcaddr + srclen).

   For zero length source and object strings, R3 and R1 contain the source and object addresses respectively.

2. If both strings have zero length or if the object string has zero length, condition code Z is set and registers R0 through R3 are left just as though the substring were found.

3. If the source string has zero length and the object string has non-zero length, condition code Z is cleared and registers R0 through R3 are left just as though the substring were not found.

MOVC   Move Character

Format:

```
opcode len.rw, srcaddr.ab, dstaddr.ab      3 operand
opcode srclen.rw, srcaddr.ab, fill.rb,
       dstlen.rw, dstaddr.ab                5 operand
```

Operation:

```
tmp1 ← len;                              !3 operand
tmp2 ← srcaddr;
tmp3 ← dstaddr;
if tmp2 GTRU tmp3 then
        begin
        while tmp1 NEQU 0 do
                begin
                (tmp3) ← (tmp2);
                tmp1 ← tmp1 - 1;
                tmp2 ← tmp2 + 1;
```

```
                        tmp3 ← tmp3 + 1;
                        end;
            R1 ← tmp2;
            R3 ← tmp3;
            end
    else
            begin
            tmp4 ← tmp1;
            tmp2 ← tmp2 + ZEXT(tmp1);
            tmp3 ← tmp3 + ZEXT(tmp1);
            while tmp1 NEQU 0 do
                        begin
                        tmp1 ← tmp1 - 1;
                        tmp2 ← tmp2 - 1;
                        tmp3 ← tmp3 - 1;
                        (tmp3) ← (tmp2);
                        end;
            R1 ← tmp2 + ZEXT(tmp4);
            R3 ← tmp3 + ZEXT(tmp4);
            end;
    R0 ← 0;
    R2 ← 0;
    R4 ← 0;
    R5 ← 0;
    tmp1 ← srclen;                              !5 operand
    tmp2 ← srcaddr;
    tmp3 ← dstlen;
    tmp4 ← dstaddr;
    if tmp2 GTRU tmp4 then
            begin
            while {tmp1 NEQU 0} AND {tmp3 NEQU 0} do
                        begin
                        (tmp4) ← (tmp2);
                        tmp1 ← tmp1 - 1;
                        tmp2 ← tmp2 + 1;
                        tmp3 ← tmp3 - 1;
                        tmp4 ← tmp4 + 1;
                        end;
```

```
while tmp3 NEQU 0 do
        begin
        (tmp4) ← fill;
        tmp3 ← tmp3 - 1;
        tmp4 ← tmp4 + 1;
        end;
R1 ← tmp2;
R3 ← tmp4;
end
else
        begin
        tmp5 ← MINU(tmp1, tmp3);
        tmp6 ← tmp3;
        tmp2 ← tmp2 + ZEXT(tmp5);
        tmp4 ← tmp4 + ZEXT(tmp6);
        while tmp3 GTRU tmp1 do
                begin
                tmp3 ← tmp3 - 1;
                tmp4 ← tmp4 - 1;
                (tmp4) ← fill;
                end;
        while tmp3 NEQU 0 do
                begin
                tmp1 ← tmp1 - 1;
                tmp2 ← tmp2 - 1;
                tmp3 ← tmp3 - 1;
                tmp4 ← tmp4 - 1;
                (tmp4) ← (tmp2);
                end;
        R1 ← tmp2 + ZEXT (tmp5);
        R3 ← tmp4 + ZEXT (tmp6);
        end;
R0 ← tmp1;
R2 ← 0;
R4 ← 0;
R5 ← 0;
```

Condition Codes:

```
N ← 0;                          !MOVC3
Z ← 1;
V ← 0;
C ← 0;
N ← srclen LSS dstlen; !MOVC5
Z ← srclen EQL dstlen;
V ← 0;
C ← srclen LSSU dstlen;
```

Exceptions:
none

Opcodes:

```
28  MOVC3  Move Character 3 Operand
2C  MOVC5  Move Character 5 Operand
```

Description:
In 3 operand format, the destination string specified by the length and destination address operands is replaced by the source string specified by the length and source address operands. In 5 operand format, the destination string specified by the destination length and destination address operands is replaced by the source string specified by the source length and source address operands. If the destination string is longer than the source string, the highest addressed bytes of the destination are replaced by the fill operand. If the destination string is shorter than the source string, the highest addressed bytes of the source string are not moved. The operation of the instruction is such that overlap of the source and destination strings does not affect the result.

Notes:
1. After execution of MOVC3:

   R0 = 0

   R1 = address of one byte beyond the source string

   R2 = 0

   R3 = address of one byte beyond the destination string.

   R4 = 0

   R5 = 0.

2. After execution of MOVC5:

   R0 = number of unmoved bytes remaining in source string; R0 is non-zero only if source string is longer than destination string

R1 = address of one byte beyond the last byte in source string that was moved

R2 = 0

R3 = address of one byte beyond the destination string

R4 = 0

R5 = 0.

3. MOVC3 is the preferred way to copy one block of memory to another.

4. MOVC5 with a zero source length operand is the preferred way to fill a block of memory with the fill character.

OVTC

Move Translated Characters

Format:

```
opcode srclen.rw, srcaddr.ab, fill.rb, tbladdr.ab,
       dstlen.rw, dstaddr.ab
```

Operation:

```
tmp1 ← srclen;
tmp2 ← srcaddr;
tmp3 ← dstlen;
tmp4 ← dstaddr;
if tmp2 GTRU tmp4 then
        begin
        while {tmp1 NEQU 0} AND {tmp3 NEQU 0} do
                begin
                (tmp4) ← (tbladdr + ZEXT((tmp2)));
                tmp1 ← tmp1 - 1;
                tmp2 ← tmp2 + 1;
                tmp3 ← tmp3 - 1;
                tmp4 ← tmp4 + 1;
                end;
        while {tmp3 NEQU 0} do
                begin
                (tmp4) ← fill;
                tmp3 ← tmp3 - 1;
                tmp4 ← tmp4 + 1;
                end;
```

```
                    R1 ← tmp2;
                    R5 ← tmp4;
                    end;
        else

                    begin
                    tmp5 ← MINU(tmp1,tmp3);
                    tmp6 ← tmp3;
                    tmp2 ← tmp2 + ZEXT(tmp5);
                    tmp4 ← tmp4 + ZEXT(tmp6);
                    while tmp3 GTRU tmp1 do
                            begin
                            tmp3 ← tmp3 - 1;
                            tmp4 ← tmp4 - 1;
                            (tmp4) ← fill;
                            end;
                    while tmp3 NEQU 0 do
                            begin
                            tmp1 ← tmp1 - 1;
                            tmp2 ← tmp2 - 1;
                            tmp3 ← tmp3 - 1;
                            tmp4 ← tmp4 - 1;
                            (tmp4) ← (tbladdr + ZEXT((tmp2)));
                            end;
                    R1 ← tmp2 + ZEXT(tmp5);
                    R5 ← tmp4 + ZEXT(tmp6);
                    end;
        R0 ← tmp1;
        R2 ← 0;
        R3 ← tbladdr;
        R4 ← 0;
```

Condition Codes:

```
N ← srclen LSS dstlen;
Z ← srclen EQL dstlen;
V ← 0;
C ← srclen LSSU dstlen;
```

Exceptions:

Opcode:

```
2E  MOVTC  Move Translated Characters
```

Description:

The source string specified by the source length and source address operands is translated and replaces the destination string specified by the destination length and destination address operands. Translation is accomplished by using each byte of the source string as an index into a 256-byte table whose zeroth entry address is specified by the table address operand. The byte selected replaces the byte of the destination string. If the destination string is longer than the source string, the highest addressed bytes of the destination string are replaced by the fill operand. If the destination string is shorter than the source string, the highest addressed bytes of the source string are not translated and moved. The operation of the instruction is such that overlap of the source and destination strings does not affect the result. If the destination string overlaps the translation table, the destination string is UNPREDICTABLE.

Notes:

After execution:

R0 = number of untranslated bytes remaining in source string; R0 is non-zero only if source string is longer than destination string

R1 = address of one byte beyond the last byte in source string that was translated

R2 = 0

R3 = address of the translation table

R4 = 0

R5 = address of one byte beyond the destination string.

MOVTUC

Move Translated Until Character

Format:

```
opcode srclen.rw, srcaddr.ab, esc.rb, tbladdr.ab, dstlen.rw,
       dstaddr.ab
```

Operation:

```
tmp1 ← srclen;
tmp2 ← srcaddr;
tmp3 ← dstlen;
tmp4 ← dstaddr;
if tmp1 GTRU 0 and tmp3 GTRU 0 then
```

```
                begin
        while {tmpl NEQU 0} AND {tmp3 NEQU 0} do
        if{(tbladdr + ZEXT(tmp2)) NEQU esc} then
                begin
                (tmp4) ← (tbladdr + ZEXT(tmp2));
                tmpl ← tmpl - 1;
                tmp2 ← tmp2 + 1;
                tmp3 ← tmp3 - 1;
                tmp4 ← tmp4 + 1;
                end;
            else exit while loop;
            end;
RO ← tmpl;
Rl ← tmp2;
R2 ← 0;
R3 ← tbladdr;
R4 ← tmp3;
R5 ← tmp4;
```

Condition Codes:

```
N ← srclen LSS dstlen;
Z ← srclen EQL dstlen;
V ← {terminated by escape};
C ← srclen LSSU dstlen;
```

Exceptions:
none

Opcode:

```
2F   MOVTUC   Move Translated Until Character
```

Description:
The source string specified by the source length and source address
operands is translated and replaces the destination string specified b
the destination length and destination address operands. Translation
is accomplished by using each byte of the source string as index into
a 256-byte table whose zeroth entry address is specified by the
table address operand. The byte selected replaces the byte of the
destination string. Translation continues until a translated byte is
equal to the escape byte or until the source string or destination strin
is exhausted. If translation is terminated because of escape, the
condition code V-bit is set; otherwise, it is cleared. If the destination

string overlaps the table, the destination string and registers R0 through R5 are UNPREDICTABLE. If the source and destination strings overlap and their addresses are not identical, the destination string and registers R0 through R5 are UNPREDICTABLE. If the source and destination string addresses are identical, the translation is performed correctly.

Notes:
After execution:

R0 = number of bytes remaining in source string (including the byte that caused the escape); R0 is zero only if the entire source string was translated and moved without escape

R1 = address of the byte that resulted in destination string exhaustion or escape; or if no exhaustion or escape, address of one byte beyond the source string

R2 = 0

R3 = address of the table

R4 = number of bytes remaining in the destination string

R5 = address of the byte in the destination string that would have received the translated byte that caused the escape or would have received a translated byte if the source string were not exhausted; or if no exhaustion or escape, the address of one byte beyond the destination string.

SCANC

Scan Characters

Format:

```
opcode len.rw, addr.ab, tbladdr.ab, mask.rb
```

Operation:

```
tmp1 ← len;
tmp2 ← addr;
if tmp1 GTRU 0 then
        begin
        while {tmp1 NEQU 0} AND {{(tbladdr + ZEXT((tmp2)))
                AND mask} EQL 0} do
                begin
                tmp1 ← tmp1 - 1;
                tmp2 ← tmp2 + 1;
                end;
        end;
```

```
RO ← tmpl;
Rl ← tmp2;
R2 ← 0;
R3 ← tbladdr;
```

Condition Codes:

```
N ← 0;
Z ← RO EQL 0;
V ← 0;
C ← 0;
```

Exceptions:
none

Opcode:

2A SCANC   Scan Characters

Description:
The bytes of the string specified by the length and address operands
are successively used to index into a 256-byte table whose zeroth
entry address is specified by the table address operand. The byte
selected from the table is ANDed with the mask operand. The
operation continues until the result of the AND is non-zero or all the
bytes of the string have been exhausted. If a non-zero AND result
is detected, the condition code Z-bit is cleared; otherwise, the Z-bit is
set.

Notes:
1. After execution:

   RO = number of bytes remaining in the string (including the byte
   that produced the non-zero AND result);

   RO is zero only if there was no non-zero AND result

   R1 = address of the byte that produced non-zero AND result; or, if
   no non-zero result, address of one byte beyond the string

   R2 = 0

   R3 = address of the table.

2. If the string has zero length, condition code Z is set just as though
   the entire string were scanned.

Skip Character

Format:

opcode char.rb, len.rw, addr.ab

Operation:

```
tmp1 ← len;
tmp2 ← addr;
if tmp1 GTRU 0 then
        begin
while {tmp1 NEQ 0} AND {(tmp2) EQL char} do
        begin
        tmp1 ← tmp1 - 1;
        tmp2 ← tmp2 + 1;
        end;
        end;
R0 ← tmp1;
R1 ← tmp2;
```

Condition Codes:

```
N ← 0;
Z ← R0 EQL 0;
V ← 0;
C ← 0;
```

Exceptions:
none

Opcode:

3B   SKPC   Skip Character

Description:
The character operand is compared with the bytes of the string specified by the length and address operands. Comparison continues until inequality is detected or all bytes of the string have been compared. If inequality is detected; the condition code Z-bit is cleared; otherwise the Z-bit is set.

Notes:
1. After execution:

    R0 = number of bytes remaining in the string (including the unequal one) if unequal byte located; otherwise, 0

R1 = address of the byte located if byte located; otherwise address of one byte beyond the string.

2. If the string has zero length, condition code Z is set just as though each byte of the entire string were equal to character.

SPANC   Span Characters

Format:

opcode len.rw, addr.ab, tbladdr.ab, mask.rb

Operation:

```
tmp1 ← len;
tmp2 ← addr;
if tmp1 GTRU 0 then
        begin
        while {tmp1 NEQU 0} AND
                {{(tbladdr + ZEXT((tmp2))) AND
                mask} NEQ 0} do
                begin
                tmp1 ← tmp1 - 1;
                tmp2 ← tmp2 + 1;
                end;
        end;
R0 ← tmp1;
R1 ← tmp2;
R2 ← 0;
R3 ← tbladdr;
```

Condition Codes:

```
N ← 0;
Z ← R0 EQL 0;
V ← 0;
C ← 0;
```

Exceptions:
none

Opcode:

2B SPANC Span Characters

Description:

The bytes of the string specified by the length and address operands are successively used to index into a 256-byte table whose zeroth entry address is specified by the table address operand. The byte selected from the table is ANDed with the mask operand. The operation continues until the result of the AND is zero or all the bytes of the string have been exhausted. If a zero AND result is detected, the condition code Z-bit is cleared; otherwise, the Z-bit is set.

Notes:

1. After execution:

   R0 = number of bytes remaining in the string (including the byte that produced the zero AND result); R0 is zero only if there was no zero AND result

   R1 = address of the byte that produced a zero AND result; or, if no non-zero result, address of one byte beyond the string

   R2 = 0

   R3 = address of the table.

2. If the string has zero length, the condition code Z is set just as though the entire string were spanned.

CYCLIC REDUNDANCY CHECK INSTRUCTION

Note

The cyclic redundancy check instructions may be omitted from subset implementations of the VAX architecture. Execution of an omitted instruction results in an emulated instruction exception. For more detail, refer to Chapter 11.

This instruction is designed to implement the calculation and checking of a cyclic redundancy check (CRC) for any CRC polynomial up to 32 bits. Cyclic redundancy checking is an error-detection method involving a division of the data stream by a CRC polynomial. The data stream is represented as a standard VAX string in memory. Error detection is accomplished by computing the CRC at the source and again at the destination, comparing the CRC computed at each end. The choice of the polynomial is such as to minimize the number of undetected block errors of specific lengths. The choice of a CRC polynomial is not given here.*

The operands to the CRC instruction are a string descriptor, a 16-longword table, and an initial CRC. The string descriptor is a standard VAX operand pair of the length of the string in bytes (up to 65,535) and the starting address of the string. The contents of the table are a

---

*See the article "Cyclic Codes for Error Detection" by W. Peterson and D. Brown in the *Proceedings of the IRE* (January 1961).

function of the CRC polynomial to be used. It can be calculated
from the polynomial by the algorithm in the notes. Several common
CRC polynomials are also included in the notes. The initial CRC
is used to start the polynomial correctly. Typically, it has the value 0
or −1, but would be different if the data stream were represented by
a sequence of non-contiguous strings.

The CRC instruction operates by scanning the string, and for each
byte of the data stream, including it in the CRC being calculated. The
byte is included by XORing it to the right 8 bits of the CRC. Then
the CRC is shifted right 1 bit, inserting zero on the left. The right-most
bit of the CRC (lost by the shift) is used to control the XORing of the
CRC polynomial with the resultant CRC. If the bit is set, the polynomi
is XORed with the CRC. Then the CRC is again shifted right, and the
polynomial is conditionally XORed with the result a total of eight
times. The actual algorithm used can shift by 1, 2, or 4 bits at a time
using the appropriate entries in a specially constructed table. The
instruction produces a 32-bit CRC. For shorter polynomials, the resul
must be extracted from the 32-bit field. The data stream must be a
multiple of 8 bits in length. If it is not, the stream must be right-
adjusted in the string with leading 0 bits.

CRC

Calculate Cyclic Redundancy Check

Format:

opcode tbl.ab, inicrc.rl, strlen.rw, stream.ab

Operation:

```
tmp1 ← strlen;
tmp2 ← stream;
tmp3 ← inicrc;
tmp4 ← tbl;
while tmp1 NEQU 0 do
        begin
        tmp3⟨7:0⟩← tmp3⟨7:0⟩ XOR (tmp2)+;
        for tmp5 ← 1,limit do !see notes for limit,s,i
                tmp3 ← ZEXT(tmp3⟨31:s⟩) XOR
                        (tmp4 + {4*ZEXT(tmp3⟨s−1:0⟩*i)};
        tmp1 ← tmp1 −1;
        end;
R0 ← tmp3;
R1 ← 0;
```

```
R2 ← 0;
R3 ← tmp2;
```

Condition Codes:

```
N ← R0 LSS 0;
Z ← R0 EQL 0;
V ← 0;
C ← 0;
```

Exceptions:
none

Opcode:

```
0B  CRC  Calculate Cyclic Redundancy Check
```

Description:
The CRC of the data stream described by the string descriptor is
calculated. The initial CRC is given by inicrc and is normally 0 or −1
unless the CRC is calculated in several steps. The result is left in
R0. If the polynomial is less than order 32, the result must be
extracted from the result. The CRC polynomial is expressed by the
contents of the 16-longword table. See the notes for the calculation of
the table.

Notes:
1. If the data stream is not a multiple of 8-bits long, it must be right-
   adjusted with leading 0 fill.

2. If the CRC polynomial is less than order 32, the result must be
   extracted from the low-order bits of R0.

3. The following algorithm can be used to calculate the CRC table
   given a polynomial expressed as follows:

   $$\text{polyn}\langle n \rangle \leftarrow \{\text{coefficient of } x^{\{order\ -1-n\}}\}$$

   This routine is available as system library routine
   LIB$CRC__TABLE (poly.rl, table.ab). The bits of the poly operand,
   taken right to left, represent the coefficients of the polynomial,
   taken left to right and skipping the most significant bit. The table is
   the location of a 64-byte (16-longword) table into which the result
   will be written.

   ```
   SUBROUTINE LIB$CRC-TABLE (POLY, TABLE)
   INTEGER*4 POLY, TABLE(0:15), TMP, X
   DO 190 INDEX = 0, 15
   TMP = INDEX
   DO 150 I = 1, 4
   ```

Table 3.1
CRC-16

Polynomial	POLY	Initialize Value	Result
CRC-16 (used for DDCMP and Bisync) $x^{16}+x^{15}+x^2+1$	0000A001	00000000	R0$\langle 15:0\rangle$
CCITT (used for ADCCP, HDLC, SDLC) $x^{16}+x^{12}+x^5+1$	00008408	0000FFFF	one's complement of R0$\langle 15:0\rangle$
AUTODIN-II $x^{32}+x^{26}+x^{23}+x^{22}+$ $x^{16}+x^{12}+x^{11}+x^{10}+$ $x^8+x^7+x^5+x^4+x^2+x+1$	EDB88320	FFFFFFFF	one's complement of R0$\langle 31:0\rangle$

```
          X   = TMP .AND. 1
          TMP = ISHFT(TMP,-1)      !logical shift right
                     one bit
          IF (X .EQ. 1) TMP = TMP .XOR. POLY
150       CONTINUE
          TABLE(INDEX) = TMP
190       CONTINUE
          RETURN
          END
```

4. Table 3.1 describes some commonly used CRC polynomials.

5. This instruction produces an UNPREDICTABLE result unless the table is well formed, such as produced in item 3 above. Note that for any well formed table, entry[0] is always 0 and entry[8] is always the polynomial expressed as in item 3 above. The operation can be implemented using shifts of 1, 2, or 4 bits at a time as shown in Table 3.2.

6. If the stream has zero length, R0 receives the initial CRC.

Table 3.2
CRC Shift Amounts

Shift Amount(s)	Steps Per Byte (Limit)	Table Index	Table Index Multiplier (1)	Table Entries Used
1	8	tmp3$\langle 0\rangle$	8	[0]=0,[8]
2	4	tmp3$\langle 1:0\rangle$	4	[0]=0,[4],[8],[12]
4	2	tmp3$\langle 3:0\rangle$	1	all

Decimal-string instructions may be omitted from subset implementations of the VAX architecture. Execution of an omitted instruction results in an emulated instruction exception. Omitted instructions may be emulated by operating system software, which may use user-mode stack space during the emulation. For more detail, refer to Chapter 11.

Decimal-string instructions operate on packed decimal strings. Convert instructions are provided between packed decimal and trailing numeric string (overpunched and zoned) and leading separate numeric string formats. Where necessary, a specific data type is identified. Where the phrase decimal string is used, it means any of the three data types.

A decimal string is specified by two operands:

- The first operand is the length; the number of digits in the string. The number of bytes in the string is a function of the length and the type of decimal string referenced (see Chapter 1).
- The second operand is the address of the lowest addressed byte of the string. This byte contains the most significant digit for trailing numeric and packed decimal strings. This byte contains a sign for left separate numeric strings. The address is specified by a byte operand of address access type.

Each of the decimal-string instructions uses general registers R0 through R3 or R0 through R5 to contain a control block that maintains updated addresses and state during the execution of the instruction. At completion, the registers containing addresses are available to the software to use as string specification operands for a subsequent instruction on the same decimal strings. During the execution of the instructions, pending interrupt conditions are tested, and if any is found, the control block is updated. First-part-done is set in the PSL, and the instruction interrupted (see Chapter 5). After the interruption, the instruction resumes transparently. The format of the control block at completion is shown in Figure 3.8. The fields address 1, address 2, and address 3 (if required) contain the address of the byte

31	0	
0		:R0
address 1		:R1
0		:R2
address 2		:R3
0		:R4
address 3		:R5

Figure 3.8
Decimal-String Instruction Control Block

containing the most significant digit of the first, second, and third (if required) string operands respectively.

The decimal-string instructions treat decimal strings as integers with the decimal point assumed immediately beyond the least significant digit of the string. If a string in which a result is to be stored is longer than the result, its most significant digits are filled with zeros.

Decimal Overflow

Decimal overflow occurs if the destination string is too short to contain all the digits (excluding leading zeros) of the result. On overflow, the destination string is replaced by the correctly signed least significant digits of the true result (even if the stored result is -0). Note that neither the high nibble of an even-length packed decimal string, nor the sign byte of a leading separate numeric string is used to store result digits.

Zero Numbers

A zero result has a positive sign for all operations that complete without decimal overflow, except for CVTPT which does not fix a -0 to a $+0$. When digits are lost because of overflow, however, a zero result receives the sign (positive or negative) of the correct result.

A decimal string with value -0 is treated as identical to a decimal string with value $+0$. For example, $+0$ compares equal to -0. When condition codes are affected on a -0 result they are affected as if the result were $+0$; that is, N is cleared and Z is set.

Reserved Operand Exception

A reserved operand abort occurs if the length of a decimal-string operand is outside the range 0 through 31, or if an invalid sign or digit is encountered in CVTSP and CVTTP. The PC points to the opcode of the instruction causing the exception.

UNPREDICTABLE Results

The result of any operation is UNPREDICTABLE if any source decimal-string operand contains invalid data. Except for CVTSP and CVTTP, the decimal-string instructions do not verify the validity of source operand data.

If the destination operands overlap any source operands, the result of an operation will, in general, be UNPREDICTABLE. The destination strings, registers used by the instruction and condition codes, will in general, be UNPREDICTABLE when a reserved operand abort occurs.

Packed decimal strings generated by the decimal-string instructions always have the preferred sign representation: 12 for "+" and 13 for "-". An even-length packed decimal string is always generated with a "0" digit in the high nibble of the first byte of the string.

A packed decimal string contains an invalid nibble if:

1. A digit occurs in the sign position

2. A sign occurs in a digit position

3. For an even-length string, a non-zero nibble occurs in the high order nibble of the lowest addressed byte.

The length of a packed decimal string can be 0. In this case, the value is zero (plus or minus) and one byte of storage is occupied. This byte must contain a "0" digit in the high nibble and the sign in the low nibble.

The length of a trailing numeric string can be 0. In this case, no storage is occupied by the string. If a destination operand is a zero-length trailing numeric string, the sign of the operation is lost. Memory access faults will not occur when a zero-length trailing numeric operand is specified because no memory reference occurs. The value of a zero-length trailing numeric string is identically 0.

The length of a leading separate numeric string can be 0. In this case, one byte of storage is occupied by the sign. Memory is accessed when a zero-length operand is specified, and a reserved operand abort occurs if an invalid sign is detected. The value of a zero-length leading separate numeric string is identically 0.

Add Packed

Format:

```
opcode addlen.rw, addaddr.ab, sumlen.rw,
       sumaddr.ab
opcode addllen.rw, addladdr.ab, add2len.rw,
       add2addr.ab, sumlen.rw, sumaddr.ab
```

Operation:

```
({sumaddr + ZEXT(sumlen/2)} : sumaddr) ←
       ({sumaddr + ZEXT(sumlen/2)} : sumaddr) +
       ({addaddr + ZEXT(addlen/2)} : addaddr); !4
```

operand

$(\{\text{sumaddr} + \text{ZEXT}(\text{sumlen}/2)\} : \text{sumaddr}) \leftarrow$

$(\{\text{add2addr} + \text{ZEXT}(\text{add2len}/2)\} : \text{add2addr}) +$

$(\{\text{addladdr} + \text{ZEXT}(\text{addllen}/2)\} : \text{addladdr}); !6$

operand

Condition Codes:

N ← {sum string} LSS 0;

Z ← {sum string} EQL 0;

V ← {decimal overflow};

C ← 0;

Exceptions:
reserved operand
decimal overflow

Opcodes:

20   ADDP4   Add Packed 4 Operand

21   ADDP6   Add Packed 6 Operand

Description:
In 4 operand format, the addend string specified by the addend lengt
and addend address operands is added to the sum string specified
by the sum length and sum address operands, and the sum string is
replaced by the result.

In 6 operand format, the addend 1 string specified by the addend 1
length and addend 1 address operands is added to the addend 2
string specified by the addend 2 length and addend 2 address
operands. The sum string specified by the sum length and sum
address operands is replaced by the result.

Notes:
1. After execution of ADDP4:

   R0 = 0

   R1 = address of the byte containing the most significant digit of
   the addend string

   R2 = 0

   R3 = address of the byte containing the most significant digit of
   the sum string.

2. After execution of ADDP6:

   R0 = 0

   R1 = address of the byte containing the most significant digit of
   the addend 1 string

R2 = 0

R3 = address of the byte containing the most significant digit of the addend 2 string

R4 = 0

R5 = address of the byte containing the most significant digit of the sum string.

3. The sum string, R0 through R3 (or R0 through R5 for ADDP6), and the condition codes are UNPREDICTABLE if the sum string overlaps the addend, addend 1, or addend 2 strings; the addend, addend 1, addend 2 or sum (4 operand only) strings contain an invalid nibble; or a reserved operand abort occurs.

Arithmetic Shift and Round Packed

Format:

```
opcode cnt.rb, srclen.rw, srcaddr.ab, round.rb
        dstlen.rw, dstaddr.ab
```

Operation:

$$(\{dstaddr + ZEXT(dstlen/2)\} : dstaddr) \leftarrow$$
$$\{(\{srcaddr + ZEXT(srclen/2)\} : srcaddr)$$
$$+ \{round \langle 3:0 \rangle * \{10 ** \{-cnt-1\}\}\}\}$$
$$* \{10 ** cnt\} ;$$

Condition Codes:

N ← {dst string} LSS 0;
Z ← {dst string} EQL 0;
V ← {decimal overflow};
C ← 0;

Exceptions:

reserved operand
decimal overflow

Opcode:

F8 ASHP Arithmetic Shift and Round Packed

Description:

The source string specified by the source length and source address operands is scaled by a power of 10 specified by the count operand. The destination string specified by the destination length and destination address operands is replaced by the result.

A positive count operand effectively multiplies; a negative count effectively divides; and a zero count just moves and affects condition codes. When a negative count is specified, the result is rounded usin the round operand.

Notes:

1. After execution:

   R0 = 0

   R1 = address of the byte containing the most significant digit of the source string

   R2 = 0

   R3 = address of the byte containing the most significant digit of the destination string.

2. The destination string, R0 through R3, and the condition codes are UNPREDICTABLE if the destination string overlaps the source string, the source string contains an invalid nibble, or a reserved operand abort occurs.

3. When the count operand is negative, the result is rounded by decimally adding bits ⟨3:0⟩ of the round operand to the most significant low-order digit discarded and propagating the carry, if any, to higher order digits. Both the source operand and the round operand are considered to be quantities of the same sign for the purpose of this addition.

4. If bits ⟨7:4⟩ of the round operand are non-zero, or if bits ⟨3:0⟩ of the round operand contain an invalid packed decimal digit, the result is UNPREDICTABLE.

5. When the count operand is zero or positive, the round operand has no effect on the result except as specified in item 4 above.

6. The round operand is normally five. Truncation may be accomplishe by using a zero round operand.

CMPP

Compare Packed

Format:

```
opcode len.rw, srcladdr.ab, src2addr.ab          3 operan
opcode srcllen.rw, srcladdr.ab, src2len.rw,
       src2addr.ab                               4
operand
```

Operation:

```
({srcladdr + ZEXT(len/2)} : srcladdr) −
       ({src2addr + ZEXT(len/2)} : src2addr); !3 operand
```

```
({srcladdr + ZEXT(srcllen/2)} : srcladdr) -
        ({src2addr + ZEXT(src2len/2)} : src2addr); !4 operand
```

Condition Codes:

```
N ← {srcl string} LSS {src2 string};
Z ← {srcl string} EQL {src2 string};
V ← 0;
C ← 0;
```

Exception:
reserved operand

Opcodes:

```
35  CMPP3   Compare Packed 3 Operand
37  CMPP4   Compare Packed 4 Operand
```

Description:
In 3 operand format, the source 1 string specified by the length and
source 1 address operands is compared to the source 2 string
specified by the length and source 2 address operands. The only
action is to affect the condition codes.

In 4 operand format, the source 1 string specified by the source 1
length and source 1 address operands is compared to the source 2
string specified by the source 2 length and source 2 address operands.
The only action is to affect the condition codes.

Notes:
1. After execution of CMPP3 or CMPP4:

   R0 = 0

   R1 = address of the byte containing the most significant digit of
   string 1

   R2 = 0

   R3 = address of the byte containing the most significant digit of
   string 2.

2. R0 through R3 and the condition codes are UNPREDICTABLE if
   the source strings overlap, if either string contains an invalid
   nibble, or if a reserved operand abort occurs.

CVTLP   Convert Long to Packed

Format:

```
opcode src.rl, dstlen.rw, dstaddr.ab
```

Operation:

```
({dstaddr + ZEXT(dstlen/2)} : dstaddr) ← conversion of src;
```

Condition Codes:

```
N ← {dst string} LSS 0;
Z ← {dst string} EQL 0;
V ← {decimal overflow};
C ← 0;
```

Exceptions:
reserved operand
decimal overflow

Opcode:

```
F9   CVTLP   Convert Long to Packed
```

Description:
The source operand is converted to a packed decimal string and the destination string operand specified by the destination length and destination address operands is replaced by the result.

Notes:
1. After execution:

   R0 = 0

   R1 = 0

   R2 = 0

   R3 = address of the byte containing the most significant digit of the destination string.
2. The destination string, R0 through R3, and the condition codes are UNPREDICTABLE on a reserved operand abort.
3. Overlapping operands produce correct results.

CVTPL   Convert Packed to Long

Format:

```
opcode srclen.rw, srcaddr.ab, dst.wl
```

Operation:

```
dst ← conversion of ({srcaddr + ZEXT(srclen/2)} : srcaddr);
```

Condition Codes:

```
N ← dst LSS 0;
Z ← dst EQL 0;
V ← {integer overflow};
C ← 0;
```

Exceptions:
reserved operand
integer overflow

Opcode:

```
36  CVTPL   Convert Packed to Long
```

Description:
The source string specified by the source length and source address operands is converted to a longword, and the destination operand is replaced by the result.

Notes:
1. After execution:

   R0 = 0

   R1 = address of the byte containing the most significant digit of the source string

   R2 = 0

   R3 = 0.

2. The destination operand, R0 through R3, and the condition codes are UNPREDICTABLE on a reserved operand abort or if the string contains an invalid nibble.

3. The destination operand is stored after the registers are updated as specified in item 1 above. Thus, R0 through R3 may be used as the destination operand.

4. If the source string has a value outside the range −2,147,483,648 through 2,147,483,647, integer overflow occurs and the destination operand is replaced by the low-order 32 bits of the correctly signed infinite precision conversion. Thus, on overflow, the sign of the destination may be different from the sign of the source.

5. Overlapping operands produce correct results.

CVTPS

Convert Packed to Leading Separate Numeric

Format:

```
opcode srclen.rw, srcaddr.ab, dstlen.rw, dstaddr.ab
```

Operation:

{dst string} ← conversion of {src string};

Condition Codes:

N ← {src string} LSS 0;
Z ← {src string} EQL 0;
V ← {decimal overflow};
C ← 0;

Exceptions:
reserved operand
decimal overflow

Opcode:

08 CVTPS Convert Packed to Leading Separate Numeric

Description:
The source packed decimal string specified by the source length and
source address operands is converted to a leading separate numeric
string. The destination string specified by the destination length
and destination address operands is replaced by the result.

Conversion is effected by replacing the lowest addressed byte of the
destination string with the ASCII character "+" or "−", determined
the sign of the source string. The remaining bytes of the destination
string are replaced by the ASCII representations of the values of
the corresponding packed decimal digits of the source string.

Notes:
1. After execution:

   R0 = 0

   R1 = address of the byte containing the most significant digit of
   the source string

   R2 = 0

   R3 = address of the sign byte of the destination string.
2. The destination string, R0 through R3, and the condition codes are
   UNPREDICTABLE if the destination string overlaps the source
   string, the source string contains an invalid nibble, or a reserved
   operand abort occurs.
3. This instruction produces an ASCII "+" or "-" in the sign byte of
   the destination string.
4. If decimal overflow occurs, the value stored in the destination may
   be different from the value indicated by the condition codes
   (Z and N bits).

5. If the conversion produces a -0 without overflow, the destination leading separate numeric string is changed to a $+0$ representation.

TPT

Convert Packed to Trailing Numeric

Format:

```
opcode srclen.rw, srcaddr.ab, tbladdr.ab, dstlen.rw,
    dstaddr.ab
```

Operation:

```
{dst string} ← conversion of {src string};
```

Condition Codes:

```
N ← {src string} LSS 0;
Z ← {src string} EQL 0;
V ← {decimal overflow};
C ← 0;
```

Exceptions:
reserved operand
decimal overflow

Opcode:

```
24  CVTPT  Convert Packed to Trailing Numeric
```

Description:
The source packed decimal string specified by the source length and source address operands is converted to a trailing numeric string. The destination string specified by the destination length and destination address operands is replaced by the result. The condition code N and Z bits are affected by the value of the source packed decimal string.

Conversion is effected by using the highest addressed byte (even if the source string value is -0) of the source string (the byte containing the sign and the least significant digit) as an unsigned index into a 256-byte table whose zeroth entry address is specified by the table address operand. The byte read out of the table replaces the least significant byte of the destination string. The remaining bytes of the destination string are replaced by the ASCII representations of the values of the corresponding packed decimal digits of the source string.

Notes:

1. After execution:

   R0 = 0

   R1 = address of the byte containing the most significant digit of the source string

   R2 = 0

   R3 = address of the most significant digit of the destination string

2. The destination string, R0 through R3, and the condition codes are UNPREDICTABLE if the destination string overlaps the source string or the table, the source string or the table contains an inval nibble, or a reserved operand abort occurs.

3. The condition codes are computed on the value of the source string even if overflow results. In particular, condition code N is se if and only if the source is non-zero and contains a minus sign.

4. By appropriate specification of the table, conversion to any form c trailing numeric string may be realized. See Chapter 1 for the preferred form of trailing overpunch, zoned and unsigned data. In addition, the table may be set up for absolute value, negative absolute value, or negated conversions. The translation table may be referenced even if the length of the destination string is zero.

5. Decimal overflow occurs if the destination string is too short to contain the converted result of a non-zero packed decimal source string (not including leading zeros). Conversion of a source string with zero value never results in overflow. Conversion of a non-zero source string to a zero-length destination string results in overflow.

6. If decimal overflow occurs, the value stored in the destination ma be different from the value indicated by the condition codes (Z and N bits).

CVTSP

Convert Leading Separate Numeric to Packed

Format:

opcode srclen.rw, srcaddr.ab, dstlen.rw, dstaddr.ab

Operation:

{dst string} ← conversion of {src string}

Condition Codes:

N ← {dst string} LSS 0;
Z ← {dst string} EQL 0;

$V \leftarrow \{\text{decimal overflow}\}$;

$C \leftarrow 0$;

Exceptions:

reserved operand

decimal overflow

Opcode:

09 CVTSP Convert Leading Separate Numeric to Packed

Description:

The source numeric string specified by the source length and source address operands is converted to a packed decimal string, and the destination string specified by the destination address and destination length operands is replaced by the result.

Notes:

1. A reserved operand abort occurs if:
   - The length of the source leading separate numeric string is outside the range 0 through 31.
   - The length of the destination packed decimal string is outside the range 0 through 31.
   - The source string contains an invalid byte. An invalid byte is any character other than an ASCII "0" through "9" in a digit byte or an ASCII "+", "⟨space⟩", or "-" in the sign byte.

2. After execution:

   R0 = 0

   R1 = address of the sign byte of the source string

   R2 = 0

   R3 = address of the byte containing the most significant digit of the destination string.

3. The destination string, R0 through R3, and the condition codes are UNPREDICTABLE if the destination string overlaps the source string, or a reserved operand abort occurs.

CVTTP

Convert Trailing Numeric to Packed

Format:

opcode srclen.rw, srcaddr.ab, tbladdr.ab, dstlen.rw,
        dstaddr.ab

Operation:

{dst string} ← conversion of {src string}

Condition Codes:

N ← {dst string}LSS 0;
Z ← {dst string} EQL 0;
V ← {decimal overflow};
C ← 0;

Exceptions:
reserved operand
decimal overflow

Opcode:

26   CVTTP   Convert Trailing Numeric to Packed

Description:
The source trailing numeric string specified by the source length and source address operands is converted to a packed decimal string, and the destination packed decimal string specified by the destination address and destination length operands is replaced by the result.

Conversion is effected by using the highest addressed (trailing) byte of the source string as an unsigned index into a 256-byte table whose zeroth entry is specified by the table address operand. The byte read out of the table replaces the highest addressed byte of the destination string (the byte containing the sign and the least significant digit). The remaining packed digits of the destination string are replaced by the low-order 4 bits of the corresponding bytes in the source string.

Notes:
1. A reserved operand abort occurs if:
   - The length of the source trailing numeric string is outside the range 0 through 31
   - The length of the destination packed decimal string is outside the range 0 through 31
   - The source string contains an invalid byte; an invalid byte is any value other than ASCII "0" through "9" in any high-order byte (any byte except the least significant byte)
   - The translation of the least significant digit produces an invalid packed decimal digit or sign nibble.
2. After execution:
   R0 = 0
   R1 = address of the most significant digit of the source string

R2 = 0

R3 = address of the byte containing the most significant digit of the destination string.

3. The destination string, R0 through R3, and the condition codes are UNPREDICTABLE if the destination string overlaps the source string or the table, or a reserved operand abort occurs.

4. If the convert instruction produces a -0 without overflow, the destination packed decimal string is changed to a $+0$ representation, condition code N is cleared, and Z is set.

5. If the length of the source string is 0, the destination packed decimal string is set identically equal to 0, and the translation table is not referenced.

6. By appropriate specification of the table, conversion from any form of trailing numeric string may be realized. See Chapter 1 for the preferred form of trailing overpunch, zoned, and unsigned data. In addition, the table may be set up for absolute value, negative absolute value, or negated conversions.

7. If the table translation produces a sign nibble containing any valid sign, the preferred sign representation is stored in the destination packed decimal string.

DVP

Divide Packed

Format:

```
opcode divrlen.rw, divraddr.ab, divdlen.rw,
        divdaddr.ab, quolen.rw, quoaddr.ab,
```

Operation:

$$(\{quoaddr + ZEXT(quolen/2)\} : quoaddr) \leftarrow$$
$$(\{divdaddr + ZEXT(divdlen/2)\} : divdaddr) /$$
$$(\{divraddr + ZEXT(divrlen/2)\} : divraddr);$$

Condition Codes:

```
N ← {quo string} LSS 0;
Z ← {quo string} EQL 0;
V ← {decimal overflow};
C ← 0;
```

Exceptions:

reserved operand
decimal overflow
divide by zero

Instructions   **177**

Opcode:

```
27  DIVP  Divide Packed
```

Description:

The dividend string specified by the dividend length and dividend address operands is divided by the divisor string specified by the divisor length and divisor address operands. The quotient string specified by the quotient length and quotient address operands is replaced by the result.

Notes:

1. This instruction allocates a 16-byte workspace on the stack. After execution, SP is restored to its original contents and the contents {(SP) − 16}:{(SP) − 1} are UNPREDICTABLE.

2. The division is performed such that:
   - The absolute value of the remainder (which is lost) is less that the absolute value of the divisor
   - The product of the absolute value of the quotient times the absolute value of the divisor is less than or equal to the absolut value of the dividend
   - The sign of the quotient is determined by the rules of algebra from the signs of the dividend and the divisor. If the value of the quotient is zero, the sign is always positive.

3. After execution:

   R0 = 0

   R1 = address of the byte containing the most significant digit of the divisor string

   R2 = 0

   R3 = address of the byte containing the most significant digit of the dividend string

   R4 = 0

   R5 = address of the byte containing the most significant digit of the quotient string.

4. The quotient string, R0 through R5, and the condition codes are UNPREDICTABLE if the quotient string overlaps the divisor or dividend strings, the divisor, dividend, or quotient strings overlap the 16 bytes of temporary storage on the stack, the divisor or dividend string contains an invalid nibble, the divisor is 0, or a reserved operand abort occurs.

Move Packed

Format:

opcode len.rw, srcaddr.ab, dstaddr.ab

Operation:

({dstaddr + ZEXT(len/2)} : dstaddr) ←
      ({srcaddr + ZEXT(len/2)} : srcaddr);

Condition Codes:

N ← {dst string} LSS 0;
Z ← {dst string} EQL 0;
V ← 0;
C ← C;

Exception:

reserved operand

Opcode:

34   MOVP   Move Packed

Description:

The destination string specified by the length and destination address operands is replaced by the source string specified by the length and source address operands.

Notes:

1. After execution:

   R0 = 0

   R1 = address of the byte containing the most significant digit of the source string

   R2 = 0

   R3 = address of the byte containing the most significant digit of the destination string.

2. The destination string, R0 through R3, and the condition codes are UNPREDICTABLE if the destination string overlaps the source string, the source string contains an invalid nibble, or a reserved operand abort occurs.

3. If the source is −0, the result is +0, N is cleared, and Z is set.

MULP   Multiply Packed

Format:

opcode mulrlen.rw, mulraddr.ab, muldlen.rw,
    muldaddr.ab, prodlen.rw, prodaddr.ab

Operation:

({prodaddr + ZEXT(prodlen/2)} : prodaddr) ←
    ({muldaddr + ZEXT(muldlen/2)} : muldaddr) *
    ({mulraddr + ZEXT(mulrlen/2)} : mulraddr);

Condition Codes:

N ← {prod string} LSS 0;
Z ← {prod string} EQL 0;
V ← {decimal overflow};
C ← 0;

Exceptions:

reserved operand
decimal overflow

Opcode:

25   MULP   Multiply Packed

Description:

The multiplicand string specified by the multiplicand length and
multiplicand address operands is multiplied by the multiplier string
specified by the multiplier length and multiplier address operands. The
product string specified by the product length and product address
operands is replaced by the result.

Notes:

1. After execution:

    R0 = 0

    R1 = address of the byte containing the most significant digit of
    the multiplier string

    R2 = 0

    R3 = address of the byte containing the most significant digit of
    the multiplicand string

    R4 = 0

    R5 = address of the byte containing the most significant digit of
    the product string.

2. The product string, R0 through R5, and the condition codes are UNPREDICTABLE if the product string overlaps the multiplier or multiplicand strings, the multiplier or multiplicand strings contain an invalid nibble, or a reserved operand abort occurs.

3P

Subtract Packed

Format:

```
opcode sublen.rw, subaddr.ab, diflen.rw,
       difaddr.ab                                4 operand
opcode sublen.rw, subaddr.ab, minlen.rw,
       minaddr.ab, diflen.rw, difaddr.ab         6 operand
```

Operation:

```
({difaddr + ZEXT(diflen/2)} : difaddr) ←
       ({difaddr + ZEXT(diflen/2)} : difaddr) −
       ({subaddr + ZEXT(sublen/2)} : subaddr); !4 operand
({difaddr + ZEXT(diflen/2)} : difaddr) ←
       ({minaddr + ZEXT(minlen/2)} : minaddr) −
       ({subaddr + ZEXT(sublen/2)} : subaddr); !6 operand
```

Condition Codes:

```
N ← {dif string} LSS 0;
Z ← {dif string} EQL 0;
V ← {decimal overflow};
C ← 0;
```

Exceptions:
reserved operand
decimal overflow

Opcodes:

```
22  SUBP4  Subtract Packed 4 Operand
23  SUBP6  Subtract Packed 6 Operand
```

Description:
In 4 operand format, the subtrahend string specified by subtrahend length and subtrahend address operands is subtracted from the difference string specified by the difference length and difference address operands, and the difference string is replaced by the result.

Instructions   **181**

In 6 operand format, the subtrahend string specified by the subtrahend length and subtrahend address operands is subtracted from the minuend string specified by the minuend length and minuend address operands. The difference string specified by the difference length and difference address operands is replaced by the result.

Notes:

1. After execution of SUBP4:

   R0 = 0

   R1 = address of the byte containing the most significant digit of the subtrahend string

   R2 = 0

   R3 = address of the byte containing the most significant digit of the difference string.

2. After execution of SUBP6:

   R0 = 0

   R1 = address of the byte containing the most significant digit of the subtrahend string

   R2 = 0

   R3 = address of the byte containing the most significant digit of the minuend string

   R4 = 0

   R5 = address of the byte containing the most significant digit of the difference string.

3. The difference string, R0 through R3 (R0 through R5 for SUBP6) and the condition codes are UNPREDICTABLE if the difference string overlaps the subtrahend or minuend strings; if the subtrahend, minuend, or difference (4 operand only) strings contain an invalid nibble; or if a reserved operand abort occurs.

EDIT INSTRUCTION

The edit instruction may be omitted from subset implementations of the VAX architecture. Execution of an omitted instruction results in emulated instruction exception. Omitted instructions may be emulated by operating system software, which may use user-mode stack space during the emulation. For more detail, refer to Chapter 11.

The edit instruction is designed to implement the common editing functions for handling fixed-format output. The instruction converts input packed decimal number to an output character string, generating characters for the output. This operation is exemplified by a MOVE a numeric edited (PICTURE) item in COBOL or PL/I, but the instruction can be used for other applications as well. When converting digits, options include leading zero fill, leading zero protection, insertion of floating sign, insertion of floating currency symbol, insertion of special sign representations, and blanking an entire field when it is zero.

The operands to the EDITPC instruction are an input packed decimal string descriptor, a pattern specification, and the starting address of the output string. The packed decimal descriptor is a standard VAX operand pair of the length of the decimal string in digits (up to 31) and the starting address of the string. The pattern specification is the starting address of a pattern operation editing sequence that is interpreted in much the same way as are the normal instructions. The output string is described by only its starting address because the pattern defines the length unambiguously.

While the EDITPC instruction is operating, it manipulates two character registers and the four condition codes. One character register contains the fill character. This is normally an ASCII blank but would be changed to asterisk for check protection. The other character register contains the sign character. Initially, this register contains either an ASCII blank or a minus sign depending upon the sign of the input. The value of the register can be changed to allow other sign representations such as plus/minus or plus/blank and can be manipulated in order to output special notations such as CR or DB. The sign register can also be changed to the currency sign in order to implement a floating currency sign. After execution, the condition codes contain the sign of the input (N), the presence of a zero source (Z), an overflow condition (V), and the presence of significant digits (C). Condition code N is determined at the start of the instruction and is not changed thereafter (except to correct a -0 input). The other condition codes are computed and updated as the instruction proceeds. When the EDITPC instruction terminates, registers R0 through R5 contain the conventional values after a decimal instruction.

PC   Edit Packed to Character String

Format:

```
opcode srclen.rw, srcaddr.ab, pattern.ab, dstaddr.ab
```

Operation:

```
if srclen GTRU 31 then {reserved operand abort};
PSW⟨V,C⟩ ← 0;
PSW⟨Z⟩ ← 1;
PSW⟨N⟩ ← {src has minus sign};
R0 ← srclen;
tmpl ← R0;
```

```
R1 ← srcaddr;
R2⟨15:8⟩ ← {if PSW⟨N⟩ EQL 0 then " " else "-"} ! sign of src
              !R2⟨7:0⟩ is used for the fill character
R3 ← pattern;
R5 ← dstaddr;
exit-flag ← false;
while NOT exit-flag do
        begin
        {fetch pattern byte};
        {if pattern 0:4 no operand};
        {if pattern 40:47 increment R3 and
                fetch one byte operand};
        {if pattern 80:AF except 80, 90, A0
                operand is rightmost nibble};
        {else {reserved operand fault}};
        {perform pattern operator};
        if NOT exit-flag then {increment R3};
        end;
if R0 NEQ 0 then {reserved operand abort};
R0 ← tmp1;                    !length of source string
R1 ← R1 - {tmp1/2}           !point to start of source string
R2 ← 0;
R4 ← 0;
if PSW⟨Z⟩ EQL 1 then PSW⟨N⟩ ← 0;
```

Condition Codes:

```
N ← {src string} LSS 0;          !N ← 0 if src is -0
Z ← {src string} EQL 0;
V ← {decimal overflow};          !non-zero digits lost
C ← {significance};
```

Exceptions:
reserved operand
decimal overflow

Opcode:

```
38  EDITPC  Edit Packed to Character String
```

Description:
The destination string specified by the pattern and destination addr
operands is replaced by the edited version of the source string
specified by the source length and source address operands. The

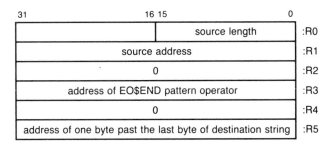

Figure 3.9
EDITPC Control Block

editing is performed according to the pattern string starting at the address pattern and extending until a pattern end (EO$END) pattern operator is encountered. The pattern string consists of one-byte pattern operators. Some pattern operators take no operands. Some take a repeat count which is contained in the right-most nibble of the pattern operator itself. The rest take a one-byte operand which immediately follows the pattern operator. This operand is either an unsigned integer length or a byte character. The individual pattern operators are described on the following pages.

Notes:

1. A reserved operand abort occurs if srclen GTRU 31.

2. The destination string is UNPREDICTABLE if the source string contains an invalid nibble, if the EO$ADJUST_INPUT operand is outside the range 1 through 31, if the source and destination strings overlap, or if the pattern and destination strings overlap.

3. After execution, the registers are as shown in Figure 3.9. If the destination string is UNPREDICTABLE, R0 through R5 and the condition codes are UNPREDICTABLE.

4. If V is set at the end and DV is enabled, numeric overflow trap occurs unless the conditions in item 9 are satisfied.

5. The destination length is specified exactly by the pattern operators in the pattern string. If the pattern is incorrectly formed or if it is modified during the execution of the instruction, the length of the destination string is UNPREDICTABLE.

6. If the source is −0, the result may be −0 unless a fixup pattern operator is included (EO$BLANK_ZERO or EO$REPLACE_ SIGN).

7. The contents of the destination string and up to one page of memory preceding it are UNPREDICTABLE if the length covered by EO$BLANK_ZERO or EO$REPLACE_SIGN is 0 or is outside the destination string.

8. If more input digits are requested by the pattern than are specifi
then a reserved operand abort is taken with R0 = − 1 and R3
location of pattern operator which requested the extra digit. The
condition codes and other registers are UNPREDICTABLE.

9. If fewer input digits are requested by the pattern than are
specified, then a reserved operand abort is taken with R3 =
location of EO$END pattern operator. The condition codes and
other registers are UNPREDICTABLE.

10. On an unimplemented or reserved pattern operator, a reserved
operand fault is taken with R3 = location of the faulting patterr
operator. This fault may be continued as long as the defined
register state is manipulated according to the pattern operator
description and the state specified as implementation depender
is preserved. FPD is set and the condition codes and registers
are as follows:

N = {src has minus sign}

Z = all source digits 0 so far

V = non-zero digits lost

C = significance

$R0\langle 31:16\rangle$ = −{count of source zeros to supply}

$R0\langle 15:0\rangle$ = remaining srclen$\langle 15:0\rangle$

R1 = current source location

$R2\langle 31:16\rangle$ = implementation dependent

$R2\langle 15:8\rangle$ = current contents of sign character register

$R2\langle 7:0\rangle$ = current contents of fill character register

R3 = location of edit pattern operator causing exception

R4 = implementation dependent

R5 = location of next destination byte

Summary of EDIT Pattern Operators

Name	Operand	Summary
insert:		
EO$INSERT	ch	insert character, fill if insignifica
EO$STORE_SIGN	–	insert sign
EO$FILL	r	insert fill
move:		
EO$MOVE	r	move digits, filling insignificant
EO$FLOAT	r	move digits, floating sign
EO$END_FLOAT	–	end floating sign

| EO$BLANK__ZERO | len | fill backward when zero |
| EO$REPLACE__SIGN | len | replace with fill if -0 |

d:

EO$LOAD__FILL	ch	load fill character
EO$LOAD__SIGN	ch	load sign character
EO$LOAD__PLUS	ch	load sign character if positive
EO$LOAD__MINUS	ch	load sign character if negative

ntrol:

EO$SET__SIGNIF	-	set significance flag
EO$CLEAR__SIGNIF	-	clear significance flag
EO$ADJUST__INPUT	len	adjust source length
EO$END	-	end edit

where:

ch = one character

r = repeat count in the range 1 through 15

len = length in the range 1 through 255

IT Pattern
erator
coding

(hex)

00	EO$END
01	EO$END__FLOAT
02	EO$CLEAR__SIGNIF
03	EO$SET__SIGNIF
04	EO$STORE__SIGN
05. .1F	Reserved to DIGITAL
20. .3F	Reserved for all time
40	EO$LOAD__FILL
41	EO$LOAD__SIGN
42	EO$LOAD__PLUS
43	EO$LOAD__MINUS
44	EO$INSERT

—character is in next byte

45	EO$BLANK__ZERO
46	EO$REPLACE__SIGN
47	EO$ADJUST__INPUT

—unsigned length is in next byte

| 48. .5F | Reserved to DIGITAL |
| 60. .7F | Reserved to DIGITAL's customers |

80,90,A0	Reserved to DIGITAL
81. .8F	EO$FILL
91. .9F	EO$MOVE } —repeat count is ⟨3:0⟩
A1. .AF	EO$FLOAT
B0. .FE	Reserved to DIGITAL
FF	Reserved for all time

On the following pages, each pattern operator is defined in a format similar to that of instruction descriptions. In each case, if there is an operand, it is either a repeat count (r) from 1 through 15, an unsigned byte length (len), or a character byte (ch). In the formal descriptions, the following two routines are invoked:

```
READ:                          !function value 0 through 9
     if R0 EQL 0 then {reserved operand};
     if R0 LSS 0 then
             begin
             READ ← 0;
             R0⟨31:16⟩ ← R0⟨31:16⟩ + 1;      !see EO$ADJUST_INPU
             end;
         else
             begin
             READ ← (R1)⟨3+4*R0⟨0⟩:4*R0⟨0⟩⟩; !get next nibble
                                            !alternating high then low
             R0 ← R0 - 1;
             if R0⟨0⟩ EQL 1 then R1 ← R1 + 1;
             end;
         return;
STORE(char):
         (R5) ← char;
         R5 ← R5 + 1;
         return;
```

Also the following definitions are used:

```
     fill = R2⟨7:0⟩
     sign = R2⟨15:8⟩
```

EO$ADJUST_ INPUT

Adjust Input Length

Purpose:
Handle source strings with lengths different from the output

Format:

```
pattern      len
```

Operation:

```
if len EQLU 0 or len GTRU 31 then {UNPREDICTABLE};
if R0⟨15:0⟩ GTRU len
then
        begin
        R0⟨31:16⟩ ← 0
        repeat R0⟨15:0⟩ - len do
                if READ NEQU 0 then
                        begin
                        PSW⟨Z⟩ ← 0;
                        PSW⟨C⟩ ← 1;      !set significance
                        PSW⟨V⟩ ← 1;
                        end;
        end;
else R0⟨31:16⟩ ← R0⟨15:0⟩ - len; !negative of number
                                 !to fill
```

Pattern operators:

```
47  EO$ADJUST_INPUT  Adjust Input Length
```

Description:

The pattern operator is followed by an unsigned byte integer length in the range 1 through 31. If the source string has more digits than this length, the excess leading digits are read and discarded. If any discarded digits are non-zero, then overflow is set, significance is set, and zero is cleared. If the source string has fewer digits than this length, a counter is set of the number of leading zeros to supply. This counter is stored as a negative number in R0⟨31:16⟩.

Note:

If length is not in the range 1 through 31, the destination string, condition codes, and R0 through R5 are UNPREDICTABLE.

$BLANK__
RO

Blank Backwards When Zero

Purpose:

Fix the destination to be blank when the value is zero

Format:

```
pattern    len
```

Operation:

```
if len EQLU O then {UNPREDICTABLE};
if PSW⟨Z⟩ EQL 1 then
        begin
        R5 ← R5 - len;
        repeat len do STORE(fill);
        end;
```

Pattern operators:

```
45   EO$BLANK-ZERO   Blank Backwards When Zero
```

Description:
The pattern operator is followed by an unsigned byte integer length.
the value of the source string is zero, then the contents of the fill
register are stored into the last length bytes of the destination string.

Notes:
1. The length must be non-zero and within the destination string
   already produced. If it is not, the contents of the destination string
   and up to one page of memory preceding it are UNPREDICTABL
2. This pattern operator is used to blank out any characters stored i
   the destination under a forced significance, such as a sign or the
   digits following the radix point.

EO$END   End Edit

Purpose:
End the edit operation

Format:
pattern

Operation:

```
exit_flag ← true;       !terminate edit loop
                        !end processing is
                        !described under EDITPC instru
```

Pattern operators:

```
00   EO$END   End Edit
```

Description:
The edit operation is terminated.

Notes:
1. If there are still input digits, a reserved operand abort is taken.
2. If the source value is -0, the N condition code is cleared.

End Floating Sign

Purpose:
End a floating sign operation

Format:
pattern

Operation:
```
if PSW(C) EQL 0 then
        begin
        STORE(sign);
        PSW(C) ← 1;    !set significance
        end;
```

Pattern operators:

01 EO$END_FLOAT End Floating Sign

Description:
If the floating sign has not yet been placed in the destination (that is, if significance is not set), the contents of the sign register are stored in the destination and significance is set.

Notes:
This pattern operator is used after a sequence of one or more EO$FLOAT pattern operators which start with significance clear. The EO$FLOAT sequence can include intermixed EO$INSERT and EO$FILL pattern operators.

Store Fill

Purpose:
Insert the fill character

Format:

```
pattern      r
```

Operation:

```
repeat r do STORE(fill);
```

Pattern operators:

```
8x   EO$FILL   Store Fill
```

Description:
The right nibble of the pattern operator is the repeat count. The
contents of the fill register is placed into the destination repeat times.

Note:
This pattern operator is used for fill (blank) insertion.

EO$FLOAT   Float Sign

Purpose:
Move digits, floating the sign across insignificant digits

Format:

```
pattern      r
```

Operation:

```
repeat r do
        begin
        tmp ← READ;
        if tmp NEQU 0 then
                begin
                if PSW⟨C⟩ EQL 0 then
                        begin
                        STORE(sign);
                        PSW⟨Z⟩ ← 0;
                        PSW⟨C⟩ ← 1;      !set significance
                        end;
                end;
        if PSW⟨C⟩ EQL 0 then STORE(fill)
                else STORE("0" + tmp);
        end;
```

Pattern operators:

```
Ax   EO$FLOAT  Float Sign
```

Description:
The right nibble of the pattern operator is the repeat count. For repeat times, the following algorithm is executed. The next digit from the source is examined. If it is non-zero and significance is not yet set, then the contents of the sign register are stored in the destination, significance is set, and zero is cleared. If the digit is significant, it is stored in the destination; otherwise, the contents of the fill register is stored in the destination.

Notes:
1. If r is greater than the number of digits remaining in the source string, a reserved operand abort is taken.
2. This pattern operator is used to move digits with a floating arithmetic sign. The sign must already be setup as for EO$STORE__SIGN. A sequence of one or more EO$FLOATs can include intermixed EO$INSERTs and EO$FILLs. Significance must be clear before the first pattern operator of the sequence. The sequence must be terminated by one EO$END__FLOAT.
3. This pattern operator is used to move digits with a floating currency sign. The sign must already be setup with a EO$LOAD__SIGN. A sequence of one or more EO$FLOATs can include intermixed EO$INSERTs and EO$FILLs. Significance must be clear before the first pattern operator of the sequence. The sequence must be terminated by one EO$END__FLOAT.

$INSERT   Insert Character

Purpose:
Insert a fixed character, substituting the fill character if not significant

Format:

```
pattern     ch
```

Operation:

```
if PSW(C) EQL 1 then STORE(ch) else STORE(fill);
```

Pattern operators:

```
44  EO$INSERT  Insert Character
```

Description:

The pattern operator is followed by a character. If significance is s
then the character is placed into the destination. If significance is
not set, then the contents of the fill register are placed into the
destination.

Notes:

This pattern operator is used for blankable inserts (comma, for
example) and fixed inserts (slash, for example). Fixed inserts requ
that significance be set (by EO$SET_SIGNIF or EO$END_FLOA

EO$LOAD_   Load Register

Purpose:
Change the contents of the fill or sign register

Format:

```
pattern    ch
```

Operation: !select one depending on pattern
operator

```
fill ← ch;              !EO$LOAD_FILL

sign ← ch;              !EO$LOAD_SIGN

if PSW⟨N⟩ EQL 0 then sign ← ch;       !EO$LOAD_PLUS

if PSW⟨N⟩ EQL 1 then sign ← ch;       !EO$LOAD_MINU
```

Pattern operators:

```
40  EO$LOAD_FILL   Load Fill Register
41  EO$LOAD_SIGN   Load Sign Register
42  EO$LOAD_PLUS   Load Sign Register If Plus
43  EO$LOAD_MINUS  Load Sign Register If Minus
```

Description:
The pattern operator is followed by a character. For EO$LOAD_F
this character is placed into the fill register. For EO$LOAD_SIGN,
this character is placed into the sign register. For EO$LOAD_PLU
this character is placed into the sign register if the source string ha
positive sign. For EO$LOAD_MINUS, this character is placed into
the sign register if the source string has a negative sign.

Notes:
1. EO$LOAD_FILL is used to setup check protection (asterisk
   instead of space).

2. EO$LOAD__SIGN is used to setup a floating currency sign.

3. EO$LOAD__PLUS is used to setup a non-blank plus sign.

4. EO$LOAD__MINUS is used to setup a non-minus minus sign (such as CR, DB, or the PL/I +).

$MOVE   Move Digits

Purpose:
Move digits, filling for insignificant digits (leading zeros)

Format:
```
pattern     r
```

Operation:
```
repeat r do
        begin
        tmp ← READ;
        if tmp NEQU 0 then
                begin
                PSW⟨Z⟩ ← 0;
                PSW⟨C⟩ ← 1;  !set significance
                end;
        if PSW⟨C⟩ EQL 0 then STORE(fill)
                else STORE(''0'' + tmp);
        end;
```

Pattern operators:
```
9x   EO$MOVE  Move Digits
```

Description:
The right nibble of the pattern operator is the repeat count. For repeat times, the following algorithm is executed. The next digit is moved from the source to the destination. If the digit is non-zero, significance is set and zero is cleared. If the digit is not significant (that is, if it is a leading zero), it is replaced by the contents of the fill register in the destination.

Notes:
1. If r is greater than the number of digits remaining in the source string, a reserved operand abort is taken.

2. This pattern operator is used to move digits without a floating sig
   If leading zero suppression is desired, significance must be clear
   If leading zeros should be explicit, significance must be set. A
   string of EO$MOVEs intermixed with EO$INSERTs and EO$FILL
   will handle suppression correctly.
3. If check protection (*) is desired, EO$LOAD_FILL must precede
   the EO$MOVE.

EO$REPLACE_
SIGN

Replace Sign When Zero

Purpose:
Fix the destination sign when the value is zero

Format:

```
pattern    len
```

Operation:

```
if len EQLU 0 then {UNPREDICTABLE};
if PSW⟨Z⟩ EQL 1 then (R5 - len) ← fill;
```

Pattern operators:

```
46  EO$REPLACE_SIGN  Replace Sign When Zero
```

Description:
The pattern operator is followed by an unsigned byte integer length.
the value of the source string is zero (that is, if Z is set), then the
contents of the fill register is stored into the byte of the destination
string which is length bytes before the current position.

Notes:
1. The length must be non-zero and within the destination string
   already produced. If it is not, the contents of the destination string
   and up to one page of memory preceding it are UNPREDICTABL
2. This pattern operator can be used to correct a stored sign
   (EO$END_FLOAT or EO$STORE_SIGN) if a minus was stored
   and the source value turned out to be zero.

EO$_SIGNIF

Significance

Purpose:
Control the significance (leading zero) indicator

Format:

pattern

Operation:

PSW⟨C⟩ ← 0;   !EO$CLEAR_SIGNIF

PSW⟨C⟩ ← 1;   !EO$SET_SIGNIF

Pattern operators:

02   EO$CLEAR_SIGNIF   Clear Significance

03   EO$SET_SIGNIF   Set Significance

Description:

The significance indicator is set or cleared. This controls the treatment of leading zeros (leading zeros are zero digits for which the significance indicator is clear).

Notes:

1. EO$CLEAR_SIGNIF is used to initialize leading zero suppression (EO$MOVE) or floating sign (EO$FLOAT) following a fixed insert (EO$INSERT with significance set).

2. EO$SET_SIGNIF is used to avoid leading zero suppression (before EO$MOVE) or to force a fixed insert (before EO$INSERT).

EO$STORE_ SIGN

Store Sign

Purpose:

Insert the sign character

Format:

pattern

Operation:

STORE(sign);

Pattern operators:

04   EO$STORE_SIGN   Store Sign

Description:

The contents of the sign register are placed into the destination.

Notes:

This pattern operator is used for any non-floating arithmetic sign. It should be preceded by a EO$LOAD_PLUS or EO$LOAD_MINUS if the default sign convention is not desired.

Memory Management   4

Memory management consists of the hardware and software that control the allocation and use of physical memory. The effect of memory management is exemplified in a multiprogramming system where several processes may reside in physical memory at the same time. To ensure that one process will not affect other processes or the operating system, VAX architecture uses memory protection and multiple address spaces.

Four hierarchical access modes provide the memory access control, which further improves software reliability. These access modes are, from most to least privileged, kernel, executive, supervisor, and user. For each of the four access modes, protection is specified at the individual page level, where a page may be inaccessible, read-only, or read/write. Any location accessible to one mode is also accessible to all more privileged modes. Furthermore, for each access mode, any location that can be written can also be read.

Memory management provides the CPU with mapping information. First, the CPU generates virtual addresses when an image is executed. Before these addresses can be used to access instructions and data, however, they must be translated into physical addresses. Memory management software maintains tables of mapping information (page tables) that keep track of where each 512-byte virtual page is located in physical memory. The CPU uses this mapping information when it translates virtual addresses to physical addresses.

Memory management, then, is the scheme that provides both the memory protection and memory mapping mechanisms of VAX architecture. Memory management accomplishes the following:

- Provides a large address space for instructions and data
- Allows data structures up to one gigabyte
- Provides convenient and efficient sharing of instructions and data
- Contributes to software reliability.

A virtual memory system provides a large address space, yet allows programs to run on hardware with small memory configurations.

Programs execute in an environment termed a process. The virtual memory system for VAX provides each process with a 4-billion-byte address space.

The virtual address space is divided into two, equal-size spaces: the system address space and the per-process address space. The system address space is the same for all processes. It contains the operating system which is written as callable procedures. Thus all system code can be available to all other system and user code via a simple CALL. Each process has its own separate process address space. However, several processes may have access to the same page, thus providing controlled sharing.

VIRTUAL ADDRESS SPACE

A virtual address is a 32-bit unsigned integer specifying a byte location in the address space. The programmer sees a linear array of 4,294,967,296 bytes. The virtual address space is broken into 512-byte units termed pages. The page is the unit of relocation, sharing, and protection.

This virtual address space is too large to be contained in any presently available main memory. Memory management provides the mechanism to map the active part of the virtual address space to the

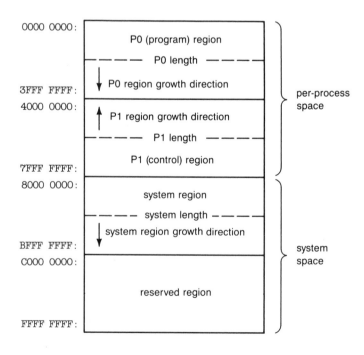

Figure 4.1
Virtual Address Space

available physical address space. Memory management also provides page protection between processes. The operating system controls the virtual-to-physical address mapping tables, and saves the inactive but used parts of the virtual address space on the external storage media.

The virtual address space is divided into two parts, per-process space and system space, discussed in the following sections. Virtual address space is illustrated in Figure 4.1.

Process Space

The half of the virtual address space with smaller addresses (addresses 00000000 through 7FFFFFFF, hex) is termed per-process space. Per-process space is divided into two equal parts: the program region (P0 region) and the control region (P1 region). Each process has a separate address translation map for per-process space, so the per-process spaces of all processes are potentially completely disjoint. The address map for per-process space is context switched (changed) when the process running on the system is changed (see Chapter 6, Process Structure).

System Space

The half of virtual address space with larger addresses (addresses 80000000 through FFFFFFFF, hex) is termed system space. All processes use the same address translation map for system space, so system space is shared among all processes. The address map for system space is not context switched.

Virtual Address Format

The VAX processor generates a 32-bit virtual address for each instruction and operand in memory. As the process executes, the system translates each virtual address to a physical address. The virtual address consists of a region field, a virtual page number (VPN) field, and a byte within page field, as shown in Figure 4.2.

The VPN field, bits $\langle 31:9 \rangle$ of a virtual address, specifies the virtual page to be referenced. The virtual address space contains 8,388,608 (2^{23}) pages. The byte-within-page field, bits $\langle 9:0 \rangle$ of a virtual address, specifies the byte offset within the page. A page contains 512 bytes.

31 30 29		9 8	0
reg	virtual page number	byte within page	

Figure 4.2
Virtual Address Format

The region field (bits ⟨31:30⟩ of a virtual address) is part of the virtual page number and specifies which of four regions the virtual address references. When bit ⟨31⟩ of a virtual address is 1, the address is in the system space. When bit ⟨31⟩ is 0, the address is in the per-process space.

Within system space, bit ⟨30⟩ distinguishes between the system region and a reserved region. When bits ⟨31:30⟩ are 11 (binary), the address refers to the reserved region. When bits ⟨31:30⟩ are 10 (binary), the address refers to the system region.

Within per-process space, bit ⟨30⟩ distinguishes between the program and control regions. When bits ⟨31:30⟩ are 01 (binary), the control region is referenced; and when bits ⟨31:30⟩ are 00 the program region is referenced.

Virtual Address Space Layout

The layout of virtual address space is illustrated in Figure 4.1. Note that access to each of the three regions (P0, P1, system) is controlled by a length register (P0LR, P1LR, SLR). Within the limits set by the length registers, the access is further controlled by page tables that specify the validity, access requirements, and physical location of each page in the memory.

MEMORY MANAGEMENT CONTROL

The action of translating a virtual address to a physical address is governed by the setting of the memory-mapping-enable (MME) bit in the MAPEN internal processor register. Figure 4.3 illustrates the privileged map-enable register.

MAPEN⟨0⟩ is the memory-mapping-enable bit. When MME is set to 1, memory management is enabled. When MME is set to 0, memory management is disabled. At processor initialization time, MAPEN is initialized to 0.

Setting MME to 0 turns off address translation and access control. Virtual address bit n, VA⟨n⟩, is copied directly to the corresponding physical address bit, PA⟨n⟩, for n = 0 to 29. VA⟨31:30⟩ are ignored; PA⟨31:30⟩ do not exist. VA⟨n⟩ is ignored if PA⟨n⟩ does not exist. (The number of PA bits is implementation dependent.)

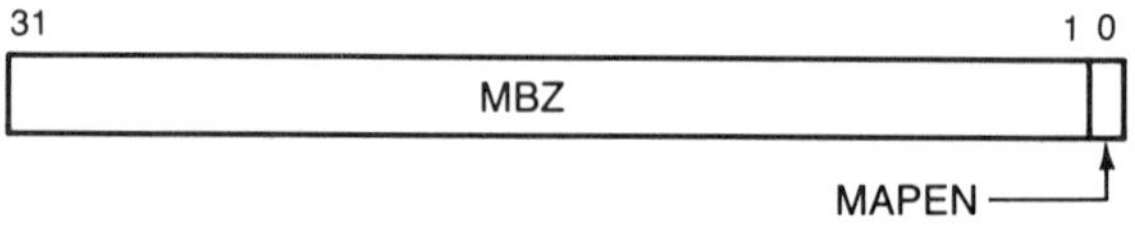

Figure 4.3
Map Enable Register (MAPEN)

```
PA = VA(29:0) modulo (2**number of PA bits)
```

There is no page protection: all accesses are allowed in all modes. No modify bit is maintained.

Note, however, that references to nonexistent memory may cause unexpected results when memory management is disabled. The accessibility of nonexistent memory is UNPREDICTABLE when memory management is disabled (see the PROBE instructions). In addition, a processor may have an instruction buffer that prefetches instructions before execution. If the instruction stream comes within 512 bytes of nonexistent memory when memory management is disabled, prefetcher references may cause UNDEFINED behavior.

ADDRESS TRANSLATION

When MME is a 1, address translation and access control are on. The processor uses the following to determine whether an intended access is allowed:

1. The virtual address, which is used to index a page table

2. The intended access type (read or write)

3. The current privilege level from the processor status longword, or kernel level for page table mapping references.

If the access is allowed and the address can be mapped (the page table entry is valid), the result is the physical address corresponding to the specified virtual address.

The intended access is READ if the operation to be performed is a read. The intended access is WRITE if the operation to be performed is a write. If the operation to be performed is a modify (that is, read followed by write), the intended access is specified as a WRITE.

If an operand is an address operand, then no reference is made. Hence the page need not be accessible and need not even exist.

Page Table Entry

The CPU uses a page table entry (PTE), shown in Figure 4.4, to translate virtual addresses to physical addresses. The fields of the PTE are described in Table 4.1.

Figure 4.4
Page Table Entry

Table 4.1
Fields of the PTE

Extent	Name	Mnemonic	Meaning
⟨31⟩	Valid	V	Indicates the validity of the M bit and PFN field. When V = 1, the M and PFN fields are valid for use by hardware; when V = 0, they are reserved for DIGITAL software.
⟨30:27⟩	Protection	PROT	Indicates at what access modes a process can reference the page. This field is always valid and is used by the CPU hardware even when V = 0.
⟨26⟩	Modify	M	When V = 0, M is not used by CPU hardware and is reserved for DIGITAL software and I/O devices. When V = 1, M shows whether the page has been modified: if M is clear, the page has not been modified; if M is set, the page may have been modified.
			M is cleared only by software. M is set by CPU hardware on a successful write or modify to the page. In addition, it may be set by the probe-write instruction (PROBEW) or by an implied probe-write. M is not set if the page is inaccessible. Beyond that, it is UNPREDICTABLE whether M is set if a fault occurs in an instruction that would otherwise have modified the page.
			For example, if a write reference crosses a page boundary where the first page is not accessible and the second page is accessible, the reference will fault. M is unchanged in the PTE mapping the first page. It is UNPREDICTABLE whether M is set in the PTE mapping the second page.
			It is UNPREDICTABLE whether the modification of a process PTE⟨M⟩ bit causes modification of the system PTE that maps that process page table. Note that the update of the M-bit is not interlocked in a multiprocessor system.
⟨25⟩	Reserved		Reserved to DIGITAL and must be 0.
⟨24:23⟩	Owner	OWN	Reserved for DIGITAL software.
⟨22:21⟩	Software		Reserved for DIGITAL software.
⟨20:0⟩	Page Frame Number	PFN	The upper 21 bits of the physical address of the base of the page. Used by CPU hardware only if V = 1.

The operating system software uses some combinations of the software bits to implement its page management data structures and functions. Among the functions implemented this way are initialize-pages-with-zeros, copy-on-reference, page sharing, and transitions between active and paged-out states. VAX/VMS encodes these functions in PTEs whose valid bit, PTE⟨31⟩, is a 0 and processes them whenever a page fault occurs.

Page Table Entry for I/O Devices

Some I/O devices, such as the DR32, use VAX memory management to translate addresses. These I/O devices use a page table entry format that is an extension of that in Figure 4.4 used by the CPU. The extended PTE implements for I/O hardware some functions that the CPU does with software using software bits and page faults. In particular, PTE bits ⟨31⟩, ⟨26⟩, and ⟨22⟩ are decoded into four combinations, as shown in Table 4.2. Some of these are used in the same way as in the CPU PTE format, and some are used in different ways.

When PTE⟨31,26,22⟩ = 1xx or as shown in Figure 4.5, PTE⟨20:0⟩ is a valid PFN field. This is identical to the PFN field illustrated in Figure 4.4 for the CPU PTE.

When PTE⟨31,26,22⟩ = 001 as shown in Figure 4.5, PTE⟨21:0⟩ is a global page table index (GPTX). The I/O device has a global page table base register (GBR) that is loaded by software with a system virtual address. The I/O device calculates GBR + GPTX * 4 to get the system virtual address of a second PTE. The second PTE must contain a valid PFN and must have PTE⟨31,26,22⟩ equal to either 000 or 1xx, binary. If either of these requirements is not met, the result is UNDEFINED. For those devices that use it, the protection field always comes from the first PTE.

When PTE⟨31,26,22⟩ = 01x, as shown in Figure 4.5, the PTE format is reserved to DIGITAL. I/O devices will abort in a device-dependent manner.

I/O devices may look at and check the protection field or modify the M-bit; this check is device dependent. Those devices that do use PTE fields use them the same way the CPU does.

Table 4.2
PTE Types

PTE⟨31,26,22⟩	PTE Type
1 x x	Valid PFN
0 0 0	Valid PFN
0 0 1	Global Page Table Entry
0 1 x	Invalid PTE, I/O Abort

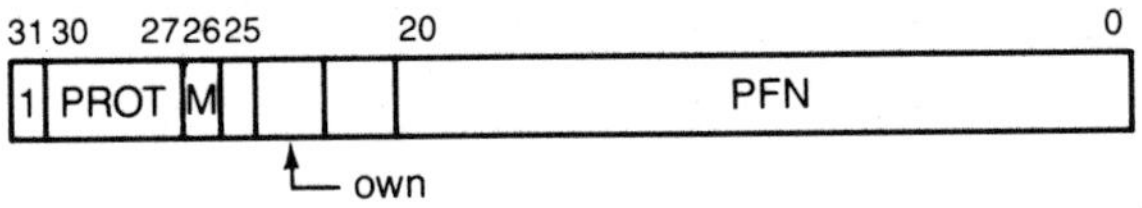

```
31 30   27 26 25      20                                    0
┌─┬────┬─┬─┬─┬─┬──────────────────────────────────┐
│1│PROT│M│ │ │ │              PFN                 │
└─┴────┴─┴─┴─┴─┴──────────────────────────────────┘
        └─ own
```

PTE with Valid Page Frame Number. PTE<31,26,22> = 1xx.

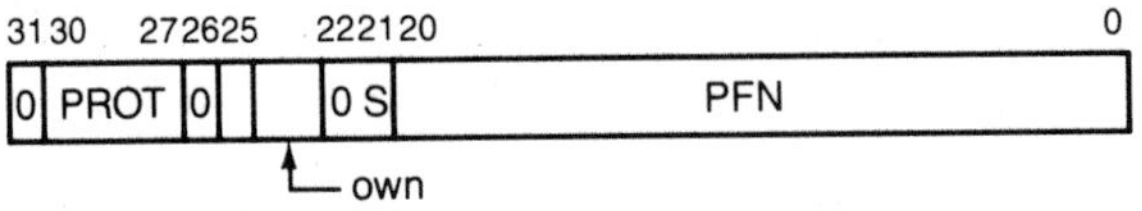

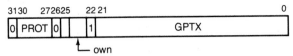

```
31 30   27 26 25   22 21 20                                 0
┌─┬────┬─┬─┬──┬─┬──────────────────────────────────┐
│0│PROT│0│ │  │0│S│           PFN                  │
└─┴────┴─┴─┴──┴─┴──────────────────────────────────┘
        └─ own
```

PTE with Valid Page Frame Number. PTE<31,26,22> = 000.

```
31 30   27 26 25   22 21                                    0
┌─┬────┬─┬─┬──┬─┬──────────────────────────────────┐
│0│PROT│0│ │  │1│              GPTX                │
└─┴────┴─┴─┴──┴─┴──────────────────────────────────┘
        └─ own
```

Global Page Table Index. PTE<31,26,22> = 001.

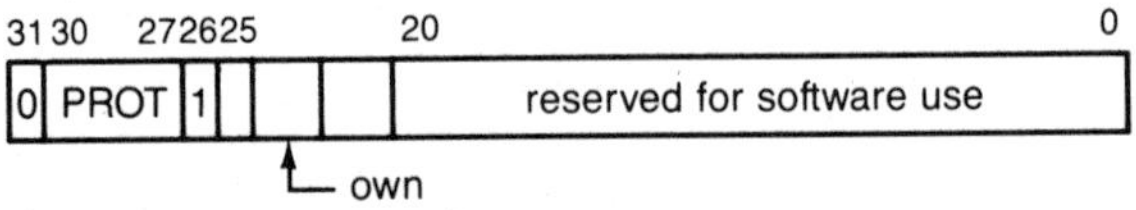

```
31 30   27 26 25      20                                    0
┌─┬────┬─┬─┬─┬─┬──────────────────────────────────┐
│0│PROT│1│ │ │ │      reserved for software use    │
└─┴────┴─┴─┴─┴─┴──────────────────────────────────┘
        └─ own
```

Invalid PTE, I/O Abort. PTE<31,26,22> = 01x.

Figure 4.5
PTE Bits Decoded into Four Combinations

I/O devices that do memory mapping use the same system page table as the CPU, but they have their own copies of the SBR and SLR. Buffer addresses are described in terms of a system virtual address of the PTE for the first buffer page and a byte offset within that page. In addition, the I/O devices use a global page table in memory and an I/O hardware global-page-table-base register that must be loaded by software.

Changes to Page Table Entries

The operating system changes PTEs as part of its memory management functions. For example, VMS sets and clears the valid bit and changes the PFN field as pages are moved to and from external storage devices.

The software must guarantee that each PTE is always consistent within itself. Changing a PTE one field at a time may give incorrect system operation. An example would be to set PTE⟨V⟩ with one instruction before establishing PTE⟨PFN⟩ with another. An interrupt routine between the two instructions could use an address that would map using the inconsistent PTE. The software can solve this problem by building a new PTE in a register and then moving the new PTE to the page table with a single instruction such as MOVL.

Multiprocessing makes the problem more complicated. Another processor, be it another CPU or an I/O processor, can reference the same page tables that the first CPU is changing. The second processor must always read consistent PTEs. In order to guarantee this, two requirements must be met (note that PTEs are longwords, longword-aligned):

1. Whenever the software modifies a PTE in more than one byte, it must use a longword, longword-aligned, and write-destination instruction such as MOVL.

2. The hardware must guarantee that a longword, longword-aligned write is an "atomic" operation. That is, a second processor cannot read (or write over) any of the first processor's partial results.

MEMORY PROTECTION

Memory protection is the function of validating whether a particular type of memory access is to be allowed to a particular page. Access to each page is controlled by a protection code that specifies for each access mode whether or not read or write references are allowed. Additionally, each address is checked to make certain that it lies within the P0, P1, or system region.

Processor Access Modes

In the order of most privileged to least privileged, the four processor modes are

Kernel	Used by the kernel of the operating system for page management, scheduling, and I/O drivers
Executive	Used for many of the operating system service calls, including the record management system
Supervisor	Used for such services as command interpretation
User	Used for user-level code, utilities, compilers, debuggers, etc.

The access mode of a running process is the current processor mode, stored in the current-mode field of the processor status longword (PSL) (see Chapter 1, Basic Architecture).

Protection Code

Every page in the virtual address space is protected according to its use. Even though all of the system space is shared, in the sense that all processes see the same system space, a program may be prevented from modifying or even reading portions of it. A program may also be prevented from reading or modifying portions of per-process space.

In system space, for example, scheduling queues are highly protected, whereas library routines may be executable by code of any privilege. Similarly, per-process accounting information may be in per-process space but highly protected; while normal user code in per-process space is executable at low privilege.

Associated with each page is a protection code that describes the accessibility of the page for each processor mode. The code allows a choice of protection for each processor mode, within the following limits:

- Each mode's access can be read-write, read-only, or no-access.
- If any level has read access, then all more privileged levels also have read access.
- If any level has write access, then all more privileged levels also have write access.

The protection codes for the 15 combinations of page protection are encoded in a 4-bit field in the page table entry, as shown in Table 4.3.

Table 4.3
PTE Protection Codes

Name	Mnemonic	Decimal	Binary	Accessibility			
				Kernel	Exec	Super	User
no access	NA	0	0000	none	none	none	none
reserved		1	0001	UNPREDICTABLE			
kernel write	KW	2	0010	write	none	none	none
kernel read	KR	3	0011	read	none	none	none
user write	UW	4	0100	write	write	write	write
exec write	EW	5	0101	write	write	none	none
exec read, kernel write	ERKW	6	0110	write	read	none	none
exec read	ER	7	0111	read	read	none	none
super write	SW	8	1000	write	write	write	none
super read, exec write	SREW	9	1001	write	write	read	none
super read, kernel write	SRKW	10	1010	write	read	read	none
super read	SR	11	1011	read	read	read	none
user read, super write	URSW	12	1100	write	write	write	read
user read, exec write	UREW	13	1101	write	write	read	read
user read, kernel write	URKW	14	1110	write	read	read	read
user read	UR	15	1111	read	read	read	read

Length Violation

Every valid virtual address lies within bounds determined by the addressing region (P0, P1, or system) and the contents of the length register associated with that region (P0LR, P1LR, or SLR). Virtual addresses outside these bounds cause a length-violation fault. The addressing bounds algorithm is a simple limit check whose formal notation is

```
case VAddr⟨31:30⟩
    set
    [0]:                                          ! P0 region
        if ZEXT( VAddr⟨29:9⟩ ) GEQU P0LR
            then {length violation};
    [1]:                                          ! P1 region
        if ZEXT( VAddr⟨29:9⟩ ) LSSU P1LR
            then {length violation};
    [2]:                                          ! System region
        if ZEXT( VAddr⟨29:9⟩ ) GEQU SLR
            then {length violation};
    [3]:                                          ! reserved region
        {length violation};
    tes;
```

Access-Control-Violation Fault

An access-control-violation fault occurs if an illegal access is attempted, as determined by the current PSL mode and the page's protection field, or if the address causes a length violation.

Access Across a Page Boundary

If an access is made across a page boundary, the order in which the pages are accessed is UNPREDICTABLE. For a single reference to a page, however, access-control-violation fault always takes precedence over translation-not-valid fault.

SYSTEM SPACE ADDRESS TRANSLATION

A virtual address with ⟨31:30⟩ = 2 is an address in the system virtual address space. A system space address is shown in Figure 4.6.

The system virtual address space is defined by the system page table, which is a vector of page table entries. The system page table is located in physical address space. Its base address is a physical address and is contained in the system base register (SBR), shown in Figure 4.6. The size of the system page table in longwords (that is, the number of PTEs) is contained in the system length register (SLR).

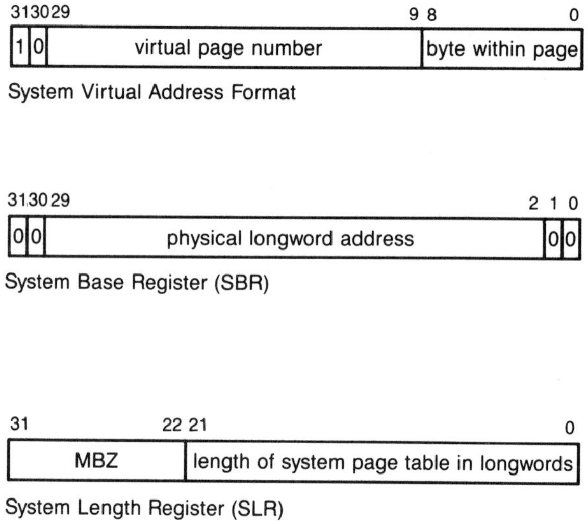

```
 313029                          9 8         0
┌─┬─┬──────────────────────────┬───────────────┐
│1│0│  virtual page number     │byte within page│
└─┴─┴──────────────────────────┴───────────────┘
```
System Virtual Address Format

```
 31.3029                        2 1 0
┌─┬─┬──────────────────────────┬─┬─┐
│0│0│ physical longword address │0│0│
└─┴─┴──────────────────────────┴─┴─┘
```
System Base Register (SBR)

```
 31        22 21                              0
┌────────────┬───────────────────────────────┐
│    MBZ     │length of system page table in longwords│
└────────────┴───────────────────────────────┘
```
System Length Register (SLR)

Figure 4.6
System Virtual Address Space Registers

The SBR points to the first PTE in the system page table. In turn, this PTE maps the first page of system space, virtual addresses 80000000 through 800001FF (hex).

The PTEs in the system page table contain the mapping information or point to the mapping information in the global page table if the PTE is in GPTX format. (See the section "Page Table Entry for I/O Devices" in this chapter for a description of the GPTX format.)

Processor initialization leaves the contents of both registers UNPRE-DICTABLE. If part or all of the system page table resides in I/O space or in nonexistent memory while memory mapping is enabled, the operation of the processor is UNDEFINED.

Bits $\langle 31:9 \rangle$ of the virtual address contain the virtual page number. However, system virtual addresses have VAddr$\langle 31:30 \rangle$ = 2. Thus, there could be as many as 2^{21} pages in the system region. The length field in the SLR requires 22 bits to express the values 0 through 2^{21} inclusive.

The algorithm to generate a physical address from a system region virtual address is

```
SYS_PA = (SBR+4*SVA⟨29:9⟩)⟨20:0⟩'SVA⟨8:0⟩  ! System Region
```

Figure 4.7 illustrates the translation of a system virtual address to a physical address.

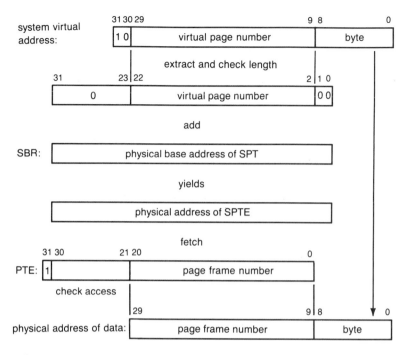

Figure 4.7
System Virtual Address to Physical Translation

The process virtual address space is divided into two, equal size, separately mapped regions. If virtual address bit ⟨30⟩ is 0, the address is in region P0. If virtual address bit ⟨30⟩ is 1, the address is in region P1. Figure 4.8 illustrates a process virtual address.

The P0 region maps a virtually contiguous area that begins at the smallest address (0) in the process virtual space and grows in the direction of larger addresses. P0 is typically used for program images and can grow dynamically.

The P1 region maps a virtually contiguous area that begins at the largest address ($2^{31} - 1$) in the process virtual space and grows in the direction of smaller addresses. P1 is typically used for system-maintained, per-process context. It may grow dynamically for the user stack.

Figure 4.8
Process Space Virtual Address Format

Each region is described by a virtually contiguous vector of page table entries. Unlike the system page table, which is addressed with a physical address, these two page tables are addressed with virtual addresses in the system region of the virtual address space. Thus, for process space, the address of the PTE is a virtual address in system space, and the fetch of the PTE is simply a longword fetch using a system virtual address.

There is a significant reason to address process page tables in virtual rather than physical space. A physically addressed process page table that required more than a page of PTEs (that is, that mapped more than 64K bytes of process virtual space) would require physically contiguous pages. Such a requirement would make dynamic allocation of process page table space very awkward since a running system tends to fragment storage into page-size areas.

A process space address translation that causes a translation buffer miss will cause one memory reference for the process PTE. If the virtual address of the page containing the process PTE is also missing from the translation buffer, a second memory reference is required.

When a process page table entry is fetched by the processor, a reference is made to system space. The system space page containing the process PTE may be marked valid or invalid. If it is marked valid, the processor can read the process space PTE. If the system space page is invalid, a translation-not-valid fault results, and the "PTE reference" bit is set in the fault parameter. This allows the process page tables to be paged.

The operating system must make process page tables accessible to kernel mode, at least. The operation of the processor is UNDEFINED if process space page tables are read-only or no-access. Thus the processor may or may not perform access checking (in kernel mode) when reading a process PTE or updating PTE⟨M⟩ in a process PTE.

When a process PTE is read, a check is made against the system-page-table-length register (SLR). Thus, the fetch of an entry from a process page table can result in translation-not-valid or length-violation faults. (See the section "Faults and Parameters" later in this chapter).

If part or all of either process page table is mapped into I/O space or nonexistent memory while memory mapping is enabled, the operation of the processor is UNDEFINED.

Region

The P0 region of the address space is mapped by the P0 page table (P0PT) which is defined by the P0 base register (P0BR) and the P0 length register (P0LR). The P0BR contains a virtual address in the system region that is the base address of the P0PT. Figure 4.9a illustrates the P0BR. The P0LR contains the size of the P0PT in longwords, that is, the number of page table entries. Figure 4.9b illustrates the P0LR. The page table entry addressed by the P0BR maps the first page of the P0 region of the virtual address space, that is, virtual byte address 0.

The PTEs in the P0PT contain the mapping information, or point to the mapping information in the global page table if the PTE is in GPTX format. (See the section "Page Table Entry for I/O Devices" in this chapter for a description of the GPTX format.)

Writing P0LR bits $\langle 26:24 \rangle$ has no effect. P0LR bits $\langle 26:24 \rangle$ read as zero. At processor initialization time, the contents of both registers are UNPREDICTABLE.

The virtual page number is contained in bits $\langle 29:9 \rangle$ of the virtual address. A 22-bit length field is required to express the values 0 through 2^{21} inclusive. There could be as many as 2^{21} pages in the P0 region. An attempt to load P0BR with a value less than 2^{31} or greater than $2^{31} + 2^{30} - 4$ results in a reserved-operand fault in some implementations.

The algorithm to generate a physical address from a P0 region virtual address is as follows:

```
PVA_PTE = P0BR+4*PVA⟨29:9⟩              ! P0 Region
PTE_PA  = (SBR+4*PVA_PTE⟨29:9⟩)⟨20:0⟩'PVA_PTE⟨8:0⟩
PROC_PA = (PTE_PA)⟨20:0⟩'PVA⟨8:0⟩
```

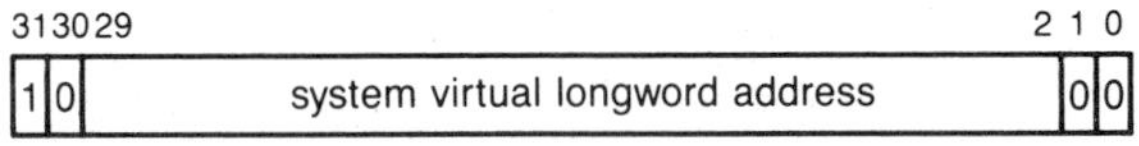

31	30	29		2	1	0
1	0		system virtual longword address		0	0

P0 Base Register (P0BR)

a

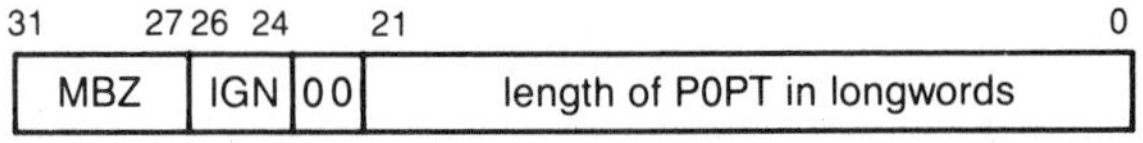

31		27	26	24		21		0
	MBZ		IGN	0 0		length of P0PT in longwords		

P0 Length Register (P0LR)

b

Figure 4.9
P0 Region Registers

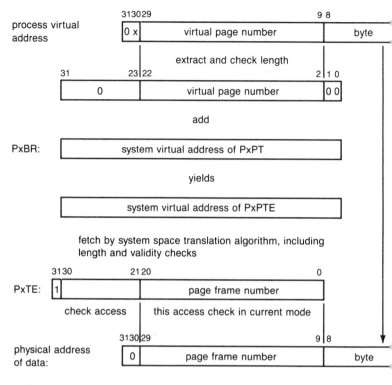

Figure 4.10
Process Virtual Address to Physical Address Translation

Figure 4.10 illustrates the process virtual address to physical address translation.

P1 Region

The P1 region of the address space is mapped by the P1 page table (P1PT). P1PT is defined by the P1 base register (P1BR) and the P1 length register (P1LR). Because P1 space grows toward smaller addresses, and because a consistent hardware interpretation of the base and length registers is desirable, P1BR and P1LR describe the portion of P1 space that is not accessible. Figure 4.11 illustrates the P1 base register and P1 length register. Note that P1LR contains the number of nonexistent PTEs. P1BR contains a virtual address of what would be the PTE for the first page of P1, that is, virtual byte address 40000000 hex).

The address in P1BR is not necessarily an address in system space, but all the addresses of PTEs must be in system space.

The PTEs in the P1PT contain the mapping information, or point to the mapping information in the GPT if the PTE is in GPTX format.

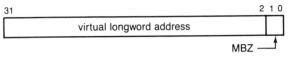

P1BR

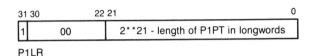

P1LR

Figure 4.11
P1 Base and Length Registers

(See the section "Page Table Entries for I/O Devices" in this chapter for a description of the GPTX format.)

At processor initialization time, the contents of both registers are UNPREDICTABLE. Writing P1LR bit ⟨31⟩ has no effect. The bit always reads as 0. An attempt to load P1BR with a value less than $2^{31} - 2^{23}$ (7F80 0000, hex) or greater than $2^{31} + 2^{30} - 2^{23} - 4$ results in a reserved-operand fault in some implementations.

The algorithm to generate a physical address from a P1 region virtual address is as follows:

```
PVA_PTE = P1BR+4*PVA⟨29:9⟩              ! P1 Region
PTE_PA  = (SBR+4*PVA_PTE⟨29:9⟩)⟨20:0⟩'PVA_PTE⟨8:0⟩
PROC_PA = (PTE_PA)⟨20:0⟩'PVA⟨8:0⟩
```

Figure 4.10 illustrates the process virtual address to physical address translation.

In order to save actual memory references when repeatedly referencing the same pages, a hardware implementation may include a mechanism to remember successful virtual address translations and page states. Such a mechanism is termed a translation buffer.

When the process context is loaded with LDPCTX, the translation buffer is automatically updated (that is, the process virtual address translations are invalidated). However, when the software changes any part of a valid PTE for the system or a current process region, it must also move a virtual address within the corresponding page to the translation-buffer-invalidate-single (TBIS) register with the MTPR instruction.

Additionally, when the software changes a System Page Table Entry which maps any part of the current process page table, all process pages so mapped must be invalidated in the translation buffer. They may be invalidated by moving an address within each such page into the TBIS register. They may also be invalidated by clearing the entire translation buffer. This is done by moving 0 to the translation-buffer-invalidate-all (TBIA) register with the MTPR instruction.

The translation buffer must not store invalid PTEs. Therefore, the software is not required to invalidate translation buffer entries when making changes for PTEs that are already invalid.

When the location or size of the system map is changed (SBR, SLR) the entire translation buffer must be cleared by moving 0 to the TBIA register with the MTPR instruction.

Whenever MME is a 0, the contents of the translation buffer are UNPREDICTABLE. Therefore, before enabling memory management at processor initialization time, or any other time, the entire translation buffer must be cleared by software.

An internal processor register is available for interrogating the presence of a valid translation in the translation buffer. When a virtual address is written to the TBCHK register with a MTPR instruction, the condition code V-bit is set if the translation buffer holds a valid translation for that virtual page.

The specification of the TBCHK register is based on VAX/VMS usage. Its specification is subject to change without prior notice.

The TBIS, TBIA, and TBCHK processor registers are write only. The operation of MFPR from any of these registers is UNDEFINED.

FAULTS AND PARAMETERS

Two types of faults are associated with memory mapping and protection. A translation-not-valid fault is taken when a read or write reference is attempted through an invalid PTE (PTE⟨31⟩ = 0). An access-control-violation fault is taken when the protection field of the PTE indicates that the intended page reference in the specified access mode would be illegal. Note that these two faults have distinct vectors in the system control block. If both faults could occur, then the access-control-violation fault takes precedence. An access-control-violation fault is also taken if the virtual address referenced is beyond the end of the associated page table. Such a "length violation" is essentially the same as referencing a PTE that specifies "No Access" in its protection field. The fault software does not have to

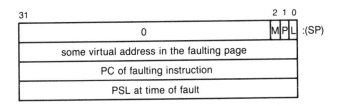

Figure 4.12
Memory Management Fault Stack Frame

compute the length check because a "length violation" indication is
stored in the memory management fault stack frame, illustrated in
Figure 4.12. See Chapter 5, Exceptions and Interrupts, for a description
of faults.
The same parameters are stored for both types of fault. The first
parameter pushed on the stack after the PSL and PC is some virtual
address in the same page with the virtual address that caused the
fault. A process-space reference can result in a system-space virtual
reference for the PTE. If the PTE reference faults, the virtual address
that is saved is the process virtual address. In addition, a 1 is stored
in bit ⟨1⟩ of the fault parameter word if the fault occurred in the per-
process PTE reference. The fields of the second parameter are
described in Table 4.4.

Table 4.4
Fields of the Memory Management Fault Parameter

Name	Extent	Meaning
modify or write intent	⟨2⟩	Set to 1 to indicate that the instruction's intended access was write or modify. This bit is 0 if the instruction's intended access was read.
PTE reference	⟨1⟩	Set to 1 to indicate that the fault occurred during the reference to the process page table associated with the virtual address. This can be set on either length-violation or translation-not-valid faults.
length violation	⟨0⟩	Set to 1 to indicate that an access-control-violation fault was the result of a length violation rather than a protection violation. This bit is always 0 for a translation-not-valid fault.

This section lists the instructions allowing access mode change, and describes two instructions that allow privileged services to check addresses passed as parameters.

Changing
Access Modes

Four instructions allow a program to change its access mode to a more privileged mode and transfer control to a service dispatcher for the new mode.

CHMK   change mode to kernel

CHME   change mode to executive

CHMS   change mode to supervisor

CHMU   change mode to user

These instructions provide the normal mechanism for less privileged code to call more privileged code; the instructions are described in detail in Chapter 5, Exceptions and Interrupts. When the mode transition takes place, the previous mode is saved in the previous-mode field of the PSL, thus allowing the more privileged code to determine the privilege of its caller.

Validating
Address
Arguments

Two instructions, PROBER and PROBEW, allow privileged services to check addresses passed as parameters. To avoid protection holes in the system, a service routine must always verify that its less privileged caller could have directly referenced the addresses passed as parameters. The PROBE instructions do this verification.

PROBEx

Probe Accessibility

Purpose: verify that arguments can be accessed

Format:

opcode mode.rb, len.rw, base.ab

Operation:

```
probe_mode ← MAXU (mode⟨1:0⟩, PSL⟨PRV_MOD⟩)
condition codes ← {accessibility of base} and
                  {accessibility of {base + ZEXT(len) − 1}}
                  using probe_mode
```

Condition Codes:

```
N ← 0 ;
Z ← if {both accessible} then 0 else 1;
V ← 0 ;
C ← C ;
```

Exception:
translation not valid

Opcodes:

```
0C  PROBER  Probe Read Accessibility
0D  PROBEW  Probe Write Accessibility
```

Description:
The PROBE instruction checks the read or write accessibility of the first and last byte specified by the base address and the zero extended length. Note that the bytes in between are not checked. System software must check all pages between the two end bytes if they will be accessed.

The protection is checked against the larger (and therefore less privileged) of the modes specified in bits ⟨1:0⟩ of the mode operand and the previous-mode field of the PSL. Note that probing with a mode operand of 0 is equivalent to probing the mode specified in PSL⟨previous-mode⟩.

Notes:
1. If the valid bit of the examined PTE is set, and write access is allowed, it is UNPREDICTABLE whether the modify bit of the examined PTE is set by a PROBEW. If the valid bit is clear or if write access is not allowed, the modify bit is not changed.
2. Except for item 1 above, the processor ignores the valid bit of the PTE mapping the probed address.
3. A length violation gives a status of "not-accessible."
4. On the probe of a process virtual address, if the valid bit of the system PTE is 0, then a translation-not-valid fault occurs. This allows for the demand paging of the process page tables.
5. An object one byte long is the smallest that can be probed. With a length of zero, the PROBE instructions test the accessibility of two bytes—base and base − 1.
6. If memory management is disabled, all memory is accessible, and probing nonexistent memory gives UNPREDICTABLE results.

Example:

```
MOVL    4(AP),R0        ; Copy the address of first argument
                        ; so that it can't be changed.
PROBER  #0,#4,(R0)      ; Verify that the longword pointed to
                        ; by the first arg could be read by
                        ; the previous access mode. (Note
                        ; that the arg list itself must alreac
                        ; have been probed.)
BEQL    violation       ; Branch if either byte gives an acces
                        ; violation.
MOVQ    8(AP),R0        ; Copy length and address of buffer ar
                        ; so that they can't change.
PROBEW  #0,R0,(R1)      ; Verify that the buffer described by
                        ; the second and third args could be
                        ; written by the previous access mode
                        ; (Note that the arg list must already
                        ; have been probed and that the seconc
                        ; arg must be less than 512.)
BEQL    violation       ; Branch if either byte gives an acces
                        ; violation.
```

Flows:

The following describes the operational flow of PROBE on each of the virtual addresses it is checking. Note that probing an address returns only the accessibility of the page(s) and has no effect on its residency However, probing a process address may cause a page fault in the system address space on the per-process page tables.

1. Look up the virtual address in the translation buffer. If found, use the associated protection field to determine the accessibility and EXIT.

2. Check for length violation for system or per-process address as appropriate. See elsewhere in this chapter for the length-violation check flows. If length violation, then return No Access and EXIT.

3. If system virtual address, form physical address of PTE, fetch the PTE, use the protection field to determine the accessibility, and EXIT.

4. For per-process virtual address, must do a virtual memory reference for the PTE.

   a. Look up the virtual address of the PTE in the translation buffer, form the physical address of the PTE if found, fetch the PTE, use the protection field to determine the accessibility, and EXIT.

b. If the virtual address of the PTE is not in the translation buffer, check the system virtual address of the PTE for length violation. If length violation, then return No Access and EXIT.

c. Read the SPTE for the system-space page containing the per-process PTE.

d. If the valid bit in the SPTE is 0, then take a translation-not-valid fault and EXIT. This case allows for the demand paging of per-process page tables.

e. Finally, calculate the physical address of the per-process PTE from the PFN field of the SPTE (see the section "System Space Address Translation" in this chapter), fetch the per-process PTE, use the protection field to determine the accessibility, and EXIT.

Exceptions and Interrupts   5

At certain times during the operation of a system, events within the system require the execution of particular pieces of software outside the explicit flow of control. The processor transfers control by forcing a change in the flow of control from that explicitly indicated in the currently executing process.

Some of the events are relevant primarily to the currently executing process and normally invoke software in the context of the current process. The notification of such an event is termed an exception.

Other events are primarily relevant to other processes, or to the system as a whole, and are therefore serviced in a system-wide context. The notification process for these events is termed an interrupt, and the system-wide context is described as "executing on the interrupt stack." Further, some interrupts are of such urgency that they require high-priority service, while others must be synchronized with independent events. To meet these needs, the processor has priority logic that grants interrupt service to the highest priority event at any point in time. The priority associated with an interrupt is termed its interrupt priority level (IPL).

Processor Interrupt Priority Levels

The processor has 31 interrupt priority levels: 15 software levels (numbered, in hex, 01 to 0F) and 16 hardware levels (10 to 1F, hex). User applications, system calls, and system services all run at process level, which may be thought of as IPL 0. Higher numbered interrupt levels have higher priority; that is to say, any requests at an interrupt level higher than the processor's current IPL will interrupt immediately, but requests at a lower or equal level are deferred.

Interrupt levels 01 through 0F (hex) exist entirely for use by software. No device can request interrupts on those levels, but software can force an interrupt by executing MTPR src, #PR$_SIRR. (See Chapter 8, and the section "Software Interrupts" later in this chapter.) Once a software interrupt request is made, it will be cleared by the hardware when the interrupt is taken.

Interrupt levels 10 to 17 (hex) are for use by devices and controllers, including UNIBUS devices; UNIBUS levels BR4 to BR7 correspond to VAX interrupt levels 14 to 17 (hex).

Interrupt levels 18 to 1F (hex) are for use by urgent conditions, serious errors, and powerfail.

Interrupts

The processor arbitrates interrupt requests according to priority. Only when the priority of an interrupt request is higher than the processor's current IPL (stored in PSL⟨20:16⟩) will the processor raise its IPL and service the interrupt request. The interrupt service routine is entered at the IPL of the interrupt request and will not usually change the IPL set by the processor. Note that this is different from the PDP–11 where the interrupt vector specifies the IPL for the interrupt service routine.

Interrupt requests can come from devices, controllers, other processors or the processor itself. Software executing in kernel mode can raise and lower the priority of the processor by executing MTPR src, #PR$__IPL where src contains the new priority desired. However, a processor cannot disable interrupts on other processors. Furthermore the priority level of one processor does not affect the priority level of the other processors. Thus in multiprocessor systems, interrupt priority levels cannot be used to synchronize access to shared resources. Even the various urgent interrupts including those exception that run at IPL 1F (hex) do so on only one processor. Consequently, special software action is required to stop other processors in a multiprocessor system.

Exceptions

Most exception service routines execute at IPL 0 in response to exception conditions caused by the software. A variation from this is serious system failures, which raise IPL to the highest level (1F, hex) to minimize processor interruption until the problem is corrected. Exception service routines are usually coded to avoid exceptions; however, nested exceptions can occur.

A trap is an exception that occurs at the end of the instruction that caused the exception. Therefore the PC saved on the stack is the address of the next instruction that would normally have been executed. Any software can enable and disable some trap conditions by using the BISPSW and BICPSW instructions described in Chapter 3.

A fault is an exception that occurs during an instruction and that leaves the registers and memory in a consistent state such that elimination of the fault condition and restarting the instruction will give correct results. After an instruction faults, the PC saved on the stack points to the instruction that faulted. Note that faults do not always leave everything as it was prior to the faulted instruction; they only restore enough to allow restarting. Thus, the state of a process that faults may not be the same as that of a process that was interrupted at the same point.

An abort is an exception that occurs during an instruction. An abort leaves the value of registers and memory UNPREDICTABLE such that the instruction cannot necessarily be correctly restarted, completed, simulated, or undone. After an instruction aborts, the PC saved on the stack points to the opcode of the aborted instruction. The following are UNPREDICTABLE:

- Destination operands (including implied operands, such as the top of the stack in an JSB instruction)

- Registers modified by operand specifier evaluation (including specifiers for implied operands)

- The PTE⟨M⟩ bit in PTEs that map destination operands, if the operands could have been written but were not written, and PTE⟨M⟩ was clear before the instruction

- Condition codes

- PSL⟨FPD⟩

- PSL⟨TP⟩, if PSL⟨T⟩ was set at the beginning of the instruction

Except where otherwise noted in the description of the abort, the rest of the PSL, other registers, and memory are unaffected.

Contrast between Exceptions and Interrupts

Generally, exceptions and interrupts are very similar. When either is initiated, both the processor status longword and the program counter are pushed onto the stack. There are, however, seven important differences:

- An exception condition is caused by the execution of the current instruction, whereas an interrupt is caused by some activity in the computing system that may be independent of the current instruction.

- An exception condition is usually serviced in the context of the process that produced the exception condition, whereas an interrupt is serviced independently from the currently running process.

- The IPL of the processor is usually not changed when the processor initiates an exception, whereas the IPL is always raised when an interrupt is initiated.

- Exception service routines usually execute on a per-process stack, whereas interrupt service routines normally execute on a per-CPU stack.

- Enabled exceptions are always initiated immediately, no matter what the processor IPL is; whereas interrupts are held off until the processor IPL drops below the IPL of the requesting interrupt.

- Most exceptions cannot be disabled. However, if an exception-causing event occurs while that exception is disabled, no exception is initiated for that event even when enabled subsequently. This includes overflow, the only exception condition whose occurrence indicated by a condition code (V). If an interrupt condition occurs while it is disabled, or the processor is at the same or higher IPL, the condition will eventually initiate an interrupt when the proper enabling conditions are met if the condition is still present.

- The previous mode field in the PSL is always set to kernel on an interrupt; but on an exception, it indicates the mode of the exception

PROCESSOR STATUS

When an exception or an interrupt is serviced, the processor status must be preserved so that the interrupted process may continue normally. Basically, this is done by automatically saving the PC and the PSL on the stack. (Refer to Chapter 1 for a description of the PC and PSL.) The PC and PSL are later restored with the Return from Exception or Interrupt instruction (REI). Any other status required to correctly resume an interruptible instruction is stored in the general registers. The terms current PSL and saved PSL are used to distinguish between this status information when it is in the processor and when copies of it are materialized in memory, as on the stack.

Process context such as the mapping information is not saved or restored on each interrupt or exception. Instead, it is saved and restored only when process context switching is performed. Refer to the LDPCTX and SVPCTX instructions in Chapter 6. Other processor status is changed even less frequently; refer to the privileged register descriptions in Chapter 8.

INTERRUPTS

The processor services interrupt requests between instructions. The processor also services interrupt requests at well-defined points during the execution of long, iterative instructions such as the string instructions. For these instructions, interrupts are initiated when the instruction state can be completely contained in the registers, PSL and PC; saving additional instruction state in memory is thus avoided The following events cause interrupts:

- Device completion (IPL 10 – 17 hex)

- Device error (IPL 10 – 17 hex)

- Device alert (IPL 10 – 17 hex)

- Device memory error (IPL 10 – 17 hex)

- Console terminal transmit and receive (IPL 14 hex)

- Interval timer (implementation dependent, IPL 16 or 18 hex)

- Recovered memory or bus or processor errors (implementation dependent, IPL 18 to 1D hex)
- Bus errors, processor errors, or uncorrectable memory errors (implementation dependent, IPL 18 to 1D hex)
- Powerfail (IPL 1E hex)
- Software interrupt invoked by MTPR src, #PR$__SIRR (IPL 01 to 0F hex)
- AST delivery when REI restores a PSL with mode greater than or equal to ASTLVL (see Chapter 6) (IPL 02)

Each device controller has a separate set of interrupt vector locations in the system control block (SCB). Thus interrupt service routines do not need to poll controllers in order to determine which controller interrupted.

In order to reduce interrupt overhead, no memory mapping information is changed when an interrupt occurs. Thus the instructions, data, and contents of the interrupt vector for an interrupt service routine must be in the system address space or present in every process at the same address.

Urgent Interrupts

The processor provides eight priority levels (18 through 1F, hex) for use by urgent conditions including serious errors and powerfail. Some implementations may not use all eight priority levels. Interrupts on these levels are initiated by the processor upon detection of certain conditions. Some of these conditions are not interrupts. For example, machine-check is usually an exception, but it runs at a high priority level on the interrupt stack.

Interrupt level 1E (hex) is reserved for powerfail. Interrupt level 1F (hex) is reserved for those exceptions that must lock out all processing until the condition has been handled. This includes the hardware and software "disasters" (machine-check and kernel-stack-not-valid aborts). It might also be used to allow a kernel-mode debugger to gain control on any exception.

Device Interrupts

The processor provides eight priority levels (10 through 17, hex) for use by peripheral devices. Some implementations may not implement all eight levels of interrupts. The minimal implementation is levels 14 through 17 (hex) that correspond to the UNIBUS levels BR4 to BR7 if the system has a UNIBUS.

Software Interrupts

The processor provides 15 interrupt levels (1 through 0F, hex) for use by software. Pending software interrupts are recorded in the software-

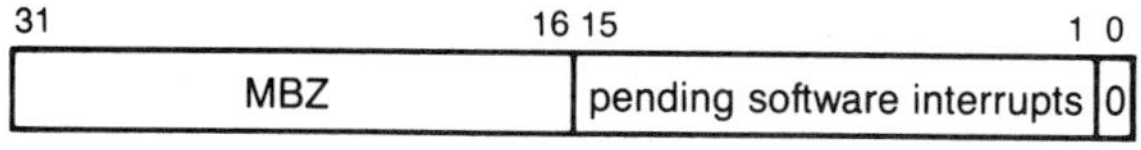

```
31                    16 15                        1 0
┌──────────────────────┬──────────────────────────┬─┐
│         MBZ          │ pending software interrupts│0│
└──────────────────────┴──────────────────────────┴─┘
```

Figure 5.1
Software Interrupt Summary Register

interrupt-summary register (SISR), as shown in Figure 5.1. The
SISR contains ones in the bit positions corresponding to levels at
which software interrupts are pending. When the processor initiates a
software interrupt, the corresponding bit in SISR is cleared. At no time
can SISR bits corresponding to levels higher than the current
processor IPL contain ones, since the processor would already have
taken the requested interrupts.

At processor initialization, SISR is cleared. The mechanism for
accessing it follows:

MFPR #PR$_SISR, dst   Reads the software interrupt summary
    register.

MTPR src, #PR$_SISR   Loads it, but this is not the normal way
    of making software interrupt requests.
    It is useful, for example, for clearing
    the software interrupt system and for
    reloading its state during powerfail
    recovery.

Software Interrupt Request Register—The software-interrupt-request
register (SIRR) is a write-only, 4-bit, privileged register used for
creating software interrupt requests. SIRR is shown in Figure 5.2.

Executing MTPR src, #PR$_SIRR requests an interrupt at the level
specified by src⟨3:0⟩. Once a software interrupt request is made, it will
be cleared by the hardware when the interrupt is taken. If src⟨3:0⟩ is
greater than the current IPL, the interrupt occurs before execution
of the following instruction. If src⟨3:0⟩ is less than or equal to the
current IPL, the interrupt will be deferred until IPL is lowered to less
than src⟨3:0⟩ and there is no higher interrupt level pending. This
lowering of IPL is by either REI or by MTPR src, #PR$_IPL. If
src⟨3:0⟩ is 0, no interrupt will occur.

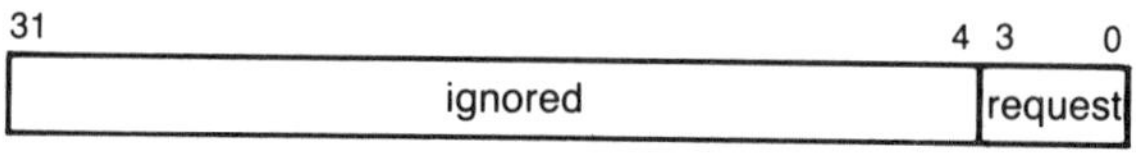

```
31                                        4 3     0
┌────────────────────────────────────────┬───────┐
│                 ignored                 │request│
└────────────────────────────────────────┴───────┘
```

Figure 5.2
Software Interrupt Request Register

Note that no indication is given if there is already a request at the selected level. The service routine, therefore, must not assume that there is a one-to-one correspondence of interrupts generated and requests made. A valid protocol for generating such a correspondence is:

1. The requester uses INSQUE to place a control block describing the request onto a queue for the service routine.

2. The requester uses MTPR src, #PR$__SIRR to request an interrupt at the appropriate level.

3. The service routine uses REMQUE to remove a control block from the queue of service requests. If REMQUE returns failure (nothing in the queue), the service routine exits with REI.

4. If REMQUE returns success (an item was removed from the queue), the service routine performs the service and returns to step 3 to look for other requests.

Interrupt Priority Level Register

Writing to the IPL register with the MTPR instruction will load the processor priority field in the PSL; that is, PSL⟨20:16⟩ is loaded from IPL⟨4:0⟩. Reading from the IPL register with the MFPR instruction will read the processor priority field from the PSL. On writing the IPL register, bits ⟨31:5⟩ are ignored; on reading the IPL register, bits ⟨31:5⟩ are returned 0. The IPL register is shown in Figure 5.3. At processor initialization, IPL is set to 31 (1F, hex).

Interrupt service routines must follow the discipline of not lowering IPL below their initial level. If they were to do so, an interrupt at an intermediate level could cause the stack nesting to be improper. This would result in REI faulting. If IPL is lowered to zero when the processor is running on the interrupt stack, the operation of the processor is UNDEFINED. Figure 5.4 is an example of interrupt processing.

EXCEPTIONS

Exceptions can be grouped into six classes:

• Arithmetic traps and faults

• Memory management exceptions

• Exceptions detected during operand reference

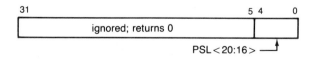

Figure 5.3
Interrupt Priority Level Register

| Event | State After Event | | |
	IPL (hex)	SISR (hex)	Stacked PSL<IPL>
Initial state:	5	00	0
Execute MTPR #8, #PR$__IPL:	8	00	0
Execute MTPR #3, #PR$__SIRR:	8	08	0
Execute MTPR #7, #PR$__SIRR:	8	88	0
Execute MTPR #9, #PR$__SIRR (interrupts at once):	9	88	8,0
Device interrupt at IPL 20 (decimal):	14	88	9,8,0
Device interrupt service routine executes REI:	9	88	8,0
IPL 9 service routine executes REI:	8	88	0
Execute MTPR #5, #PR$__IPL: *	7	08	5,0
IPL 7 service routine executes REI:	5	08	0
Initial IPL 5 service routine executes REI: *	3	00	0
IPL 3 service routine executes REI:	0	00	—

*This operation lowers IPL below that of an outstanding software interrupt request. The software interrupt occurs at once.

Figure 5.4
An Example of Interrupt Processing

- Exceptions occurring as a consequence of an instruction
- Tracing
- Serious system failures

Arithmetic Traps and Faults

This section contains the descriptions of the exceptions that occur as the result of an arithmetic or conversion operation. These exceptions are mutually exclusive and all are assigned the same vector in the SCB, and hence the same signal "reason" code. Each of them indicates that an exception had occurred during the last instruction and that the instruction has been completed (trap) or backed up (fault). An appropriate distinguishing code is pushed on the stack as a longword, as shown in Figure 5.5. Table 5.1 lists the arithmetic exception type codes.

Integer Overflow Trap—An integer overflow trap is an exception that indicates that the last instruction executed had an integer overflow setting PSL⟨V⟩ and that integer overflow was enabled (IV set). The result stored is the low-order part of the correct result. N and Z

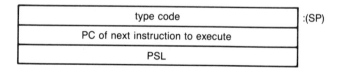

Figure 5.5
Arithmetic Exception Stack Frame

Table 5.1

Arithmetic Exception Type Codes

Exception Type	Mnemonic	Decimal	Hex
Traps			
integer overflow	SS$_INTOVF	1	1
integer divide-by-zero	SS$_INTDIV	2	2
floating overflow	SS$_FLTOVF	3	3
floating or decimal divide-by-zero	SS$_FLTDIV	4	4
floating underflow	SS$_FLTUND	5	5
decimal overflow	SS$_DECOVF	6	6
subscript range	SS$_SUBRNG	7	7
Faults			
floating overflow	SS$_FLTOVF_F	8	8
floating divide-by-zero	SS$_FLTDIV_F	9	9
floating underflow	SS$_FLTUND_F	10	A

are set according to the stored result. The type code pushed on the stack is 1 (SS$_INTOVF).

Integer Divide-By-Zero Trap—An integer divide-by-zero trap is an exception that indicates that the last instruction executed had an integer zero divisor. The result stored is equal to the dividend, and condition code V is set. The type code pushed on the stack is 2 (SS$_INTDIV).

Floating Overflow Trap—A floating overflow trap is an exception that indicates that the last instruction executed resulted in an exponent greater than the largest representable exponent for the data type after normalization and rounding. The result stored contains a one in the sign and zeros in the exponent and fraction fields. This is a reserved operand and will cause a reserved operand fault if used in a subsequent floating-point instruction. The N and V condition code bits are set, and Z and C are cleared. The type code pushed on the stack is 3 (SS$_FLTOVF).

Divide-By-Zero Trap—A floating divide-by-zero trap is an exception that indicates that the last instruction executed had a floating zero divisor. The result stored is the reserved operand, as described above for floating overflow trap, and the condition codes are set as in floating overflow.

A decimal string divide-by-zero trap is an exception that indicates that the last instruction executed had a decimal-string zero divisor. The destination, R0 through R5, and condition codes are UNPREDICTABLE. The zero divisor can be either +0 or −0.

The type code pushed on the stack for both types of divide-by-zero is 4 (SS$_FLTDIV).

Floating Underflow Trap—A floating underflow trap is an exception that indicates that the last instruction executed resulted in an exponent less than the smallest representable exponent for the data type after normalization and rounding, and that floating underflow was enabled (FU set). The result stored is zero. Except for POLYx, the N, V, and C condition codes are cleared, and Z is set. In POLYx, the trap occurs on completion of the instruction, which may be many operations after the underflow. The condition codes are set on the final result in POLYx. The type code pushed on the stack is 5 (SS$_FLTUND).

Decimal-String Overflow Trap—A decimal-string overflow trap is an exception that indicates that the last instruction executed had a decimal-string result too large for the destination string provided and that decimal overflow was enabled (DV set). The V condition code is always set. Refer to the individual instruction descriptions in Chapter 3 for the value of the result and of the condition codes. The type code pushed on the stack is 6 (SS$_DECOVF).

Subscript-Range Trap—A subscript-range trap is an exception that indicates that the last instruction was an INDEX instruction with a subscript operand that failed the range check. The value of the subscript operand is lower than the low operand or greater than the high operand. The result is stored in indexout, and the condition codes are set as if the subscript were within range. The type code pushed on the stack is 7 (SS$_SUBRNG).

Floating Overflow Fault—A floating overflow fault is an exception that indicates that the last instruction executed resulted in an exponent greater than the largest representable exponent for the data type after normalization and rounding. The destination was unaffected, and the saved condition codes are UNPREDICTABLE. The saved PC points to the instruction causing the fault. In the case of a POLY instruction, the instruction is suspended with FPD set. The type code pushed on the stack is 8 (SS$_FLTOVF_F).

Floating Divide-By-Zero Fault—A floating divide-by-zero fault is an exception that indicates that the last instruction executed had a floating zero divisor. The quotient operand was unaffected, and the saved condition codes are UNPREDICTABLE. The saved PC points to the instruction causing the fault. The type code pushed on the stack is 9 (SS$_FLTDIV_F).

Floating Underflow Fault—A floating underflow fault is an exception that indicates that the last instruction executed resulted in an exponent less than the smallest representable exponent for the data type after normalization and rounding, and that floating underflow was enabled (FU set). The destination operand is unaffected. The saved condition codes are UNPREDICTABLE. The saved PC points to the instruction causing the fault. In the case of a POLY instruction, the instruction is suspended with FPD set. The type code pushed on the stack is 10 (SS$__FLTUND__F).

Memory Management Exceptions

A memory management exception can be either an access-control-violation fault or a translation-not-valid fault.

Access-Control-Violation Fault—An access-control-violation fault is an exception indicating that the process attempted a reference not allowed at the current access mode. See Chapter 4, Memory Management, for a description of the information pushed on the stack as parameters. Software may restart the process after changing the address translation information.

Translation-Not-Valid Fault—A translation-not-valid fault is an exception indicating that the process attempted a reference to a page for which the valid bit in the page table was not set. See Chapter 4, Memory Management, for a description of the information pushed on the stack as parameters.

Note that if a process attempts to reference a page for which the page table entry specifies both not-valid and access-control violation, an access-control-violation fault occurs.

Exceptions Detected During Operand Reference

Reserved-Addressing-Mode Fault—A reserved-addressing-mode fault is an exception indicating that an operand specifier attempted to use an addressing mode that is not allowed in the situation in which it occurred. No parameters are pushed.

See Chapter 2 for details of reserved addressing modes and for combinations of addressing modes and registers that cause UNPRE-DICTABLE results.

Reserved-Operand Exception—A reserved-operand exception is an exception indicating that an operand accessed has a format reserved for future use by DIGITAL. No parameters are pushed. This exception always backs up the saved PC to point to the opcode. The exception service routine may determine the type of operand by examining the opcode using the saved PC.

Note that only the changes made by instruction fetch and because of operand specifier evaluation may be restored. Therefore, some instructions are not restartable. These exceptions are labeled as aborts rather than faults. The saved PC is always restored properly unless the instruction attempted to modify it in a manner that results in UNPREDICTABLE results.

The reserved-operand exceptions are caused by:
1. Bit field too wide (fault)
2. Invalid combination of bits in PSL restored by REI (fault)
3. Invalid combination of bits in PSW mask longword during RET (fault)
4. Invalid combination of bits in BISPSW or BICPSW (fault)
5. Invalid CALLS or CALLG entry mask (fault)
6. Invalid register number in MFPR or MTPR (fault)
7. Invalid PCB contents in LDPCTX for some implementations (abort)
8. Unaligned operand in ADAWI (fault)
9. Invalid register contents in MTPR for some implementations (fault)
10. Invalid operand addresses in INSQHI, INSQTI, REMQHI, or REMQTI (fault)
11. A floating-point number that has the sign bit set and the exponent zero except in the POLY table (fault)
12. A floating-point number that has the sign bit set and the exponent zero in the POLY table (fault) (see Chapter 3 for restartability)
13. POLY degree too large (fault)
14. Decimal string too long (abort)
15. Invalid digit in CVTTP or CVTSP (abort)
16. Reserved pattern operator in EDITPC (fault) (see Chapter 3 for restartability)
17. Incorrect source-string length at completion of EDITPC (abort)

Exceptions Occurring as the Consequence of an Instruction

Reserved- or Privileged-Instruction Fault—A reserved- or privileged-instruction fault occurs when the processor encounters an opcode that is not specifically defined, or that requires higher privileges than the current mode. No parameters are pushed. Opcode FFFF (hex) will always fault.

An Opcode-Reserved-To-Customers Fault—An opcode-reserved-to-customers fault is an exception that occurs when an opcode reserved to customers or to DIGITAL is executed. The operation is identical to the reserved-or-privileged-instruction fault except that the event is caused by a different set of opcodes, and faults through a different vector. All opcodes reserved to customers start with FC (hex), which is the XFC instruction. If the special instruction needs to generate a unique exception, one of the reserved-to-customer vectors should be used. An example might be an unrecognized second byte of the instruction.

The XFC fault is intended primarily for use with writable control store to implement installation-dependent instructions. The method used to enable and disable the handling of an XFC fault in user-written microcode is implementation-dependent. Some implementations may transfer control to microcode without checking bits ⟨1:0⟩ of the exception vector.

Instruction-Emulation Exceptions—When a subset processor executes a string instruction that is omitted from its instruction set, an emulation exception results. An emulation exception can occur through either of two SCB vectors, depending on whether or not PSL⟨FPD⟩ was set at the beginning of the instruction. If PSL⟨FPD⟩ is clear, a subset-emulation trap occurs through the SCB vector at offset C8 (hex), and a subset-emulation trap frame is pushed onto the current stack. If PSL⟨FPD⟩ is set, a suspended-emulation fault occurs through the SCB vector at offset CC (hex); and PC and PSL are pushed onto the current stack.

The emulation exception handler runs in the mode of the emulated instruction, on the same stack, and at the same IPL. The exception parameters are pushed onto the current stack. See Chapter 11 for details of instruction emulation and the emulation exceptions.

Compatibility-Mode Exceptions—A compatibility-mode exception is an exception that occurs when the processor is in compatibility mode. A longword of information is pushed on the stack, which contains a code indicating the exception type. The stack frame is the same as that for arithmetic exceptions, shown in Table 5.1. The compatibility mode exception type codes are shown in Table 5.2.

Table 5.2
Compatibility Mode Exception Type Codes

Exception Type	Decimal
Faults	
reserved opcode	0
BPT instruction	1
IOT instruction	2
EMT instruction	3
TRAP instruction	4
illegal instruction	5
Aborts	
odd address	6

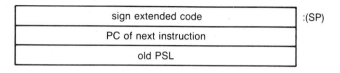

sign extended code	:(SP)
PC of next instruction	
old PSL	

Figure 5.6
CHMx Instruction Stack Frame

All other exceptions in compatibility mode occur to the regular native
mode vector; for example, access-control-violation fault, translation-
not-valid fault, and machine-check abort. See Chapter 9, PDP – 11
Compatibility Mode.

Change-Mode Trap—A change-mode trap is an exception that occur
when one of the change-mode instructions (CHMK, CHME, CHMS,
CHMU) is executed. The instruction operand is pushed on the
exception stack, as shown in Figure 5.6. See the description of the
change-mode instructions for details.

Breakpoint Fault—A breakpoint fault is an exception that occurs whe
the breakpoint instruction (BPT) is executed. No parameters are
pushed.

To proceed from a breakpoint, a debugger or tracing program typical
restores the original contents of the location containing the BPT, sets
T in the PSL saved by the BPT fault, and resumes. When the
instruction completes, a trace exception will occur (see section on
tracing). At this point, the tracing program can again re-insert the BP
instruction, restore T to its original state (usually clear), and resume.
Note that if both tracing and breakpointing are in progress (if PSL⟨T⟩
was set at the time of the BPT), then on the trace exception both
the BPT restoration and a normal trace exception should be processe
by the trace handler.

Trace Fault

A trace is an exception that occurs between instructions when trace i
enabled. Tracing is used for tracing programs, for performance
evaluation, or for debugging purposes. It is designed so that one and
only one trace exception occurs before the execution of each traced
instruction. The saved PC on a trace is the address of the next
instruction that would normally be executed. If a trace fault and a
memory management fault (or an odd address abort during a
compatibility mode instruction fetch) occur simultaneously, the order i
which the exceptions are taken is UNPREDICTABLE. The trace fault
for an instruction takes precedence over all other exceptions.
In order to ensure that exactly one trace occurs per instruction despit
other traps and faults, the PSL contains two bits: trace enable (T)

and trace pending (TP). If only one bit were used, then the occurrence of an interrupt at the end of an instruction would either produce zero or two traces, depending on the design. Instead of the PSL⟨T⟩ bit being defined to produce a trap after any other traps or aborts at the end of an instruction, the trap effect is implemented by copying PSL⟨T⟩ to a second bit (PSL⟨TP⟩) that is actually used to generate the exception. PSL⟨TP⟩ generates a fault before any other processing at the start of the next instruction.

The rules of operation for trace are as follows:

1. At the beginning of an instruction, if TP is set, then a trace fault is taken after clearing TP.

2. TP is loaded with the value of T.

3. If the instruction faults or an interrupt is serviced, PSL⟨TP⟩ is cleared before the PSL is saved on the stack. The saved PC is set to the start of the faulting or interrupted instruction. Instruction execution is resumed at step 1.

4. If the instruction aborts or takes an arithmetic trap, PSL⟨TP⟩ is not changed before the PSL is saved on the stack.

5. If an interrupt is serviced after instruction completion and arithmetic traps but before tracing is checked for at the start of the next instruction, then PSL⟨TP⟩ is not changed before the PSL is saved on the stack.

The routine entered by a CHMx is not traced because CHMx clears T and TP in the new PSL. However, if T was set at the beginning of CHMx, the saved PSL will have both T and TP set. Trace faults resume with the instruction following the REI in the routine entered by the CHMx. An instruction following an REI will fault either if T was set when the REI was executed or if TP in the saved PSL is set; in both cases, TP is set after the REI. Note that a trace fault that occurs for an instruction following an REI that sets TP will be taken with the new PSL. Thus, special care must be taken if exception or interrupt routines are traced. If the T-bit is set by a BISPSW instruction, trace faults begin with the second instruction after the BISPSW.

In addition, the CALLS and CALLG instructions save a clear T, although T in the PSL is unchanged. This is done so that a debugger or trace program proceeding from a BPT fault does not get a spurious trace from the RET that matches the CALL.

The detection of reserved-instruction faults occurs after the trace fault. The detection of interrupts and other exceptions can occur during instruction execution. In this case, TP is cleared before the exception or interrupt is initiated. The entire PSL (including T and TP) is automatically saved on interrupt or exception initiation and is restored at the end with an REI. This makes interrupts and benign exceptions totally transparent to the executing program.

Table 5.3 shows the operation of tracing during execution of ordinary instructions, instructions that have special effects on tracing, and other system events that effect tracing.

Table 5.3
Tracing

Event	Before the Event Current T	TP	Stacked T	TP	After the Event Current T	TP	Stacked T	TP	Exception
ordinary instruction execution	0	0			0	0			
	1	0			1	1			
	x	1			0	0	1	0	trace fault
BISPSW that sets T	0	0			1	0			
	0	1			0	0	0	0	trace fault
	1	0			1	1			
	1	1			0	0	1	0	trace fault
BICPSW that clears T	0	0			0	0			
	0	1			0	0	0	0	trace fault
	1	0			0	1			
	1	1			0	0	1	0	trace fault
CALLS or CALLG	0	0			0	0	0		
	0	1			0	0	0	0	trace fault
	1	0			1	1	0		
	1	1			0	0	1	0	trace fault
RET	0	0	0		0	0			
	0	0	1		1	0			
	0	1	0		0	0	0,0	0	trace fault
	0	1	1		0	0	0,1	0	trace fault
	1	0	0		0	0			
	1	0	1		1	1			
	1	1	0		0	0	1,0	0	trace fault
	1	1	1		0	0	1,1	0	trace fault
CHMx . . . REI	0	0			0	0			
	1	0			1	1			
	x	1			0	0	1	0	trace fault
interrupt or exception . . . REI	0	0			0	0			
	1	0			1	1			
	x	1			0	0	1	0	trace fault
CHMx	0	0			0	0	0	0	CHMx
	1	0			0	0	1	1	CHMx
	x	1			0	0	1	0	trace fault

	Before the Event				After the Event				
	Current		Stacked		Current		Stacked		
Event	T	TP	T	TP	T	TP	T	TP	Exception
REI	0	0	0	0	0	0			
	0	0	0	1	0	1			
	0	0	1	0	1	0			
	0	0	1	1	1	1			
	0	1	0	0	0	0	0,0	0,0	trace fault*
	0	1	0	1	0	0	0,0	0,1	trace fault*
	0	1	1	0	0	0	0,1	0,0	trace fault*
	0	1	1	1	0	0	0,1	0,1	trace fault*
	1	0	0	0	0	1			
	1	0	0	1	0	1			
	1	0	1	0	1	1			
	1	0	1	1	1	1			
	1	1	0	0	0	0	1,0	0,0	trace fault*
	1	1	0	1	0	0	1,0	0,1	trace fault*
	1	1	1	0	0	0	1,1	0,0	trace fault*
	1	1	1	1	0	0	1,1	0,1	trace fault*
Interrupt or exception	0	0			0	0	0	0	
	1	0			0	0	1	0	
	0	1			0	0	0	1	
	1	1			0	0	1	1	

Where two entries are shown stacked, the first shown is on the kernel or interrupt stack for
the trace fault handler. The second shown is on the original stack, unchanged by the trace
fault.

Routines using the trace facility are termed trace handlers. They
should observe the following conventions and restrictions:

1. When the trace handler performs its REI back to the traced
   program, it should always force the T-bit on in the PSL that will be
   restored. This defends against programs clearing T via RET, REI,
   or BICPSW.

2. The trace handler should never examine or alter the TP bit when
   continuing tracing. The hardware flows ensure that this bit is
   maintained correctly to continue tracing.

3. When tracing is to be ended, both T and TP should be cleared.
   This ensures that no further traces will occur.

4. Tracing a service routine that completes with an REI will give a
   trace in the restored mode after the REI. If the program being
   restored to was also being traced, only one trace exception
   is generated.

5. If a routine entered by a CALLS or CALLG instruction is executed at full speed by turning off T, then trace control can be regained b setting T in the PSW in its call frame. Tracing will resume after the instruction following the RET.

6. Tracing is disabled for routines entered by a CHMx instruction or any exception. Thus, if a CHMx or exception service routine is to be traced, a breakpoint instruction must be placed at its entry point. If such a routine is recursive, breakpointing will catch each recursion only if the breakpoint is not on the CHMx or instruction with the exception.

7. If it is desired to allow multiple trace handlers, all handlers should preserve T when turning on and off trace. They also would have t simulate traced code that alters or reads T.

Serious System Failures

Kernel-stack-not-valid abort is an exception that indicates that the kernel stack was not valid while the processor was pushing informatic onto the kernel stack during the initiation of an exception or interrupt. Usually this is an indication of a stack overflow or other operating system error. The attempted exception is transformed into an abort that uses the interrupt stack. No extra information is pushed on the interrupt stack in addition to PSL and PC of the original exceptior IPL is raised to 1F (hex). If the exception vector ⟨1:0⟩ is not 1, the operation of the processor is UNDEFINED.

Software may abort the process without aborting the system. Becaus of the lost information, however, the process cannot be continued. If the kernel stack is not valid during the normal execution of an instruction (including CHMx or REI), the normal memory managemen fault is initiated.

An interrupt-stack-not-valid halt results when the interrupt stack was not valid, or a memory error occurred, while the processor was pushing information onto the interrupt stack during the initiation of an exception or interrupt. No further interrupt requests are acknowledgec on the processor. The processor leaves the PC, the PSL, and the reason for the halt in registers so that they are available to a debugge to the normal bootstrap routine, or to an optional watch-dog bootstrap routine. A watch-dog bootstrap can cause the processor to leave the halted state.

A machine-check exception indicates that the processor detected an internal error in itself. As is usual for exceptions, machine-check is taken regardless of current IPL. The machine-check exception vector bits⟨1:0⟩ must specify 1 or the operation of the processor is UNDE-FINED. The exception is taken on the interrupt stack, and IPL is raised to 1F (hex).

00000010 (hex)	:(SP)
1st longword of error report	
2nd longword of error report	
3rd longword of error report	
4th longword of error report	
PC	
PSL	

Figure 5.7
An Example Machine-Check Stack Frame

The processor pushes a machine-check stack frame onto the interrupt stack, consisting of a count longword, an implementation-dependent number of error report longwords, and a PC and PSL. The count longword reports the number of bytes of error report pushed. For example, if 4 longwords of error report are pushed, the count longword will contain 16 (decimal). An example machine-check stack frame is shown in Figure 5.7.

Software can decide, on the basis of the information presented, whether to abort the current process if the machine-check came from the process. Machine-check includes uncorrected bus and memory errors anywhere, and any other processor-detected errors. Some processor errors cannot ensure the state of the machine at all. For such errors, the state will be preserved on a "best effort" basis.

SERIALIZATION OF NOTIFICATION OF MULTIPLE EVENTS

The interaction between arithmetic traps, tracing, other exceptions, and multiple interrupts is complex. In order to ensure consistent and useful implementations, it is necessary to understand this interaction at a detailed level. As an example, if an instruction is started with PSL⟨T⟩ = 1 and PSL⟨TP⟩ = 0, and it gets an arithmetic trap, and an interrupt request is recognized, the following sequence occurs:

1. The instruction finishes, storing all its results. PSL⟨TP⟩ is set at the end of this instruction since PSL⟨T⟩ was set at the beginning.

2. The overflow trap sequence is initiated, saving PC and PSL (with TP = 1), loading a new PC from the overflow trap vector, and creating a new PSL.

3. The interrupt sequence is initiated, saving the PC and PSL appropriate to the overflow-trap service routine, loading a new PC from the interrupt vector, and creating a new PSL.

4. If a higher priority interrupt is noticed, the first instruction of the interrupt service routine is not executed. Instead, the PC and PSL appropriate to that routine are saved as part of initiating the new

interrupt. The original interrupt service routine will then be executed when the higher priority routine terminates via REI.

5. The interrupt service routine runs and then exits with REI.

6. The overflow-trap service routine runs and then exits with REI, which sets PSL⟨TP⟩ since the saved PSL⟨TP⟩ was set.

7. The trace fault occurs, again pushing PC and PSL but this time with PSL⟨TP⟩ = 0.

8. Trace service routine runs and then exits with REI.

9. The next instruction is executed.

This sequence is accomplished by the following operation between instructions:

```
        ! Here at completion of instruction, including
        ! at end of REI from an exception or interrupt routine.
1$:  {possibly take interrupts or console halt};
        ! If so, PSL⟨TP⟩ is not modified before PSL is saved.
        if PSL⟨TP⟩ EQLU 1 then      ! If trace pending, then fault.
                begin               ! Trace fault takes precedence
                PSL⟨TP⟩ ← 0;        ! over other exceptions.
                {initiate trace fault};
                end;
        {possibly take interrupts or console halt};
        ! If so, PSL⟨TP⟩ is not modified before PSL is saved.
        PSL⟨TP⟩ ← PSL⟨T⟩;           !if trace enable, set trace pending
        {go start instruction execution};
        ! Reserved instruction faults are taken here.
        ! FPD is tested here, thus TP takes
        ! precedence over FPD if both are set.
        if {instruction faults} OR {an interrupt or console halt
            is taken before end of instruction} then
                begin
                {back up PC to start of opcode};
                {either set PSL⟨FPD⟩ or back up all general
                register side effects};
                PSL⟨TP⟩ ← 0;
                {initiate exception or interrupt};
                end;
        if {arithmetic trap needed and no other abort or trap}
            then {initiate arithmetic trap};
        ! Note: All instructions end by flowing
        ! through 1$, thus the REI from a service
        ! routine will return to 1$.
```

The system control block is a page containing the vectors by which exceptions and interrupts are dispatched to the appropriate service routines. Table 5.4 shows the interrupt and exception vectors in the SCB.

Table 5.4
System Control Block Vectors

Offset	Name	Type	Parameters	Notes
00	passive release	interrupt		IPL is that of the request.
04	machine check	abort, fault, or trap		Number of parameters is implementation-dependent.
08	kernel stack not valid	abort	0	
0C	power fail	interrupt		IPL is 1E.
10	reserved or privileged instruction	fault	0	Opcodes reserved to DIGITAL and privileged instruction.
14	customer reserved instruction	fault	0	XFC instruction.
18	reserved operand	fault or abort	0	
1C	reserved addressing mode	fault	0	
20	access-control violation	fault	2	Virtual address and fault parameter are pushed.
24	translation not valid	fault	2	Virtual address and fault parameter are pushed.
28	trace pending	fault	0	
2C	breakpoint instruction	fault	0	
30	compatibility	fault or abort	1	A type code is pushed.
34	arithmetic	trap or fault	1	A type code is pushed.
38	unused			Reserved to DIGITAL.
3C	unused			Reserved to DIGITAL.
40	CHMK	trap	1	The operand word is sign-extended and pushed.
44	CHME	trap	1	The operand word is sign-extended and pushed.
48	CHMS	trap	1	The operand word is sign-extended and pushed.
4C	CHMU	trap	1	The operand word is sign-extended and pushed.
50-60	reserved for bus or memory error	interrupt		IPL is implementation dependent.
64-80	unused			Reserved to DIGITAL.
84	software level 1	interrupt		IPL is 1.
88	software level 2	interrupt		IPL is 2. Ordinarily used for AST delivery.

Table 5.4
System Control Block Vectors (*continued*)

Offset	Name	Type	Parameters	Notes
8C	software level 3	interrupt		IPL is 3. Ordinarily used for process scheduling.
90-BC	software levels 4-F	interrupt		Vector corresponds to IPl
C0	interval timer	interrupt		IPL is 16 or 18 (hex), implementation-dependent.
C4	unused			Reserved to DIGITAL.
C8	subset emulation	trap	10	FPD clear. Emulation frame is pushed.
CC	suspended emulation	fault	0	FPD set.
DO-DC	unused			Reserved to DIGITAL.
EO-EC	unused			Reserved to owners.
FO	console storage receive	interrupt		11/750 and 11/730. IPL is implementation-dependent.
F4	console storage transmit	interrupt		11/750 and 11/730. IPL is implementation-dependent.
F8	console terminal receive	interrupt		IPL is 14 (hex).
FC	console terminal transmit	interrupt		IPL is 14 (hex).
100-13C	adapter vectors	interrupt		IPL is 14 (hex). Implementation-dependent.
140-17C	adapter vectors	interrupt		IPL is 15 (hex). Implementation-dependent.
180-1BC	adapter vectors	interrupt		IPL is 16 (hex). Implementation-dependent.
1CO-IFC	adapter vectors	interrupt		IPL is 17 (hex). Implementation-dependent.
200-3FC	device vectors	interrupt		Implementation-dependent.
400-5FC	device vectors	interrupt		Implementation-dependent.

System Control Block Base

The system control block base (SCBB) is a privileged register containing the physical address of the system control block, which must be page-aligned. Figure 5.8 shows the SCBB.

The actual length is implementation dependent because it represents a physical address. Processor initialization leaves the contents of SCBB UNPREDICTABLE.

```
31 30 29                              9 8              0
┌─┬─┬────────────────────────────────┬──────────────┐
│0│0│   physical page address of SCB │     MBZ      │
└─┴─┴────────────────────────────────┴──────────────┘
```

Figure 5.8
System Control Block Base

If the SCBB points to I/O space or nonexistent memory when an exception or interrupt occurs, the operation of the processor is UNDEFINED.

A vector is a longword in the SCB. The processor examines the vector when an exception or interrupt occurs in order to determine how to service the event.

Separate vectors are defined for each interrupting device controller and each class of exceptions. Each vector is interpreted as follows by the hardware. Bits ⟨1:0⟩ contain a code interpreted:

0 Service this event on the kernel stack unless already running on the interrupt stack, in which case service on the interrupt stack.

1 Service this event on the interrupt stack. If this event is an exception, the IPL is raised to 1F (hex).

2 Service this event in writable control store, passing bits ⟨15:2⟩ to the installation-dependent microcode there. If writable control store does not exist or is not loaded, the operation is UNDEFINED.

3 Operation UNDEFINED. Reserved to DIGITAL.

For codes 0 and 1, bits ⟨31:2⟩ contain the virtual address of the service routine, which must begin on a longword boundary and will ordinarily be in the system space. CHMx is serviced on the stack selected by the new mode. Bits ⟨1:0⟩ in the CHMx vectors must be zero or the operation of the processor is UNDEFINED. Emulation exceptions are serviced on the current stack. Bits ⟨1:0⟩ in the emulation exception vectors must be zero or the operation of the processor is UNDEFINED.

The assignment of SCB offsets and priority levels for controllers, adapters, and other devices connecting to the system bus is implementation dependent. Typically, interrupt priority levels 14 through 17 (hex) are used to signal I/O device, controller, and adapter events. Typically, one interrupt vector is assigned to each priority level for each adapter.

The use of second or third SCB pages (offsets 200-3FC and 400-5FC) is implementation dependent. In some processors (VAX-11/750 and VAX-11/730, for example) UNIBUS devices interrupt the processor directly, and the second SCB page contains the UNIBUS device vectors. When a UNIBUS device connected to such a system requests an interrupt, the vector is determined by adding 2 hex) to th vector supplied by the device. If a second UNIBUS adapter is installed, the third SCB page contains its device vectors, and 400 (hex) is added to the vector supplied by the device attached to the second UNIBUS. Only device vectors in the range 0 to 1FC (hex) are allowed. Interrupt priority levels 14 through 17 (hex) correspond to UNIBUS levels BR4 through BR7.

STACKS

At any time, the processor is either in a process context (and PSL⟨IS⟩ = 0) in one of four modes (kernel, executive, supervisor, user), or is in the system-wide interrupt service context (and PSL⟨IS⟩ = 1) that operates with kernel privileges. There is a stack pointer associated with each of these five states; any time the processor changes from one of these states to another, the stack pointer (SP or R14) is store in the process context stack pointer for the old state and is loaded from that for the new state. The five stack pointers are accessible as internal processor registers.

KSP   Kernel-mode stack pointer

ESP   Executive-mode stack pointer

SSP   Supervisor-mode stack pointer

USP   User-mode stack pointer

ISP   Interrupt stack pointer

Operating system design must choose a priority level that is the boundary between kernel and interrupt stack use. The SCB interrupt vectors must be set such that interrupts to levels above this boundary run on the interrupt stack (vector⟨1:0⟩ = 1) and interrupts below this boundary run on the kernel stack (vector⟨1:0⟩ = 0). Typically, AST delivery (IPL 2) is on the kernel stack, and all higher levels are on the interrupt stack.

Stack Residency

The user, supervisor, and executive mode stacks do not need to be resident. Kernel-mode code can bring in or allocate process stack pages as translation-not-valid faults occur. The kernel stack for the current process and the interrupt stack (which is process-independent however, must be resident and accessible. Translation-not-valid and access-control-violation faults occurring on references to either of these stacks are regarded as serious system failures.

If either of these faults occurs on a reference to the kernel stack, the processor aborts the current sequence and initiates kernel-stack-not-valid abort on hardware level 1F (hex). If either of these faults occurs on a reference to the interrupt stack, the processor halts. Note that this does not mean that every possible reference is checked, but rather that the processor will not loop on these conditions.

It is not necessary that the kernel stack for a process other than the current one be resident, but it must be resident before that process is selected to run by the software's process dispatcher. Further, any mechanism that uses translation-not-valid or access-control-violation faults to gather process statistics, for instance, must exercise care not to invalidate kernel-stack pages.

Except on CALLS and CALLG instructions, the hardware makes no attempt to align the stacks. For best performance on all processors, the software should align the stack on a longword boundary and allocate the stack in longword increments. The convert-byte-to-long (CVTBL and MOVZBL), convert-word-to-long (CVTWL and MOVZWL), convert-long-to-byte (CVTLB), and convert-long-to-word (CVTLW) instructions are recommended for pushing bytes and words on the stack and popping them off in order to keep it longword aligned.

The interrupt stack bit (IS) and current mode bits in the privileged processor status longword specify which of the five stack pointers is currently in use, as shown in Table 5.5.

The processor does not allow current mode to be non-zero when IS = 1. This is achieved by clearing the mode bits when taking an interrupt or exception, and by causing reserved operand fault if REI attempts to load a PSL in which both IS and mode are non-zero.

The stack to be used for an interrupt or exception is selected by the current PSL⟨IS⟩ and bits⟨1:0⟩ of the vector. If the current PSL⟨IS⟩ is 1 or if the low bits of the vector are 01 (binary), then the interrupt stack is used. If the current PSL⟨IS⟩ is 0 and the low bits of the vector are then the kernel stack is used. Values 10 (binary) and 11 (binary) of the vector⟨1:0⟩ are used for other purposes. Refer to the section "System Control Block" earlier in this chapter for details.

Table 5.5
Indication of Current Stack Pointer

Stack Pointer	Mnemonic	PSL⟨IS⟩	PSL⟨CUR_MOD⟩
Interrupt stack pointer	ISP	1	0
Kernel stack pointer	KSP	0	0
Executive pointer	ESP	0	1
Supervisor stack pointer	SSP	0	2
User stack pointer	USP	0	3

Accessing Stack Registers

Reference to SP (the stack pointer) in the general registers will access one of five possible architecturally defined stack pointers—the user, supervisor, executive, kernel, or interrupt—depending on the values of the current mode and IS bits in the PSL. Some processors may implement these five stack pointers as five internal processor registers. Other processors may store the four per-process stack pointers in memory in the PCB and store only the interrupt stack pointer in an internal register (see Chapter 8). In either case, software can access any of the five stack pointers with the MTPR and MFPR instructions. Results are correct even if the stack pointer specified by the current mode and IS bits in the PSL is referenced in the internal processor register space by an MTPR or MFPR instruction.

If the four process stack pointers are implemented as registers, then these instructions are the only method for accessing the stack pointers of the current process. See Chapter 8 for conventions to be followed when referencing other per-process registers in the internal processor register space.

The internal processor register numbers were chosen to be the same as PSL⟨26:24⟩. The previous stack pointer is the same as PSL⟨23:22⟩ unless PSL⟨IS⟩ is set. If PSL⟨IS⟩ is set, the previous mode cannot be determined from the PSL since interrupts always clear PSL⟨23:22⟩. Processor initialization leaves the contents of all stack pointers UNPREDICTABLE.

INITIATE EXCEPTION OR INTERRUPT

Initiate Exception or Interrupt

Operation:

```
! Read the vector into a temporary register, and check it for validit
! The vector number is determined by the exception or interrupt type.
vector ← SCB[vector_number];
case vector(1:0) of
        0:      if {machine check OR kernel-stack-not-valid}
                        then {UNDEFINED};
        1:      if {CHMx OR subset emulation exception}
                        then {UNDEFINED};
        2:      if {writable control store exists and is loaded}
                        then {enter writable control store}
                        else {UNDEFINED};
        3:      {UNDEFINED};
end;
```

```
! Save the current PSL in a temporary register.
saved_PSL ← PSL;
! Create and load a new PSL.
case {exception or interrupt type} of
        {interrupt}:
                begin
                PSL⟨CM,TP,FPD,DV,FU,IV,T,N,Z,V,C⟩ ← 0;
                PSL⟨CUR_MOD,PRV_MOD⟩ ← 0;
                if vector⟨1:0⟩ EQLU 1
                        then PSL⟨IS⟩ ← 1
                        else PSL⟨IS⟩ ← saved_PSL⟨IS⟩;
                PSL⟨IPL⟩ ← new_IPL;
                end;
        {CHMx}:
                begin
                PSL⟨CM,TP,FPD,DV,FU,IV,T,N,Z,V,C⟩ ← 0;
                PSL⟨CUR_MOD⟩ ← new_mode;
                PSL⟨PRV_MOD⟩ ← saved_PSL⟨CUR_MOD⟩;
                PSL⟨IS⟩ ← saved_PSL⟨IS⟩;
                PSL⟨IPL⟩ ← saved_PSL⟨IPL⟩;
                end;
        {subset emulation exception}:
                begin
                PSL⟨CM,TP,FPD,DV,FU,IV,T⟩ ← 0;
                PSL⟨CUR_MOD⟩ ← saved_PSL⟨CUR_MOD⟩;
                PSL⟨PRV_MOD⟩ ← saved_PSL⟨PRV_MOD⟩;
                PSL⟨IS⟩ ← saved_PSL⟨IS⟩;
                PSL⟨IPL⟩ ← saved_PSL⟨IPL⟩;
                PSL⟨N,Z,V,C⟩ ← saved_PSL⟨N,Z,V,C⟩;
                end;
        otherwise                    ! (Other exceptions.)
                begin
                PSL⟨CM,TP,FPD,DV,FU,IV,T,N,Z,V,C⟩ ← 0;
                PSL⟨CUR_MOD⟩ ← 0;
                PSL⟨PRV_MOD⟩ ← saved_PSL⟨CUR_MOD⟩;
                if vector⟨1:0⟩ EQLU 1
                        then PSL⟨IS⟩ ← 1
                        else PSL⟨IS⟩ ← saved_PSL⟨IS⟩;
                if vector⟨1:0⟩ EQLU 1
                        then PSL⟨IPL⟩ ← 31
                        else PSL⟨IPL⟩ ← saved_PSL⟨IPL⟩;
                end;
        end;
```

```
! If necessary, save the current stack pointer and load a new one.
if saved_PSL⟨IS⟩ EQLU 0 then
        begin
        IPR[saved_PSL⟨CUR_MOD⟩] ← SP;
        SP ← IPR[ PSL⟨IS⟩'PSL⟨CUR_MOD⟩ ];
        end;
! Push PC, the saved PSL, and any parameters onto the new stack,
! in the new mode.
-(SP) ← saved_PSL;
-(SP) ← PC;
{push parameters if any};
! Load PC with the address of the exception or interrupt handler.
PC ← vector⟨31:2⟩ ' 0⟨1:0⟩;
! Software interrupts clear the software-interrupt-pending bit.
if {software interrupt} then SISR⟨ PSL⟨IPL⟩ ⟩ ← 0;
```

Condition Codes:

```
N ← 0;
Z ← 0;
V ← 0;
C ← 0;
```

Exceptions:
kernel-stack not valid
interrupt-stack not valid

Description:
The vector associated with the exception or interrupt is read from the
system control block. The current PSL is saved and a new PSL is
created and loaded. If this is an interrupt, the new PSL has all fields
cleared except ⟨IS⟩ and ⟨IPL⟩. IPL is raised to the priority level of
the interrupt request. IS is set to 1 if the low bits of the vector contain
01 (binary); otherwise, it is unchanged from the old PSL. If this is a
CHMx exception, current mode is loaded with the new mode, previous
mode is loaded with the old value of current mode, ⟨IS⟩ and ⟨IPL⟩ are
retained from the old PSL, and all other fields are cleared. If this is an
emulation exception, current mode, previous mode, ⟨IS⟩, ⟨IPL⟩, and
the condition codes are all retained from the old PSL, and all other
fields are cleared. If this is any other kind of exception, previous mode
is loaded with the old value of current mode, ⟨IS⟩ and ⟨IPL⟩ are
loaded according to the low bits of the vector, and all other fields are
cleared. If the low bits of the vector are 01 (binary), then ⟨IS⟩ is
loaded with 1 and ⟨IPL⟩ is raised to 31; otherwise, ⟨IS⟩ and ⟨IPL⟩ are
retained from the old PSL. Unless the processor is already running on
the interrupt stack, the old stack pointer is saved and a new one is

loaded. The saved PSL and the PC are pushed onto the stack, along with any exception parameters. PC is loaded with the address of the interrupt or exception service routine indicated by bits ⟨31:2⟩ of the vector.

Notes:

1. Interrupts are disabled during this sequence.

2. On a fault or interrupt, the saved condition codes are UNPRE-DICTABLE; they are only saved to the extent necessary to ensure correct completion of the instruction when resumed.

3. After an abort, all the explicit and implicit operands of the aborted instruction are UNPREDICTABLE (see Appendix B). The PC pushed on the stack points to the opcode of the aborted instruction, unless the instruction modified PC in a way that produces UNPREDICTABLE results.

4. After an abort or fault or interrupt that pushes a PSL with FPD set, the general registers except PC, SP, and FP are UNPREDICTABLE unless the instruction description specifies a setting. If FP is the destination in this case, then it is also UNPREDICTABLE. On a kernel-stack-not-valid abort, both SP and FP are UNPREDICT-ABLE. This implies that processes stopped with FPD set cannot be resumed on processors of a different type or engineering-change level.

5. If the processor gets an access-control-violation or translation-not-valid condition while attempting to push information on the kernel stack, a kernel-stack-not-valid abort is initiated instead, and IPL is raised to 31. The PSL and PC saved on the interrupt stack are those that would have been pushed on the kernel stack by the original exception. Additional information, if any, associated with the original exception is lost. If vector⟨1:0⟩ for kernel-stack-not-valid abort is 0, the operation of the processor is UNDEFINED. (Kernel stack not valid will not occur with CHMx or subset emulation exceptions, since they explicitly probe the destination stack and fault if it is invalid or inaccessible.)

6. If the processor gets an access-control-violation or translation-not-valid condition while attempting to push information on the interrupt stack, the processor is halted and only the state of ISP, PC, and PSL is ensured to be correct for subsequent analysis. The PSL and PC have the values that would have been pushed on the interrupt stack.

7. The value of PSL⟨TP⟩ that is saved on the stack is as follows:

fault	clear
trace	clear
interrupt	clear (if FPD set)
	from PSL⟨TP⟩ (if after traps, before trace)

abort	UNPREDICTABLE
trap	from PSL⟨TP⟩
CHMx	from PSL⟨TP⟩
BPT, XFC	clear
reserved instr.	clear

8. The value of PC that is saved on the stack points to the following:

fault	instruction faulting
trace	next instruction to execute (instruction at the beginning of which the trace fault was taken)
interrupt	instruction interrupted or next instruction to execute
abort	instruction aborting or detecting kernel-stack-not-valid (not ensured on machine-check)
trap	next instruction to execute
CHMx	next instruction to execute
BPT, XFC	BPT, XFC instruction
reserved instr.	reserved instruction

INSTRUCTIONS RELATED TO EXCEPTIONS AND INTERRUPTS

REI

Return from Exception or Interrupt

Format:

Opcode

Operation:

```
tmp1 ← (SP)+; ! Pick up saved PC
tmp2 ← (SP)+; ! and PSL
if {tmp2⟨IS⟩ EQLU 1 AND tmp2⟨IPL⟩ EQLU 0} OR
   {tmp2⟨IPL⟩ GTRU 0 AND tmp2⟨CUR–MOD⟩ NEQU 0} OR
   {tmp2⟨PRV–MOD⟩ LSSU tmp2⟨CUR–MOD⟩} OR
   {tmp2⟨PSL–MBZ⟩ NEQU 0} OR
```

```
        {tmp2⟨CUR-MOD⟩ LSSU PSL⟨CUR-MOD⟩} OR

        {tmp2⟨IS⟩ EQLU 1 AND PSL⟨IS⟩ EQLU 0} OR

        {tmp2⟨IPL⟩ GTRU PSL⟨IPL⟩} then {reserved operand fault};
if {compatibility mode implemented} then
        begin
        if {tmp2⟨CM⟩ EQLU 1} AND

            {{tmp2⟨FPD,IS,DV,FU,IV⟩ NEQU 0} OR

            {tmp2⟨CUR-MOD⟩ NEQU 3}} then
                    {reserved operand fault};

        end
else if {tmp2⟨CM⟩ EQLU 1} then {reserved operand fault};
if PSL⟨IS⟩ EQLU 1 then ISP ← SP     !save old stack pointer
        else PSL⟨CUR-MOD⟩-SP ← SP;
if PSL⟨TP⟩ EQLU 1 then tmp2⟨TP⟩ ← 1; !TP ← TP or stack TP
PC ← tmp1;
PSL ← tmp2;
if PSL⟨IS⟩ EQLU 0 then
        begin
        SP ← PSL⟨CUR-MOD⟩-SP;               !switch stack
        if PSL⟨CUR-MOD⟩ GEQU ASTLVL        !check for AST delivery
                    then {request interrupt at IPL 2};
        end;
{check for software interrupts};
{clear instruction look-ahead}
```

Condition Codes:

```
N ← saved PSL⟨3⟩;
Z ← saved PSL⟨2⟩;
V ← saved PSL⟨1⟩;
C ← saved PSL⟨0⟩;
```

Exception:
reserved operand

Opcode:

```
02  REI  Return from Exception or Interrupt
```

Description:
A longword is popped from the current stack and held in a temporary
PC. A second longword is popped from the current stack and held

in a temporary PSL. The popped PSL is checked for internal consistency. The popped PSL is compared with the current PSL to make sure that the transition from current PSL to popped PSL is allowed. The current stack pointer is saved, and a new stack pointer is selected according to the new PSL⟨CUR—MOD⟩ and ⟨IS⟩ fields (see section "Stack Status Bits" earlier in this chapter). The level of the highest privileged AST is checked against the current mode to see whether a pending AST can be delivered (see Chapter 6). Execution resumes with the instruction being executed at the time of the exception or interrupt. Any instruction lookahead in the processor is reinitialized.

Notes:

1. The exception or interrupt service routine is responsible for restoring any registers saved and removing any parameters from the stack.

2. As usual for faults, if access-control-violation or translation-not-valid occurs while popping PC or PSL from the stack, the stack pointer is restored as part of the initiation of the fault.

3. REI to compatibility mode results in a reserved operand fault if compatibility mode is not implemented.

CHM

Change Mode

Purpose:
request services of more privileged software

Format:
opcode code.rw

Operation:

```
tmp1 ← {mode selected by opcode (K=0, E=1, S=2, U=3)};
tmp2 ← MINU(tmp1, PSL⟨CUR—MOD⟩);        !maximize privilege
tmp3 ← SEXT(code);
if {PSL⟨IS⟩ EQLU 1} then HALT;          !illegal from I stack
PSL⟨CUR—MOD⟩–SP ← SP;                   !save old stack pointer
tmp4 ← tmp2–SP;                         !get new stack pointer
PROBEW (from tmp4−1 through tmp4−12 with mode=tmp2);   !check
                                       ! new stack access
    if {access—control violation} then
        {initiate access—control—violation fault};
    if {translation not valid} then
        {initiate translation—not—valid fault};
```

```
{initiate CHMx exception with new—mode = tmp2
        and parameter = tmp3
        using 40 + tmpl*4 (hex) as SCB offset
        using tmp4 as the new SP
        and not storing SP again};
```

Condition Codes:

N ← 0;
Z ← 0;
V ← 0;
C ← 0;

Exception:
halt

Opcodes:

```
BC   CHMK   Change Mode to Kernel
BD   CHME   Change Mode to Executive
BE   CHMS   Change Mode to Supervisor
BF   CHMU   Change Mode to User
```

Description:
Change-mode instructions allow processes to change their access mode in a controlled manner. The instruction only increases privilege (decreases the access mode) or leaves it unchanged.

A change in mode also results in a change of stack pointers: the old pointer is saved, the new pointer is loaded. The PSL, PC, and code passed by the instruction are pushed onto the stack of the new mode. The saved PC addresses the instruction following the CHMx instruction. The code is sign extended. Figure 5.6 illustrates the new stack's appearance after execution.

The destination mode selected by the opcode is used to obtain a location from the system control block. This location addresses the CHMx dispatcher for the specified mode. If the vector$\langle 1{:}0 \rangle$ code NEQU is 0, then the operation is UNDEFINED.

Notes:
1. As usual for faults, any access-control-violation or translation-not-valid fault saves PC and PSL and leaves SP as it was at the beginning of the instruction except for any pushes onto the kernel stack.
2. By software convention, negative codes are reserved to DIGITAL and DIGITAL's customers.

Table 5.6
Processor State Transitions

Initial State	Final State					
	User Mode	Super Mode	Exec Mode	Kernel, Stack, IPL = 0	Kernel Stack, IPL > 0	Interrupt Stack
User Mode	REI or CHMU	CHMS	CHME	CHMK or e(0)	i(0)	e(1) or i(1)
Super Mode	REI	REI, CHMU, or CHME	CHME	CHMK or e(0)	i(0)	e(1) or i(1)
Exec Mode	REI	REI	REI, CHMU, CHMS, or CHME	CHMK or e(0)	i(0)	e(1) or i(1)
Kernel Stack, IPL = 0	REI	REI	REI	REI, CHMx, LDPCTX, e(0), or MTPR IPL	MTPR IPL or i(0)	e(1), i(1), or SVPCTX
Kernel Stack, IPL > 0	REI	REI	REI	REI or MTPR IPL	REI, CHMx, LDPCTX, e(0), or i(0)	e(1), i(1), or SVPCTX
Interrupt Stack	REI	REI	REI	REI	REI or LDPCTX	REI, SVPCTX, MTPR IPL, exception or interrupt

e(0) means exception with vector⟨1:0⟩ = 0
e(1) means exception with vector⟨1:0⟩ = 1
i(0) means interrupt with vector⟨1:0⟩ = 0
i(1) means interrupt with vector⟨1:0⟩ = 1

Examples:

```
CHMK    #7      ; Request the kernel-mode service
                ; specified by code 7.
CHME    #4      ; Request the executive-mode service
                ; specified by code 4.
CHMS    #-2     ; Request the supervisor-mode service
                ; specified by customer code -2.
```

Process Structure

6

A process is a single thread of execution. It is the basic scheduling entity that is executed by the processor. A process consists of an address space and both hardware and software context. The hardware context of a process is defined by a process control block (PCB) that contains images of the 14 general-purpose registers, the processor status longword, the program counter, the four per-process stack pointers, the process virtual memory defined by the base and length registers P0BR, P0LR, P1BR, and P1LR, and several minor control fields. In order for a process to execute, the majority of the PCB must be moved into the internal registers. While a process is executing, some of its hardware context is being updated in the internal registers. When a process is not being executed, its hardware context is stored in a data structure termed the process control block. Saving the contents of the privileged registers in the PCB of the currently executing process and then loading a new context from another PCB is termed context switching. Context switching occurs as one process after another is scheduled for execution.

**PROCESS
CONTEXT**

Shown in Figure 6.1 is the process control block for the currently executing process. The PCB is pointed to by the process control block base (PCBB) register, an internal privileged register. Figure 6.2 shows the PCBB. When the processor is initialized, the contents of PCBB are UNPREDICTABLE.

The PCB contains all of the switchable process context collected into a compact form for ease of movement to and from the privileged internal registers. Although in any normal operating system there is additional software context for each process, the following description is limited to that portion of the PCB known to the hardware. The PCB's contents are described in Table 6.1.

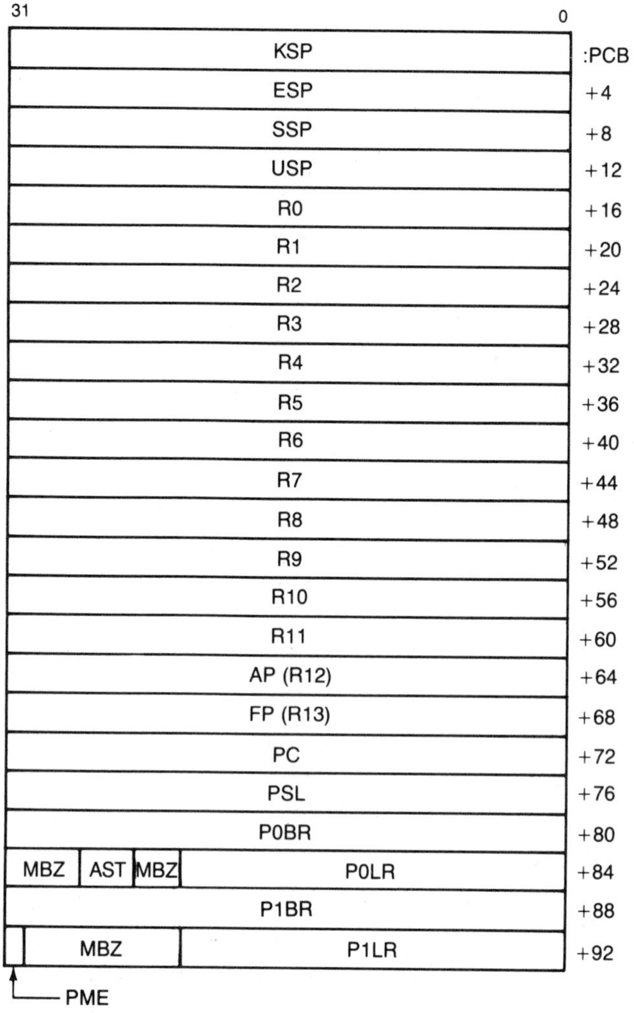

31   0

KSP	:PCB
ESP	+4
SSP	+8
USP	+12
R0	+16
R1	+20
R2	+24
R3	+28
R4	+32
R5	+36
R6	+40
R7	+44
R8	+48
R9	+52
R10	+56
R11	+60
AP (R12)	+64
FP (R13)	+68
PC	+72
PSL	+76
P0BR	+80
MBZ AST MBZ P0LR	+84
P1BR	+88
MBZ P1LR	+92

└── PME

Figure 6.1
Process Control Block (PCB)

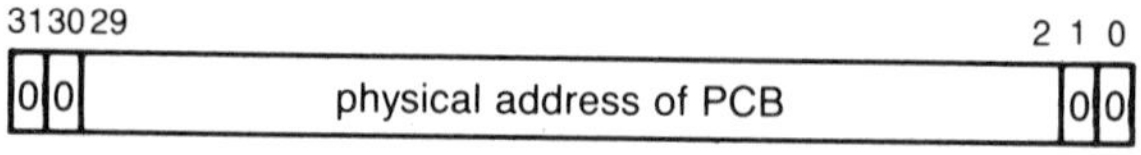

31 30 29   2 1 0

| 0 | 0 | physical address of PCB | 0 | 0 |

Figure 6.2
Process Control Block Base Register (PCBB)

Table 6.1
Contents of the Process Control Block

Name	Mnemonic	Offset (hex)	Extent
kernel stack pointer	KSP	0	$\langle 31{:}0 \rangle$
executive stack pointer	ESP	4	$\langle 31{:}0 \rangle$
supervisor stack pointer	SSP	8	$\langle 31{:}0 \rangle$
user stack pointer	USP	C	$\langle 31{:}0 \rangle$
general registers	R0–R13	10–44	$\langle 31{:}0 \rangle$
program counter	PC	48	$\langle 31{:}0 \rangle$
processor status longword	PSL	4C	$\langle 31{:}0 \rangle$
P0 base register	P0BR	50	$\langle 31{:}0 \rangle$
P0 length register	P0LR	54	$\langle 21{:}0 \rangle$
AST level	ASTLVL	54	$\langle 26{:}24 \rangle$
P1 base register	P1BR	58	$\langle 31{:}0 \rangle$
P1 length register	P1LR	5C	$\langle 21{:}0 \rangle$
performance monitor enable	PME	5C	$\langle 31 \rangle$

To alter its P0BR, P1BR, P0LR, P1LR, ASTLVL or PME, a process must be executing in kernel mode. The process must first store the desired new value in the memory image of the PCB, then move the value to the appropriate privileged register. This protocol results from the fact that these are read-only fields (for the context switch instructions) in the PCB.

The ASTLVL and PME fields of the PCB may be contained in internal processor registers when the process is running.

Performance Monitor Enable Register

The performance-monitor-enable (PME) register controls a signal visible to an external hardware performance monitor. PME allows the system to identify those processes for which monitoring is desired and so permits their behavior to be observed without interference caused by the activity of other processes. Figure 6.3 shows PME. Processor initialization sets PME to zero.

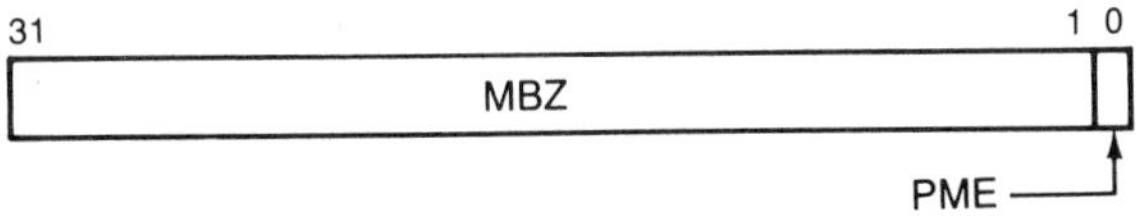

Figure 6.3
Performance Monitor Enable Register (PME)

Asynchronous System Traps

Asynchronous system traps (AST) are a technique for notifying a process of events that are not synchronized with its execution and for initiating processing of asynchronous events with the least possible delay. This delay in delivery of the AST may be due to either process non-residence or to an access mode mismatch. The efficient handling of ASTs in the VAX system requires some hardware assistance to detect changes in access mode (current mode in PSL). A process in any of the four access modes (kernel, executive, supervisor, and user) may receive ASTs; however, an AST for a less privileged access mode must not be permitted to interrupt execution in a more protected access mode. Since outward access mode transitions occur only in the REI instruction, comparison of the current access mode field is made with a privileged register, ASTLVL, shown in Figure 6.4. ASTLVL contains the most privileged access mode number for which an AST is pending. If the new access mode is greater than or equal to the pending ASTLVL, an IPL 2 interrupt is posted to cause delivery of the pending AST.

The software flow for AST processing follows:

1. An event associated with an AST causes software enqueuing of an AST control block to the software PCB, and the software sets the ASTLVL field in the hardware PCB to the most privileged access mode for which an AST is pending. If the target process is currently executing, the ASTLVL privileged register also has to be set.

2. When an REI instruction detects a transition to an access mode that can be interrupted by a pending AST, an IPL 2 interrupt is triggered to cause delivery of the AST. Note that the REI instruction does not make pending AST checks while returning to a routine executing on the interrupt stack.

3. The (IPL 2) interrupt service routine should compute the correct new value for ASTLVL that prevents additional AST delivery interrupts while in kernel mode and move that value to the PCB and the ASTLVL register before lowering IPL and actually dispatching the AST. This interrupt service routine normally executes on the kernel stack in the context of the process receiving the AST.

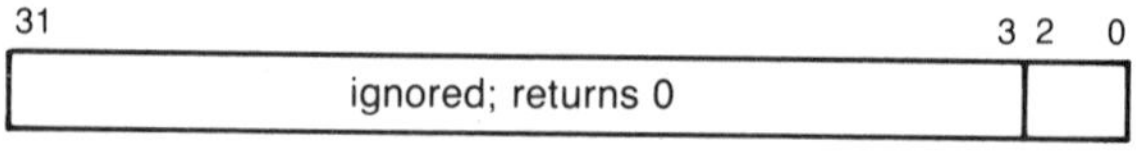

```
31                                            3 2   0
+---------------------------------------------+-----+
|            ignored; returns 0               |     |
+---------------------------------------------+-----+
```

Figure 6.4
AST Level Register (ASTLVL)

4. At the conclusion of processing for an AST, the ASTLVL is again computed and moved to the PCB and ASTLVL register by software.

If ASTLVL contains 4, no AST is pending for the current process. If ASTLVL is less than 4, an AST is pending for the mode corresponding to the value of ASTLVL.

Values of ASTLVL greater than 4 are reserved. Execution of MTPR src, #PR$__ASTLVL with src⟨2:0⟩ GEQU 5 results in UNDEFINED behavior. The preferred implementation is to cause reserved-operand fault. Processor initialization sets ASTLVL to 4. Note that loading ASTLVL with MTPR does not affect SISR or request a software interrupt. Those affects of ASTLVL occur only during REI.

PROCESS SCHEDULING INTERRUPTS

Two of the software interrupt priorities are reserved for process scheduling software.

They are:

(IPL 2)   AST delivery interrupt. This interrupt is triggered by an REI that detects PSL⟨CUR__MOD⟩ GEQU ASTLVL and indicates that a pending AST may now be delivered for the currently executing process.

(IPL 3)   Process scheduling interrupt. This interrupt is triggered by software. It indicates that a process has changed software priority and that the process scheduler should reschedule to find the highest priority executable process to run.

PROCESS STRUCTURE INSTRUCTIONS

Process scheduling software must execute on the interrupt stack (PSL⟨IS⟩ set) in order to have a non-context-switched stack available for use. If the scheduler were running on a process's kernel stack, then any state information it had there would disappear when a new process is selected. Running on the interrupt stack can occur as the result of the interrupt origin of scheduling events. However, some synchronous scheduling requests such as a WAIT service may want to cause rescheduling without any interrupt occurrence. For this reason, the save-process-context (SVPCTX) instruction can be executed while on either the kernel or the interrupt stack, and forces a transition to execution on the interrupt stack.

All of the process structure instructions are privileged and require kernel mode.

Load Process Context

Purpose:

restore register and memory management context

Format:

opcode

Operation:

```
if PSL⟨CUR_MOD⟩ NEQU 0
        then {privileged instruction fault};
if PSL⟨IS⟩ NEQU 1 then {UNDEFINED};
{invalidate per-process translation buffer entries};
! The PCB is located by the physical address in PCBB.
if {internal registers for stack pointers} then
        begin
        KSP ← (PCB);
        ESP ← (PCB+4);
        SSP ← (PCB+8);
        USP ← (PCB+12);
        end;
R0  ← (PCB+16);
R1  ← (PCB+20);
R2  ← (PCB+24);
R3  ← (PCB+28);
R4  ← (PCB+32);
R5  ← (PCB+36);
R6  ← (PCB+40);
R7  ← (PCB+44);
R8  ← (PCB+48);
R9  ← (PCB+52);
R10 ← (PCB+56);
R11 ← (PCB+60);
AP  ← (PCB+64);
FP  ← (PCB+68);
tmp1 ← (PCB+80);
if {tmp1⟨31:30⟩ NEQU 2} OR {tmp1⟨1:0⟩ NEQU 0} then
                {UNDEFINED};
POBR ← tmp1;
if (PCB+84)⟨31:27⟩ NEQU 0 then {UNDEFINED};
if (PCB+84)⟨23:22⟩ NEQU 0 then {UNDEFINED};
POLR ← (PCB+84)⟨21:0⟩;
if (PCB+84)⟨26:24⟩ GEQU 5 then {UNDEFINED};
```

```
ASTLVL ← (PCB+84)⟨26:24⟩;
tmp1 ← (PCB+88);
tmp2 ← tmp1 + 2**23;
if {tmp2⟨31:30⟩ NEQU 2} OR {tmp2⟨1:0⟩ NEQU 0} then
        {UNDEFINED};
P1BR ← tmp1;
if (PCB+92)⟨30:22⟩ NEQU 0 then {UNDEFINED};
P1LR ← (PCB+92)⟨21:0⟩;
PME ← (PCB+92)⟨31⟩;
ISP ← SP;                        ! Save the interrupt stack pointer.
{interrupts off};
PSL⟨IS⟩ ← 0;                     ! Change from the interrupt stack
SP ← (PCB);                      ! to the new kernel stack.
{interrupts on};
-(SP) ← (PCB+76);                ! Push PSL onto kernel stack.
-(SP) ← (PCB+72);                ! Push PC onto kernel stack.
                                 ! (If kernel stack is inaccessible
                                 ! or invalid, then UNDEFINED.)
```

Condition Codes:

```
N ← N;
Z ← Z;
V ← V;
C ← C;
```

Exceptions:
reserved operand
privileged instruction

Opcode:

06   LDPCTX   Load Process Context

Description:
The process control block is specified by the privileged PCBB register. The general registers are loaded from the PCB. The memory management registers describing the process address space are also loaded, and the process entries in the translation buffer are cleared. Execution is switched to the kernel stack. The PC and PSL are moved from the PCB to the stack, suitable for use by a subsequent REI instruction.

Note:
1. Some processors keep a copy of each of the per-process stack pointers in internal registers. In those processors, LDPCTX loads

Process Structure   **265**

the internal registers from the PCB. Other processors do not keep
a copy of all four per-process stack pointers in internal registers.
Rather such processors keep only the stack pointer for the current
access mode in an internal register and switch this with the PCB
contents whenever the current access mode changes.

2. The preferred implementation of UNDEFINED operation is reserved
operand abort.

3. To guarantee correct operation, a LDPCTX must be followed by an
REI instruction.

SVPCTX Save Process Context

Purpose:
save register context

Format:
opcode

Operation:

```
if PSL⟨CUR_MOD⟩ NEQU 0 then
        {privileged instruction fault};
!PCB is located by physical address in PCBB
if {internal registers for stack pointers} then
        begin
        (PCB) ← KSP;
        (PCB+4) ← ESP;
        (PCB+8) ← SSP;
        (PCB+12) ← USP;
        end;
(PCB+16) ← R0;
(PCB+20) ← R1;
(PCB+24) ← R2;
(PCB+28) ← R3;
(PCB+32) ← R4;
(PCB+36) ← R5;
(PCB+40) ← R6;
(PCB+44) ← R7;
(PCB+48) ← R8;
(PCB+52) ← R9;
(PCB+56) ← R10;
```

```
(PCB+60) ← R11;
(PCB+64) ← AP;
(PCB+68) ← FP;
(PCB+72) ← (SP)+;                    !pop PC
(PCB+76) ← (SP)+;                    !pop PSL
If PSL⟨IS⟩ EQLU 0 then
        begin
        PSL⟨IPL⟩ ← MAXU(1, PSL⟨IPL⟩);
        (PCB) ← SP;      !save KSP
        KSP ← SP;
        {interrupts off};
        PSL⟨IS⟩ ← 1;
        SP ← ISP;
        {interrupts on};
        end;
```

Condition Codes:

```
N ← N;
Z ← Z;
V ← V;
C ← C;
```

Exception:
privileged instruction

Opcode:

```
07  SVPCTX   Save Process Context
```

Description:
The process control block is specified by the privileged PCBB register. The general registers are saved into the PCB. The PC and PSL currently on the top of the current stack are popped and stored in the PCB. If a SVPCTX instruction is executed when IS is clear, then IS is set, the interrupt stack pointer activated, and IPL is maximized with 1 because of the switch to the interrupt stack.

Notes:
1. The map, ASTLVL, and PME from the PCB are not saved because they are rarely changed. Thus, not writing them saves overhead.
2. Some processors keep a copy of each of the per-process stack pointers in internal registers. In those processors, SVPCTX stores

the internal registers into the PCB. Other processors do not keep copy of all four per-process stack pointers in internal registers. Rather these processors keep only the stack pointer for the current access mode in an internal register and switch this with the PCB contents whenever the current access mode changes.

3. Between the SVPCTX instruction that saves state for one process and the LDPCTX that loads the state of another, the internal stack pointers may not be referenced by MFPR or MTPR instructions. This implies that interrupt service routines invoked at priority higher than the lowest one used for context switching must not reference the process stack pointers.

The following example illustrates how the process structure instructions can be used to implement process dispatching software. is assumed that this simple dispatch routine is always entered via an interrupt.

```
;
;                    ENTERED VIA INTERRUPT
;                    IPL = 3
RESCHED:             SVPCTX                 ; Save context in PCB
                       .
                       .
                       .

                     (set state to runnable)
                     (and place current PCB)
                     (on proper RUN queue)
                       .
                       .

                       .
                     (Remove head of highest)
                     (priority, non-empty, )
                     (RUN queue.)
                     MTPR @#PHYSPCB, #PR$_PCBB ; Set physical PCB address

                                            ; in PCBB
                     LDPCTX                 ; Load context from PCB
                                            ; For new process
                     REI                    ; Place process in execution
```

System Architecture and Programming Implications

7

Certain portions of the VAX architecture have implications for the system structure of implementations and programming considerations. The broad categories of interaction are data sharing and synchronization, memory reference behavior, restartability, I/O structure, interrupts, and errors. Of these, data sharing is most visible to the programmer.

The memory system must be implemented such that the granularity of access for independent modification is the byte. Note that this does not imply a maximum reference size of one byte but only that independent modifying accesses to adjacent bytes produce the same results regardless of the order of execution. For example, suppose locations 0 and 1 contain the values 5 and 6. Suppose one processor executes INCB 0 and another executes INCB 1. Then, regardless of the order of execution, including effectively simultaneous execution, the final contents must be 6 and 7.

Access to explicitly shared data that may be written must be synchronized by the programmer or hardware designer. Before accessing shared writable data, the programmer must acquire control of the data structure. Seven instructions (BBSSI, BBCCI, ADAWI, INSQHI, INSQTI, REMQHI, REMQTI) are provided to allow the programmer to control, or interlock, access to a control variable. These interlocked instructions are implemented in such a way that once an interlocked read has occurred, other processors and I/O devices are locked out of performing interlocked operations on the same control variable until the interlock is released. This is termed an interlocked sequence. The interlocked instructions operate on a control variable within an interlocked sequence. Only interlocked accesses are locked out by the interlock. On the VAX-11/780 system, the SBI primitive operations are interlock-read and interlock-write. The interlocked read operation sets the interlock, and the interlocked write releases it.

BBSSI and BBCCI instructions use hardware-provided primitive operations to read a single byte, test and modify a bit within that byte and then write the byte, in an interlocked sequence. The ADAWI instruction uses a hardware-provided primitive operation to make a read and then a write operation to a single aligned word in an interlocked sequence to allow counters to be maintained without other interlocks. The ADAWI instruction takes the hardware lock on the read of the .mw operand (the second operand which is the one being modified).

The INSQUE and REMQUE instructions provide a series of longword reads and writes in an uninterruptible sequence to allow queues to be maintained without other interlocks in a uniprocessor system. The INSQHI, INSQTI, REMQHI, and REMQTI instructions use an interlock on the queue header to allow queues to be maintained consistently in a multiprocessor system.

In order to provide a function upon which some UNIBUS peripheral devices rely, processors must ensure that all instructions making byte or word-sized modifying references (.mb and .mw) use the DATIP - DATO(B) functions when the operand physical address selects a UNIBUS device. This constraint does not apply to longword, quadword, field, all floating, or string operations if implemented using byte- or word-modifying references. This constraint also does not apply to instructions precluded from I/O space references.

In a multiprocessor system, any software clearing PTE⟨V⟩ or changing the protection code of a page table entry for system space such that it issues a MTPR src, #PR$—TBIS must arrange for all other processors to issue a similar TBIS. The original processor must wait until all the other processors have completed their TBIS before it allows access to the system page.

SEPARATION OF PROCEDURE AND DATA

The VAX architecture encourages (and provides the mechanisms to facilitate) separation of procedure (instructions) and writable data. Native mode procedures may not write data that is to be subsequently executed as an instruction without an intervening REI instruction being executed (see Chapter 5). If no REI occurs between a procedure writing data as instructions to be executed and those instructions being executed, the instructions executed are UNPREDICTABLE. A compatibility mode procedure can write data and subsequently execute it as an instruction without any additional synchronization.

MEMORY REFERENCES

The memory references made by each instruction (and therefore the possible memory exceptions) are specified as part of the VAX architecture. Any required or permitted memory reference (read, modify, or write) may be made more than once, except for references to I/O space which are made once and only once. Operands requiring interlocked access are always referenced. In general, for operands not requiring interlocked access, it is UNPREDICTABLE whether an operand is referenced if it does not affect the result (including condition codes). Further clarifications and exceptions to this simplified rule are listed below. Software must not rely on the occurrence of memory management exceptions on operands that do not affect the result of an instruction. The probe instructions should be used to determine the accessibility of a memory location. Note that no results are written unless the instruction can be completed or can be suspended with FPD set.

1. It is UNPREDICTABLE whether longwords containing indirect addresses are read. For example, MULL3 #0, @16(R5), A may or may not access the longword containing the address of the second operand.

2. If a branch is not taken, it is UNPREDICTABLE whether the branch displacement is read.

3. It is UNPREDICTABLE whether all bytes for .r operands are read. For example, TSTF may only read the word containing the sign and exponent. BLBC and BLBS may only read the low byte of the source operand.

4. All bytes for .w operands are always written.

5. It is UNPREDICTABLE whether all bytes for .m operands are either read (with modify intent) or written. However, a modify operand requiring interlocked read and write is always accessed. For example, ADDL2 #0, A may only read A (without modify intent). INCL A may only write the bytes of A that changed. The sum operand of ADAWI #0, A is always read and written back interlocked.

6. For .a operands (and for .v operands when .v is not a register), the memory reference behavior is peculiar to each instruction or instruction group. Overriding the rules given below, it is UNPRE-DICTABLE whether an otherwise unreadable operand is read or not if it appears as an immediate mode operand. For example, PUSHAB (R0) cannot read the byte at (R0), but PUSHAB #512 can read the value 512.

   a. POLY{F,D,G,H}. If the argument is not zero, each entry in the coefficient table is read unless an arithmetic exception occurs before the instruction completes. If the argument is zero, it is UNPREDICTABLE whether the entire table or only the last coefficient is read.

   b. MOVA{B,W,L,Q,O} and PUSHA{B,W,L,Q,O}. The address operand is not referenced.

   c. Field Instructions (EXTV, EXTZV, INSV, CMPV, CMPZV, FFS,

FFC). The aligned longword(s) containing the field specified by FIELD (pos, size, base) can be read. For INSV, only this aligned longword(s) can be written. It is UNPREDICTABLE whether all or some of the bytes in these longwords are accessed.

d. BB{S,C}, BB{S,C}{S,C}. Only the single byte containing the test bit specified by the base and position operands is read. If the test bit does not need to change state, it is UNPREDICTABLE whether the byte is written back.

e. BB{SS,CC}I. Only the single byte containing the test bit specified by the base and position operands is referenced using the interlocked forms of read and write. The test bit is written even if its state is unchanged.

f. JMP and JSB. The address is not referenced by the JMP or JSB (but will be read as instruction stream data for the next instruction).

g. CALL{S,G}. The two bytes (containing the entry mask) at the destination address are read. The argument list for CALLG is not referenced.

h. Interlocked Queue. It is UNPREDICTABLE whether the backward pointer of the queue header is accessed for INSQHI, REMQHI.

7. Some of the character string instructions (MOVTUC, CMPC3, CMPC5, SCANC, SPANC, LOCC, SKPC, and MATCHC) can stop before the whole source string is processed. Three definitions help define the required memory references for these instructions. The stop byte is the byte that ends the instruction execution without using the string length end condition. It is the last byte on which the answer of the instruction depends. (The stop byte may have any position in the string, including first or last, or it may not exist at all. For string matches, it is the last byte of the matched string.)

A source string consists of a body concatenated with a tail.

The body of a source string is the substring from the first byte up to and including the stop byte, if one exists, or up to and including the last byte (as determined by the source string's length) if no stop byte exists. (The body may be null only if the source string has a zero length.)

The tail of a source string is the substring from the first byte after the body up to and including the last byte in the source string as determined by the source string's length. (The tail will be null if there is no stop byte or if the STOP byte is the last byte.)

Character strings are defined by length and starting address. Some strings (ASCIZ strings) are delimited by a specific character. The "real" length of the string is not known, and 64K is used as the length. Only some of the VAX character string instructions can be reasonably used on character delimited strings. These instructions are MOVTUC, SPANC, SCANC, LOCC, and SKPC. For these five instructions, it is necessary to guarantee that no memory management exceptions will occur beyond the page containing the delimiting character. The absence of such a requirement could cause a program that works on one processor to fail on another because of access violations on data that is not necessary to produce the correct result.

For string operands specified by length and starting address, one of the following rules applies:

a. For MOVC3, MOVTC, and CRC, all bytes are referenced. These instructions have no end condition other than string length.

b. For MOVC5, the stop byte is defined as the last byte moved from the source string. MOVC5 references all bytes except when the source string is longer than the destination string; in the latter case, no bytes in the source string's tail beyond the page containing the stop byte are referenced.

c. For CMPC3, CMPC5, and MATCHC, all bytes in a string's body are referenced. It is UNPREDICTABLE whether any bytes in a string's tail are referenced.

d. For MOVTUC, SCANC, SPANC, LOCC, and SKPC, all bytes in the source string's body are referenced, and no bytes in the source string's tail beyond the page containing the stop byte are referenced. For MOVTUC, the destination address which would receive the translated escape character is not written into, nor is any larger address written into.

For table operands, one of the following rules applies:

a. In the table for MOVTC, MOVTUC, SCANC, and SPANC, entries are accessed for the corresponding source characters or values. It is UNPREDICTABLE whether the other table entries are accessed.

b. For the CRC table operand, it is UNPREDICTABLE whether all or only part of the table is accessed.

8. If a packed decimal source string contains invalid digits, it is UNPREDICTABLE whether the entire source string is read and whether any or all of the destination is written.

If there are no invalid digits in a packed decimal source string, one of the following rules applies:

a. EDITPC, MOVP, ADDP6, SUBP6, MULP, DIVP, CVTPT, CVTTP, CVTPS, CVTSP, and ASHP. All bytes of the source strings are read, and all bytes of the result are written, unless an exception condition is detected and the instruction can be completed without reading all the bytes in the source strings.

b. CMPP3 and CMPP4. It is UNPREDICTABLE whether all bytes of the two source strings are read.

c. ADDP4 and SUBP4. All bytes of the addend (or subtrahend) string are read. It is UNPREDICTABLE whether all bytes of the result are written.

d. CVTLP. All bytes of the destination string are written.

e. CVTPL. All bytes of the source string are read.

f. EDITPC, CVTPT, CVTTP. The table entries are accessed for the corresponding source bytes. It is UNPREDICTABLE whether the other table entries are accessed.

9. PROBER and PROBEW. The first and last bytes specified by the base and length operand are not accessed.

CACHE

A hardware implementation may include a mechanism to reduce access time by making local copies of recently used memory content. Such a mechanism is termed a cache. A cache must be implemented in such a way that its existence is transparent to software (except for timing and error reporting, control, and recovery). In particular, the following must be true:

1. An I/O transfer from memory to a peripheral, started after a program write to the same memory, must output the updated memory value.

2. A program memory read, executed after the completion of an I/O transfer from a peripheral to the same memory, must read the updated memory value. On the VAX-11/780 system, this is achieved by a cache that writes through to memory and that watches the memory bus for all external writes to memory.

3. If one processor writes or modifies memory and then executes HALTs, a read or modify of the same memory by another processor must read the updated value.

4. If a processor writes or modifies memory and then halts as a result of power failure, a read or modify of the same memory must read the updated value (provided that the duration of the power failure does not exceed the maximum non-volatile period of the main memory).

5. In multiprocessor systems, access to variables shared between processors must be interlocked by software executing one of the interlocked instructions (BBSSI, BBCCI, ADAWI, INSQHI, INSQTI, REMQHI, REMQTI).

6. Valid accesses to I/O registers must not be cached.

7. A cache may prefetch instructions or data. In a virtual cache, memory management exception conditions could occur during

prefetch. Such exceptions should not be taken until the prefetched data is referenced by an instruction.

Processor initialization must leave the cache either empty or valid.

RESTART-ABILITY

The VAX architecture requires that all instructions be restartable after a fault or interrupt that terminated execution before the instruction was completed. Generally, this means that modified registers are restored to the value they had at the start of execution. For some complex or iterative instructions, described in Chapter 3, intermediate results are stored in the general registers. In the latter case, memory contents may have been altered; but the former case requires that no operand be written unless the instruction can be completed. For most instructions with only a single modified or written operand, this implies special processing only when a multiple-byte operand spans a protection boundary making it necessary to test accessibility of both parts of the operand.

Instructions that store intermediate results in the general registers must not compromise system integrity. Therefore they must ensure that any addresses stored or used are virtual addresses, subject to protection checking. In addition, any state information stored or used cannot result in a non-interruptible or non-terminating sequence.

Instruction operands that are peripheral-device registers having access side effects may produce UNPREDICTABLE results due to instruction restarting after faults or interrupts. In order that software may dependably access peripheral-device registers, instructions used to access them must not permit a fault or interrupt after the first I/O space access.

Memory modifications produced as a side effect of instruction execution (memory access statistics, for example) are specifically excluded from the constraint that memory not be altered until the instruction can be completed.

Instructions that abort are constrained only by memory protection.

INTERRUPTS

Underlying the VAX architectural concept of an interrupt is the notion that an interrupt request is a static condition, not a transient event, which can be sampled by a processor at appropriate times. Further, if the need for an interrupt disappears before a processor has honored an interrupt request, the interrupt request can be removed (subject to implementation-dependent timing constraints) without consequence.

In order for software to operate deterministically, any instruction changing the processor priority (IPL) such that a pending interrupt is enabled must allow the interrupt to occur before executing the next instruction that would have been executed had the interrupt not been pending.

Similarly, instructions that generate requests at the software interrupt levels must allow the interrupt to occur, if processor priority permits, before executing the apparently subsequent instruction.

ERRORS

Processor errors, if not inconsistent with instruction completion, should create high priority interrupt requests. Otherwise, they must terminate instruction execution with an exception (fault, trap or abort), in which case there may also be an associated interrupt request.

Error notification interrupts may be delayed from the apparent completion of the instruction in execution at the time of the error. But if enabled, the interrupt must be requested before processor context is switched, priority permitting.

An example of a case where both an interrupt and an exception are associated with the same event occurs when the VAX-11/780 instruction buffer gets a read data substitution (that is, an uncorrectable memory read error). In this case, the interrupt request associated with error will not be taken if the priority of the running program is high; but an abort will occur when an attempt is made to execute the instruction. The interrupt is still pending, however, and will be taken when the priority is lowered.

I/O STRUCTURE

The VAX I/O architecture is very similar to the PDP-11 structure. The principal difference is the method by which internal processor registers (such as the memory management registers) are accessed. Peripheral device control and status registers and data registers appear at locations in the physical address space and can therefore be manipulated by most memory reference instructions. Use of general instructions permits all the virtual address mapping and protection mechanisms described in Chapter 4 to be used when referencing I/O registers. Note: Implementations that include a cache feature must suppress caching for references in the I/O space.

For any member of the VAX series implementing the UNIBUS, there will be one or more areas of the I/O physical address space, each 2^{18} bytes in length, that "map through" to UNIBUS addresses. The collection of these areas is referred to as the UNIBUS space.

The following is a list of both hardware and programming constraints on I/O registers. These items affect both hardware register design and programming considerations.

1. The physical address of an I/O register must be an integral multiple of the register size in bytes (which must be a power of two); that is, all registers must be aligned on natural boundaries.

2. References using a length attribute other than the length of the register, or to unaligned addresses, may produce UNPREDICTABLE results. For example, a byte reference to a word-length register will not necessarily respond by supplying or modifying the byte addressed.

3. In all peripheral devices, error and status bits that may be asynchronously set by the device must be cleared by software writing a 1 to that bit position and are not affected by writing a 0. This is to prevent clearing bits that may be asynchronously set between reading and writing a register.

4. Only byte and word references of read-modify-write type (.mb or .mw access type) in UNIBUS I/O spaces are guaranteed to interlock correctly. References in the I/O space other than in UNIBUS spaces are UNDEFINED with respect to interlocking. This includes the BBSSI and BBCCI instructions.

5. String, quadword, octaword, F__floating, D__floating, G__floating, H__floating, and field references in the I/O space result in UNDEFINED behavior.

6. Page tables must not be located in I/O space. References to page table entries located in I/O space result in UNDEFINED behavior.

7. The PCB and SCB must not be located in I/O space. References to the PCB or to SCB entries located in I/O space result in UNDEFINED behavior.

Some of the instructions are not usable for referencing I/O space. The reasons for this are as follows:

1. String instructions are restartable via PSL⟨FPD⟩.

2. The instruction is not in the kernel set.

3. The PC, SP, or PCBB cannot point to I/O space.

4. I/O space does not support operand types of quad, floating, field, or queue; nor can the position, size, length, or base of them be from I/O space.

5. The instruction may be interruptible because it is potentially a slow instruction in some implementations.

6. Only instructions with a maximum of one modify or write destination can be used. The destination must be the last operand.

For any memory reference to I/O space, the programmer must use an instruction from the following lists and must ensure that no interrupts or exceptions will occur, including page fault and overflow trap, after the first I/O space reference. To ensure no interrupts, the programmer must avoid operand specifier modes 9, 11, 13, and 15, and these modes indexed. (Symbolically, these are @(Rn)+, @B^D(Rn), @W^D(Rn), and @L^D(Rn), and these indexed.) The hardware may allow interrupts for these modes in order to minimize interrupt latency. For the instructions in the following lists, the hardware ensures that no other interrupts will occur after the first I/O space access.

Since these instructions are not interruptible after I/O space accesses (except for the addressing modes above), their execution will extend the interrupt latency. The programmer should make some effort to keep them short by minimizing the number of memory references. Use R0 through R13 instead, for example.

Instructions for which any explicit operand can be in I/O space:

ADAWI	CHM{K,E,S,U}	MOVZ{BW,BL,WL}
ADD{B,W,L}2	CMP{B,W,L}	MTPR
ADD{B,W,L}3	CVT{BW,BL,WB,WL,LB,LW}	PROBE{R,W}
ADWC	DEC{B,W,L}	PUSHA{B,W,L}
BIC{B,W,L}2	INC{B,W,L}	PUSHAQ
BIC{B,W,L}3	MCOM{B,W,L}	PUSHL
BICPSW	MFPR	SBWC
BIS{B,W,L}2	MNEG{B,W,L}	SUB{B,W,L}2
BIS{B,W,L}3	MOV{B,W,L}	SUB{B,W,L}3
BISPSW	MOVA{B,W,L}	TST{B,W,L}
BIT{B,W,L}	MOVAQ	XOR{B,W,L}2
CASE{B,W,L}	MOVPSL	XOR{B,W,L}3
CLR{B,W,L}		

Instructions for which some operand can be in I/O space are as follows:

BLB{S,C}	(any operands but branch displacement)
XFC	(depending on implementation)
REMQUE	addr (destination)
REMQHI	addr (destination)
REMQTI	addr (destination)

Notwithstanding the above rules, it is possible for a specific hardware implementation to execute macro code from the I/O space or to allow the stack or PCB to be in I/O space. This might, for example, be used as part of the bootstrap process. If this is done, then it is valid for software to transfer to this code.

Privileged Registers

8

The internal processor register (IPR) space provides access to many types of CPU control and status registers such as the memory management base registers, parts of the PSL, and the multiple stack pointers. These registers are explicitly accessible only by the move-to-processor-register (MTPR) and move-from-processor-register (MFPR) instructions which require kernel-mode privileges.

All the internal processor registers are summarized in Table 8.1. Those internal processor registers that require further explanation are described below. Reference to general registers means R0 through R13, the SP, and the PC (see Chapter 1). Registers referenced by the MTPR and MFPR instructions are designated processor registers and appear in the processor register space.

**PER-PROCESS
REGISTERS
AND CONTEXT
SWITCHING**

Several per-process registers are loaded from the PCB during a context load operation and, with the exception of the memory mapping registers, PME, and AST level, are written back to the PCB during a context save operation (see Chapter 6). Some implementations may copy some or all of these registers from the PCB into scratchpad registers and write them back into the PCB during a context save operation. Other implementations may retain the registers in main memory in the PCB.

An implementation may retain some or all per-process stack pointers only in the PCB. In this case, MTPR and MFPR for these registers must access the corresponding PCB location. However, implementations that have per-process stack pointers in hardware scratchpads are not required to access the corresponding PCB locations for MTPR and MFPR. The PCB locations get updated when a SVPCTX instruction is executed.

Table 8.1

Architecturally Defined Internal Processor Registers

Name	Mnemonic	Decimal	Hex	Type	Scope
kernel stack pointer	KSP	0	0	R/W	process
executive stack pointer	ESP	1	1	R/W	process
supervisor stack pointer	SSP	2	2	R/W	process
user stack pointer	USP	3	3	R/W	process
interrupt stack pointer	ISP	4	4	R/W	CPU
P0 base register	P0BR	8	8	R/W	process
P0 length register	P0LR	9	9	R/W	process
P1 base register	P1BR	10	A	R/W	process
P1 length register	P1LR	11	B	R/W	process
system base register	SBR	12	C	R/W	CPU
system limit register	SLR	13	D	R/W	CPU
process control block base	PCBB	16	10	R/W	CPU
system control block base	SCBB	17	11	R/W	CPU
interrupt priority level	IPL	18	12	R/W	CPU
AST level	ASTLVL	19	13	R/W	process
software interrupt request	SIRR	20	14	W	CPU
software interrupt summary	SISR	21	15	R/W	CPU
interval clock control*	ICCS	24	18	R/W	CPU
next interval count*	NICR	25	19	W	CPU
interval count*	ICR	26	1A	R	CPU
time of year*	TODR	27	1B	R/W	CPU
console receiver status*	RXCS	32	20	R/W	CPU
console receiver data buffer*	RXDB	33	21	R	CPU
console transmit status*	TXCS	34	22	R/W	CPU
console transmit data buffer*	TXDB	35	23	W	CPU
memory management enable	MAPEN	56	38	R/W	CPU
translation buffer invalidate all	TBIA	57	39	W	CPU
translation buffer invalidate single	TBIS	58	3A	W	CPU
performance monitor enable*	PME	61	3D	R/W	process
system identification	SID	62	3E	R	CPU
translation buffer check	TBCHK	63	3F	W	CPU

Key: process one copy per process, loaded by LDPCTX
     CPU   one copy per processor, not affected by LDPCTX
     R   register can be read but cannot be written
     W   register can be written but cannot be read
     R/W   register can be both read and written

*Subset implementations are not required to include NICR, ICR, TODR, RXCS, RXDB, TXCS, TXDB, and PME. Only a subset of ICCS is required.

It is possible that some implementations will retain some or all of the memory mapping registers (P0BR, P0LR, P1BR, P1LR), ASTLVL, and PME only in the PCB. These processors will implement MTPR and MFPR for those registers as a no-op, at least in the sense that the destination or register is not written. Other implementations may copy some or all of these registers from the PCB into scratchpad registers. The SVPCTX instruction does not write these registers back into the PCB. To ensure that the PCB is always correctly updated, software must use the following convention when referencing any of the memory mapping registers (P0BR, P0LR, P1BR, P1LR), or ASTLVL, or PME.

1. Write. Software must first write the value directly into the proper location in the current PCB by using a MOVL (for example), then execute an MTPR with the same source as the MOVL. Implementations that do not retain internal copies of these registers will effectively no-op the MTPR instruction. They will not take a reserved operand fault which would normally occur for a non-existent register.

2. Read. Software can read the value directly from the proper location in the current PCB by using a EXTZV (for example). It is not necessary to execute a MFPR from the corresponding internal register, since the PCB location always contains an updated value due to the software convention for writing these registers.

STACK POINTER IMAGES

Reference to SP (the stack pointer) in the general registers will access one of five possible stack pointers---user, supervisor, executive, kernel, or interrupt---depending on the values of the current mode and IS bits in the PSL (see Chapter 5). Additionally, software can access any of the five stack pointers (including the one currently selected by the current mode and IS bits in the PSL) via the MTPR and MFPR instructions (even on processors that implement the KSP, SSP, ESP, or USP only in the PCB). Results are correct even if the stack pointer specified by the current mode and IS bits in the PSL is referenced in the internal processor register address space by an MTPR or MFPR instruction. This means that a MFPR or MTPR to the KSP (if IS = 0) or the ISP (if IS = 1) is equivalent to a MOVL from or to the SP.

MTPR AND MFPR INSTRUCTIONS

MTPR

Move To Processor Register

Format:

```
opcode src.rl, procreg.rl
```

Operation:

```
if PSL ⟨CUR[cb3]-[cb0]MOD⟩ NEQ 0 then {reserved
        instruction fault};
IPR[procreg] ← src;
```

Condition Codes:

```
N ← src LSS 0;   !if register is replaced
Z ← src EQL 0;
V ← 0:           !except TBCHK register (see Chapter 4
C ← C;
N ← N;           !if register is not replaced
Z ← Z;
V ← V;
C ← C;
```

Exception:
reserved instruction fault

Opcode:

```
DA   MTPR   Move To Processor Register
```

Description:
MTPR loads the source operand specified by source into the processe
register specified by procreg. The procreg operand is a longword tha
contains the processor register number. Execution may have registe
dependent side effects.

Notes:
1. A reserved instruction fault occurs if instruction execution is
   attempted in other than kernel mode.
2. If a register is implemented only as a PCB location, MTPR to that
   register has no effect.
3. The operation of the processor is UNDEFINED after execution of
   MTPR to a read-only register, MTPR to a nonexistent register,
   MTPR of a non-zero value to an MBZ field, or MTPR of a reserve
   value to a register. The preferred implementation is to cause
   reserved-operand fault.

Move From Processor Register

Format:

opcode procreg.rl, dst.wl

Operation:

if PSL ⟨CUR[cb3]-[cb0]MOD⟩ NEQ 0 then {reserved
        instruction fault};
dst ← IPR[procreg];

Condition Codes:

N ← dst LSS 0;   !if destination is replaced
Z ← dst EQL 0;
V ← 0;
C ← C;
N ← N;   !if destination is not replaced
Z ← Z;
V ← V;
C ← C;

Exception:
reserved instruction fault

Opcode:

DB   MFPR   Move From Processor Register

Description:
The destination operand is replaced by the contents of the processor
register specified by procreg. The procreg operand is a longword
which contains the processor register number. Execution may have
register-dependent side effects.

Notes:
1. A reserved instruction fault occurs if instruction execution is
   attempted in other than kernel mode.
2. If a register is implemented only as a PCB location, MFPR from
   that register has no effect.
3. The operation of the processor is UNDEFINED after execution of
   MFPR from a register that does not exist, or after execution of
   MFPR from a write-only register. The preferred implementation is
   to cause reserved-operand fault.

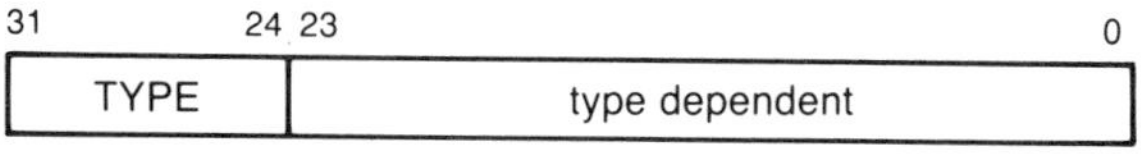

TYPE	type dependent

Figure 8.1
System Identification Register (SID)

System Identification Register

The system identification register (SID) specifies the processor type and includes an inplementation-dependent field. The processor type field is used by software in handling implementation-dependent processor features. The implementation-dependent field typically specifies additional information, such as hardware revision level and microcode revision level, and is included in the error log to more finely distinguish processor types. The SID is shown in Figure 8.1. Table 8.2 shows the processor type codes. See Appendix B for details on particular implementations.

For systems based on the MicroVAX chip, the different system implementations can be distinguished by the contents of the MicroVAX system type register (SYS_TYPE), at physical address 20040004 (hex). SYS_TYPE is shown in Figure 8.2, and the system type codes are shown in Table 8.3.

Table 8.2
Processor Type Codes

Code	Processor
0	Reserved to DIGITAL
1	VAX-11/780 or VAX-11/785
2	VAX-11/750
3	VAX-11/730
4	VAX 8600
5	Reserved to DIGITAL
6	Reserved to DIGITAL
7	MicroVAX I
8	MicroVAX II chip
9-255	Reserved to DIGITAL

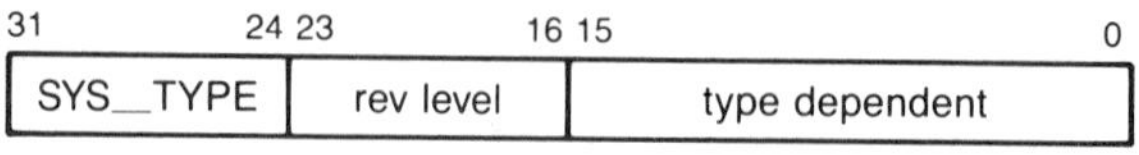

31   24 23   16 15   0

SYS_TYPE	rev level	type dependent

Figure 8.2
MicroVAX System Type Register (SYS-TYPE)

Table 8.3
MicroVAX System Type Codes

Code	System
0	Reserved to DIGITAL
1	MicroVAX II
2–127	Reserved to DIGITAL
128–255	Reserved to owners

Time-of-Year Clock Register

The time-of-year clock is used to measure the duration of power failures and is required for unattended restart after a power failure.

The time-of-year clock consists of one longword register, shown in Figure 8.3. The register forms an unsigned 32-bit binary counter that is driven by a precision clock source with at least .0025% accuracy (approximately 65 seconds per month). The least significant bit of the counter represents a resolution of 10 milliseconds. Thus, the counter cycles to 0 after approximately 497 days.

The counter has an optional battery back-up power supply sufficient for at least 100 hours of operation, and the clock does not gain or lose any ticks during transition to or from stand-by power. The battery is recharged automatically. If the battery has failed, so that time is not accurate, then the register is cleared upon power-up. One of two things then happens:

1. The register starts counting from 0. Thus, if software initializes this clock to a value corresponding to a large time (say, a month), it can check for loss of time after a power restore by checking the clock value. This is the VAX-11/780 implementation.

2. The register stays at 0 until the software writes a non-zero value into it. It counts only when it contains a non-zero value. This is the VAX-11/750 implementation.

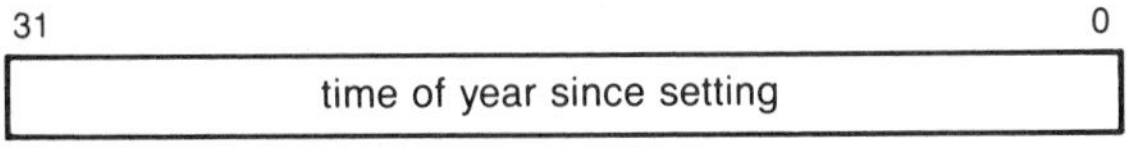

```
31                                                    0
+----------------------------------------------------+
|              time of year since setting            |
+----------------------------------------------------+
```

Figure 8.3
Time of Year (TODR)

Privileged Registers   **285**

Interval Clock Registers

The interval clock is used for accounting, for time-dependent events, and to maintain the software date and time. It provides an interrupt at IPL 22 or 24 at programmed intervals. IPL 24 is used on the VAX-11/780, VAX-11/750, and VAX-11/730 systems. The preferred implementation is at IPL 22. The counter is incremented at 1-microsecond intervals, with at least .01% accuracy (8.64 seconds per day). The clock interface consists of three internal processor registers, shown in Figure 8.4:

• Interval Count Register (ICR)—The interval count register is a read-only register incremented once every microsecond. Upon a carry out (overflow) from bit ⟨31⟩, it is automatically loaded from NICR; an interrupt is generated if the interrupt is enabled. That is, the value of ICR on successive microseconds will be FFFFFFFD (hex), FFFFFFFE, FFFFFFFF, ⟨value of NICR⟩.

• Next Interval Count Register (NICR)—This reload register is a write-only register that holds the value to be loaded into ICR when ICR overflows. The value is retained when ICR is loaded.

• Interval Clock Control Status Register (ICCS)—The ICCS register contains control and status information for the interval clock.

```
31                                                    0
┌─────────────────────────────────────────────────────┐
│                  interval count                       │
└─────────────────────────────────────────────────────┘
```
Interval Count (ICR)

```
31                                                    0
┌─────────────────────────────────────────────────────┐
│                next interval count                    │
└─────────────────────────────────────────────────────┘
```
Next Interval Count (NICR)

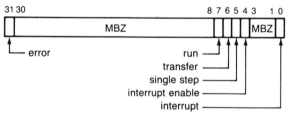

Interval Clock Control and Status (ICCS)

Figure 8.4
Clock Interface Internal Processor Registers

Table 8.4
Fields of the Interval Clock Control and Status Register

Name	Extent	Description
Error	$\langle 31 \rangle$	When ICR overflows, if interrupt is already set, then error is set. Thus, error indicates a missed clock tick. Writing 1 to clear.
Interrupt	$\langle 7 \rangle$	Set by hardware every time ICR overflows. If interrupt-enable is set, then an interrupt is also generated. Writing a 1 to this bit with MTPR clears it, thereby re-enabling the clock tick interrupt.
Interrupt enable	$\langle 6 \rangle$	When set, an interrupt request is generated every time ICR overflows (every time interrupt is set). When clear, no interrupt is requested. Similarly, if interrupt is already set and the software sets interrupt enable, an interrupt is generated. That is, an interrupt is generated whenever the function (interrupt enable and interrupt) changes from 0 to 1. Processor initialization clears interrupt enable.
Single step	$\langle 5 \rangle$	If run is clear, each time this bit is set, ICR is incremented by one. Write only.
Transfer	$\langle 4 \rangle$	When a 1 is written to this bit, NICR is transferred to ICR. Write only.
Run	$\langle 0 \rangle$	When set, ICR increments each microsecond. When clear, ICR does not increment automatically. Processor initialization clears run.

The fields of the interval clock control and status register are described in Table 8.4.

Note

Subset processors may omit NICR and ICR, and are required only to implement ICCS⟨IE⟩. If this bit is set, an interrupt request at IPL 22 is generated once every 10 milliseconds.

Thus, to use the interval clock, load the negative of the desired interval into NICR. Then a MTPR #X51,#PR$_ICCS will enable interrupts, reload ICR with the NICR interval, and set run. Every "interval count" microseconds will cause interrupt to be set and an interrupt to be requested. The interrupt routine should execute a MTPR #XC1,#PR$_ICCS to clear the interrupt. If interrupt has not been cleared (the interrupt has not been handled) by the time of the next ICR overflow, error will be set.

Note

If NICR is written while the clock is running, the clock may lose or add a few ticks. If the interval clock interrupt is enabled, this may cause the loss of an interrupt.

Processor initialization leaves ICR and NICR UNPREDICTABLE, clears ICCS ⟨6⟩ and ⟨0⟩, and leaves the rest of ICCS UNPREDICTABLE

PDP-11 Compatibility Mode $\qquad$ 9

Implementation of PDP-11 compatibility mode is optional. Processors that do implement compatibility mode do so as specified in this chapter. Operating system software may emulate compatibility mode on processors that omit this mode.

VAX compatibility mode hardware, in conjunction with a compatibility mode software executive (which runs in VAX mode), can emulate the environment provided to user programs on a PDP-11 system. This environment does not include the following features of normal PDP-11 system operation:

- Privileged instructions such as HALT and RESET
- Special instructions such as traps and WAIT
- Access to internal processor registers such as the PSW and the console switch register
- Direct access to trap and interrupt vectors
- Direct access to I/O devices
- Interrupt servicing
- Stack overflow protection
- Alternate general register sets
- Any processor mode other than user (that is, kernel and supervisor modes are not supported) and separate I and D spaces
- Floating-point instructions

This specification is based on the behavior of all PDP-11 implementations. Compatibility mode behavior is defined as UNPREDICTABLE where there is a difference between any two PDP-11 implementations.

GENERAL REGISTERS AND ADDRESSING MODES

All of the PDP-11 general registers and addressing modes are provided in compatibility mode. Side effects caused by a destination address calculation have no effect on source values (except in JSR), and autoincrement modes in JMP and JSR do not affect the new PC. Side effects caused by a source address calculation, however, affect the value of a register used for destination address calculation.

All PDP-11 addresses are 16-bits wide. In compatibility mode, a 16-bit PDP-11 address is zero-extended to 32 bits.

The operands of some PDP-11 instructions are implied by the instruction type, whereas others are specified as part of the instruction. The different kinds of operand specifiers appearing in PDP-11 instructions are shown in Figure 9.1. Address mode operand specifiers include a 3-bit mode field, specifying one of eight modes: register, register deferred, autoincrement, autoincrement deferred, autodecrement, autodecrement deferred, index, or index deferred mode. These modes are discussed in the following sections.

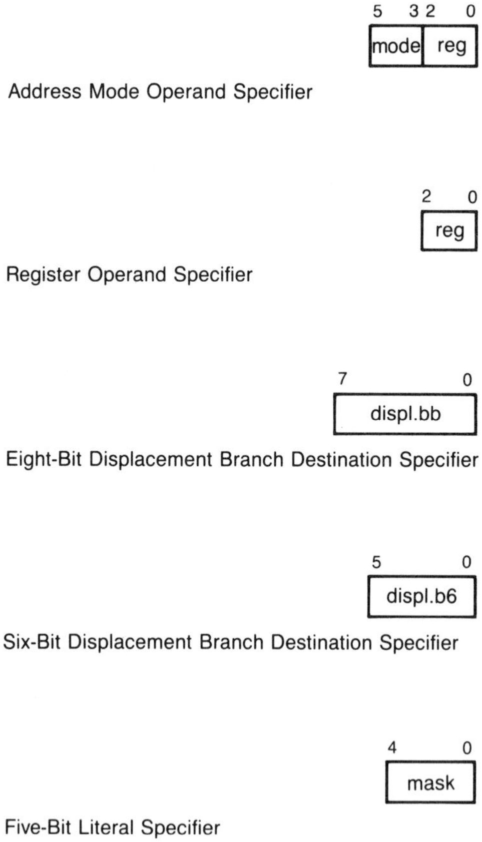

```
 5   3 2   0
+----+-----+
|mode| reg |
+----+-----+
```

Address Mode Operand Specifier

```
 2     0
+-------+
|  reg  |
+-------+
```

Register Operand Specifier

```
 7          0
+-----------+
|  displ.bb |
+-----------+
```

Eight-Bit Displacement Branch Destination Specifier

```
 5          0
+-----------+
|  displ.b6 |
+-----------+
```

Six-Bit Displacement Branch Destination Specifier

```
 4         0
+----------+
|   mask   |
+----------+
```

Five-Bit Literal Specifier

Figure 9.1
PDP-11 Instruction Operand Specifiers

Register Mode

In register mode addressing, the operand is the contents of register n:

```
operand = Rn
```

Byte operations, except for MOVB to a register, access the low order byte, that is, bits $\langle 7:0 \rangle$. The low byte is sign-extended if a register is used as the destination of a MOVB instruction. If the PC is used as the destination of a byte instruction, the result is UNPREDICTABLE.

The assembler notation for register mode is Rn.

Register Deferred Mode

In register deferred mode addressing, the address of the operand is the contents of register n:

```
OA = Rn
operand = (OA)
```

The assembler notation for register deferred mode is (Rn) or @Rn.

Autoincrement Mode

In autoincrement mode addressing, the address of the operand is the contents of register n. After the operand address is determined, the size of the operand in bytes (1 for byte, 2 for word) is added to the contents of register n (except in the case of SP and PC); the register is then replaced by the result. If Rn denotes SP or PC, the register is incremented by 2 and the register is replaced by the result.

```
OA = Rn
if n LEQ 5 then Rn ← Rn + size else Rn ← Rn + 2
operand = (OA)
```

If Rn denotes PC, immediate data follows the instruction. The mode is termed immediate mode.

The assembler notation for autoincrement mode is (Rn)+. For immediate mode, the notation is #constant where constant is the data immediately following the instruction.

Autoincrement Deferred Mode

In autoincrement deferred mode addressing, the address of the operand is the contents of a word whose address is the contents of register n. After the operand address is determined, 2 is added to the contents of register n, and the register is replaced by the result.

```
OA = (Rn)
Rn ← Rn + 2
operand = (OA)
```

If Rn denotes PC, a 16-bit address follows the instruction. The mode is termed absolute mode.

The assembler notation for autoincrement deferred mode is @(Rn)+. For absolute mode, the notation is @#address where address is the word that follows the instruction.

Autodecrement Mode

In autodecrement mode addressing, the size of the operand in bytes (1 for byte, 2 for word) is subtracted from the contents of register n (except in the case of SP and PC); the register is then replaced by the result. If Rn denotes SP or PC, the register is decremented by 2 and the register is replaced by the result. The updated contents of register n is the address of the operand:

```
if n LEQ 5 then Rn ← Rn - size else Rn ← Rn - 2
OA = Rn
operand = (OA)
```

The assembler notation for autodecrement mode is -(Rn).

Autodecrement Deferred Mode

In autodecrement deferred mode addressing, 2 is subtracted from the contents of register n; the register is replaced by the result. The updated contents of register n is the address of the word whose contents is the address of the operand:

```
Rn ← Rn - 2
OA = (Rn)
operand = (OA)
```

The assembler notation for autodecrement deferred mode is @-(Rn).

Index Mode

In index mode, the index (contents of the word following the instruction) is added to the contents of register n. The result is the address of the operand:

```
OA = Rn + index
operand = (OA)
```

If Rn denotes PC, the updated contents of the PC is used. The mode is termed relative mode.

The assembler notation for index mode is index(Rn), where the index value is the word following the instruction.

Index Deferred Mode

In index deferred mode, the index (contents of the word following the instruction) is added to the contents of register n. The result is the address of a word whose contents are the address of the operand:

```
OA = (Rn + index)
operand = (OA)
```

If Rn denotes PC, the updated contents of the PC are used. The mode is termed relative deferred mode.

The assembler notation for index deferred mode is @index(Rn), where the index value is the word following the instruction.

HE STACK

General register R6 is used as the stack pointer by certain instructions, as in the PDP-11 system. It is not, however, used by the hardware for any exceptions or interrupts. There is also no stack overflow protection in compatibility mode.

ROCESSOR TATUS WORD

PDP-11 compatibility mode uses a subset of the full PDP-11 processor status word. Only bits $\langle 4:0 \rangle$ are used; bits $\langle 15:5 \rangle$ are zero. When an RTI or RTT instruction is executed, bits $\langle 15:5 \rangle$ in the saved PSW on the stack are ignored. Compatibility mode PSW bits $\langle 4:0 \rangle$ have the same meaning as do VAX PSL bits $\langle 4:0 \rangle$. They are, respectively, PSL$\langle T,N,Z,V,C \rangle$. See Chapter 1 for a description of the PSL.

NSTRUCTIONS

Table 9.1 lists the instructions provided in compatibility mode.

Table 9.1
Compatibility Mode Instructions

Opcode (Octal)	Mnemonic
000002	RTI
000006	RTT
0001DD	JMP
00020R	RTS
000240–000277	Condition codes
0003DD	SWAB
000400–003777	Branches
100000–103777	Branches
004RDD	JSR
.050DD	CLR(B)
.051DD	COM(B)
.052DD	INC(B)
.053DD	DEC(B)
.054DD	NEG(B)

Table 9.1

Compatibility Mode Instructions (*continued*)

Opcode (Octal)	Mnemonic
.055DD	ADC(B)
.056DD	SBC(B)
.057SS	TST(B)
.060dd	ROR(B)
.061DD	ROL(B)
.062DD	ASR(B)
.063DD	ASL(B)
0065SS	MFPI*
0066DD	MTPI*
1065SS	MFPD*
1066DD	MTPD*
0067DD	SXT
070RSS	MUL
071RSS	DIV
072RSS	ASH
073RSS	ASHC
074RDD	XOR
077RNN	SOB
.1SSDD	MOV(B)
.2SSSS	CMP(B)
.3SSSS	BIT(B)
.4SSDD	BIC(B)
.5SSDD	BIS(B)
06SSDD	ADD
16SSDD	SUB

Key: R   Register specifier
      SS   Source operand specifier
      DD   Destination operand specifier
          0 for word operations and 1 for byte operations

*These instructions execute exactly as they would on a PDP-11 in user mode with Instruction and Data space overmapped. More specifically, the ignore the previous access level and act like PUSH and POP instructions referencing the current stack.

Table 9.2 lists the trap instructions that cause the processor to fault to VAX mode, where either the complete trap may be serviced or where the instruction may be simulated.

Table 9.2

Compatibility Mode Trap Instructions

Opcode (Octal)	Mnemonic
000003	BPT
000004	IOT
104000–104377	EMT
104400–104777	TRAP

The instructions listed in Table 9.3 and all other opcodes not listed in Tables 9.1 or 9.2 are considered reserved instructions in compatibility mode. These instructions fault to VAX mode.

Table 9.3

Compatibility Mode Reserved Instructions

Opcode (Octal)	Mnemonic
000000	HALT
000001	WAIT
000005	RESET
000007	MFPT
00023N	SPL
0064NN	MARK
0070DD	CSM
07500R	FADD–FIS
07501R	FSUB–FIS
07502R	FMUL–FIS
07503R	FDIV–FIS
076XXX	Extended Instructions
1064SS	MTPS
1067DD	MFPS
17XXXX	FP11 Floating Point

Key: R Register specifier
      SS Source operand specifier
      DD Destination operand specifier

Note that no floating-point instructions are included in compatibility mode.

Figure 9.2 shows seven compatibility mode instruction formats.

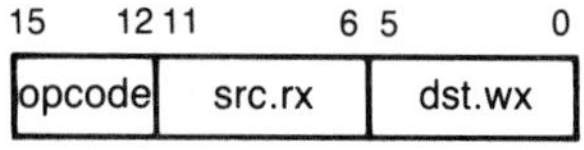

```
 15    1211      6 5      0
+------+--------+--------+
|opcode| src.rx | dst.wx |
+------+--------+--------+
```
Double Operand Format with Two Address Mode Specifiers

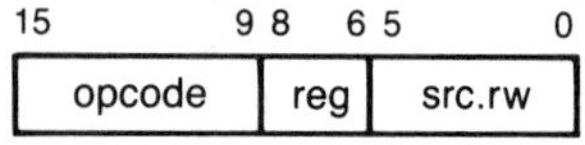

```
 15         9 8  6 5      0
+----------+----+--------+
|  opcode  |reg | src.rw |
+----------+----+--------+
```
Double Operand Format with Register and Address Mode Specifiers

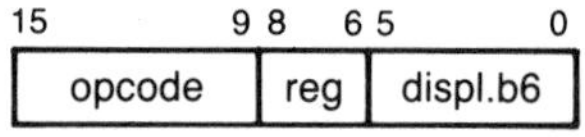

```
 15         9 8  6 5      0
+----------+----+--------+
|  opcode  |reg |displ.b6|
+----------+----+--------+
```
Loop Format with Register and 6-Bit Branch Displacement Specifiers

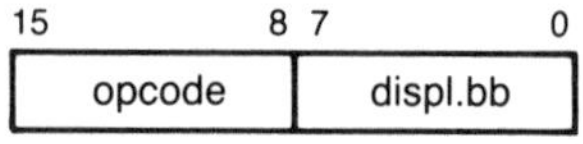

```
 15          8 7         0
+-----------+-----------+
|  opcode   |  displ.bb |
+-----------+-----------+
```
Branch Format 8-Bit Branch Displacement Specifier

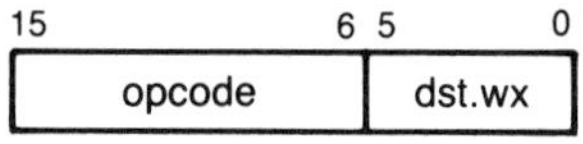

```
 15            6 5       0
+-------------+---------+
|   opcode    | dst.wx  |
+-------------+---------+
```
Single Operand Format with Address Mode Specifier

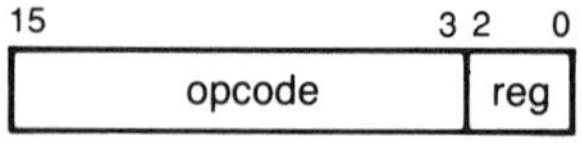

```
 15               3 2    0
+----------------+------+
|    opcode      | reg  |
+----------------+------+
```
Single Operand Format with Register Specifier

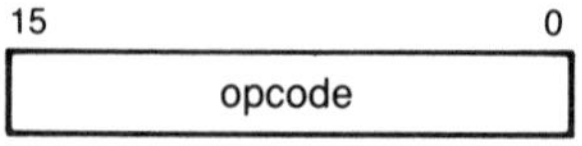

```
 15                      0
+-----------------------+
|         opcode        |
+-----------------------+
```
Zero Operand Format

Figure 9.2
Seven Compatibility Mode Instruction Formats

The following single operand instructions are described in this section. The instructions are grouped according to type: arithmetic, logical, shifts, multiprecision, and rotates.

Arithmetic:
CLR(B) dst.wx

DEC(B) dst.mx

INC(B) dst.mx

NEG(B) dst.mx

TST(B) src.rx

Logical:
COM(B) dst.mx

Shifts:
ASR(B) dst.mx

ASL(B) dst.mx

Multiprecision:
ADC(B) dst.mx

SBC(B) dst.mx

SXT dst.ww

Rotates:
ROL(B) dst.mx

ROR(B) dst.mx

SWAB dst.mw

CLR

Clear

Format:

opcode dst.wx

Operation:

dst ← 0;

Condition Codes:

N ← 0;

Z ← 1;

V ← 0;

C ← 0;

Exceptions:
none

Opcodes (octal):

```
0050   CLR    Clear Word
1050   CLRB   Clear Byte
```

Description:
The destination operand is replaced by zero. The instruction is single operand format with address mode specifier. See Figure 9.2.

DEC   Decrement

Format:

```
opcode dst.mx
```

Operation:

```
dst ← dst − 1;
```

Condition Codes:

```
N ← dst LSS 0;
Z ← dst EQL 0;
V ← {integer overflow};
C ← C;
```

Exceptions:
none

Opcodes (octal):

```
0053   DEC    Decrement Word
1053   DECB   Decrement Byte
```

Description:
One is subtracted from the destination operand, and the destination operand is replaced by the result. The instruction is single operand format with address mode specifier. See Figure 9.2.

Note:
Integer overflow occurs if the largest negative integer is decremented. On overflow, the destination operand is replaced by the largest positive integer.

C

Increment

Format:

opcode dst.mx

Operation:

dst ← dst + 1;

Condition Codes:

N ← dst LSS 0;
Z ← dst EQL 0;
V ← {integer overflow};
C ← C;

Exceptions:
none

Opcodes (octal):

0052   INC   Increment Word
1052   INCB Increment Byte

Description:
One is added to the destination operand, and the destination operand
is replaced by the result. The instruction is single operand format
with address mode specifier. See Figure 9.2.

Note:
Integer overflow occurs if the largest positive integer is incremented.
On overflow, the destination operand is replaced by the largest
negative integer.

EG

Negate

Format:

opcode dst.mx

Operation:

dst ← −dst;

Condition Codes:

```
N ← dst LSS 0;
Z ← dst EQL 0;
V ← dst EQL most negative integer;
C ← dst NEQ 0;
```

Exceptions:
none

Opcodes (octal):

```
0054  NEG   Negate Word
1054  NEGB  Negate Byte
```

Description:
The destination operand is negated (two's complement), and the destination operand is replaced by the result. The instruction is single operand format with address mode specifier. See Figure 9.2.

Note:
Integer overflow occurs if the operand is the most negative integer (which has no positive counterpart). On overflow, the destination operand is replaced by itself.

TST   Test

Format:

```
opcode src.rx
```

Operation:

```
src − 0;
```

Condition Codes:

```
N ← src LSS 0;
Z ← src EQL 0;
V ← 0;
C ← 0;
```

Exceptions:

Opcodes (octal):

```
0057   TST    Test Word
1057   TSTB   Test Byte
```

Description:
The condition codes are affected according to the value of the source operand. The instruction is single operand format with address mode specifier. See Figure 9.2.

Complement

Format:

```
opcode dst.mx
```

Operation:

```
dst ← NOT dst;
```

Condition Codes:

```
N ← dst LSS 0;
Z ← dst EQL 0;
V ← 0;
C ← 1;
```

Exceptions:
none

Opcodes (octal):

```
0051   COM    Complement Word
1051   COMB   Complement Byte
```

Description:
The destination operand is complemented (one's complement), and the destination operand is replaced by the result. The instruction is single operand format with address mode specifier. See Figure 9.2.

Arithmetic Shift Right

Format:

```
opcode dst.mx
```

Operation:

```
dst ← dst shifted one place to the right;
```

Condition Codes:

```
N ← dst LSS 0;
Z ← dst EQL 0;
V ← {bit shifted out} XOR {dst LSS 0};
C ← bit shifted out;
```

Exceptions:
none

Opcodes (octal):

```
0062  ASR   Arithmetic Shift Right Word
1062  ASRB  Arithmetic Shift Right Byte
```

Description:
The destination operand is arithmetically shifted right by one bit and the destination operand is replaced by the result. The instruction is single operand format with address mode specifier. See Figure 9.2.

Notes:
1. The sign bit of the destination operand is replicated in shifts to the right. The condition code C-bit stores the bit shifted out.

2. If the PC is used as the destination operand, the result and the next instruction executed are UNPREDICTABLE.

ASL

Arithmetic Shift Left

Format:

```
opcode dst.mx
```

Operation:

```
dst ← dst shifted one place to the left;
```

Condition Codes:

```
N ← dst LSS 0;
Z ← dst EQL 0;
V ← {integer overflow};
C ← bit shifted out;
```

Exceptions:
none

Opcodes (octal):

0063   ASL   Arithmetic Shift Left Word

1063   ASLB   Arithmetic Shift Left Byte

Description:
The destination operand is arithmetically shifted left by one bit, and the destination operand is replaced by the result. The instruction is single operand format with address mode specifier. See Figure 9.2.

Notes:
1. The least significant bit is filled with zero in shifts to the left. The condition code C-bit stores the bit shifted out.
2. Integer overflow occurs if the destination changes sign due to the shift.

DC   Add Carry

Format:

opcode dst.mx

Operation:

dst ← dst + C;

Condition Codes:

N ← dst LSS 0;

Z ← dst EQL 0;

V ← {integer overflow};

C ← {carry from most significant bit};

Exceptions:
none

Opcodes (octal):

0055   ADC   Add Carry to Word

1055   ADCB   Add Carry to Byte

Description:
The contents of the condition code C-bit are added to the destination operand, and the destination operand is replaced by the result. The

instruction is single operand format with address mode specifier. See Figure 9.2.

Note:
Integer overflow occurs if the most positive integer is incremented. On overflow, the result is the most negative integer.

SBC   Subtract Carry

Format:

opcode dst.mx

Operation:

dst ← dst − C;

Condition Codes:

N ← dst LSS 0;
Z ← dst EQL 0;
V ← {integer overflow};
C ← {borrow into most significant bit};

Exceptions:
none

Opcodes (octal):

0056   SBC   Subtract Carry from Word
1056   SBCB   Subtract Carry from Byte

Description:
The contents of the condition code C-bit are subtracted from the destination operand, and the destination operand is replaced by the result. The instruction is single operand format with address mode specifier. See Figure 9.2.

Note:
Integer overflow occurs if the most negative integer is decremented. On overflow, the result is the most positive integer.

SXT   Sign Extend Word

Format:

opcode dst.ww

Operation:

```
if N EQL 1 then dst ← -1 else dst ← 0;
```

Condition Codes:

```
N ← dst LSS 0;  !N ← N
Z ← dst EQL 0;
V ← 0;
C ← C;
```

Exceptions:
none

Opcode (octal):

```
0067   SXT   Sign Extend
```

Description:
If the condition code N-bit is set, then the destination operand is replaced by −1; otherwise, the destination operand is cleared. The instruction is single operand format with address mode specifier. See Figure 9.2.

Note:
If the PC is used as the destination operand, the results and the next instruction executed are UNPREDICTABLE.

OL

Rotate Left

Format:

```
opcode dst.mx
```

Operation:

```
dst'C ← dst'C rotated left;
```

Condition Codes:

```
N ← dst LSS 0;
Z ← dst EQL 0;
V ← {integer overflow};
C ← {bit rotated out of dst};
```

Exceptions:

Opcodes (octal):

```
0061   ROL    Rotate Left Word
1061   ROLB   Rotate Left Byte
```

Description:
The condition code C-bit and the destination operand are rotated left by one bit position; that is, the C-bit gets the most significant bit of the destination operand, and the destination is replaced by the destination shifted left by one bit with the initial C-bit filling the least significant bit. The instruction is single operand format with address mode specifier. See Figure 9.2.

Notes:
1. The rotate instructions operate on the destination operand and the condition code C-bit taken as a circular datum.

2. Integer overflow occurs if the destination changes sign because of the rotate.

ROR   Rotate Right

Format:

```
opcode dst.mx
```

Operation:

```
dst'C ← dst'C rotated right;
```

Condition Codes:

```
N ← dst LSS 0;
Z ← dst EQL 0;
V ← {C bit changed due to rotate};
C ← {bit rotated out of dst};
```

Exceptions:
none

Opcodes (octal):

```
0060   ROR    Rotate Right Word
1060   RORB   Rotate Right Byte
```

Description:
The condition code C-bit and the destination operand are rotated right by one bit position; that is, the C-bit gets the least significant bit of

the destination operand, and the destination is replaced by the destination shifted right by one bit with the initial C-bit filling the most significant bit. The instruction is single operand format with address mode specifier. See Figure 9.2.

Note:
The rotate instructions operate on the destination operand and the condition code C-bit taken as a circular datum.

SWAB

Swap Bytes

Format:

opcode dst.mw

Operation:

dst ← dst⟨7:0⟩'dst⟨15:8⟩;

Condition Codes:

N ← dst⟨7:0⟩ LSS 0;
Z ← dst⟨7:0⟩ EQL 0;
V ← 0;
C ← 0;

Exceptions:
none

Opcode (octal):

0003   SWAB   Swap Bytes

Description:
The high and low bytes of the destination word operand are swapped. The instruction is single operand format with address mode specifier. See Figure 9.2.

Note:
If the PC is used as the destination operand, the result and the next instruction executed are UNPREDICTABLE.

Double Operand Instructions

The following PDP-11 compatibility mode double operand instructions are described in this section. The instructions are grouped according to type: arithmetic and logical, and shift.

Arithmetic and Logical:

MOV(B) src.rx, dst.mx

ADD src.rw, dst.mw

SUB src.rw, dst.mw

CMP(B) src1.rx, src2.rx

MUL reg, src.rw

DIV reg, src.rw

XOR reg, dst.mw

BIS(B) src.rx, dst.mx

BIC(B) src.rx, dst.mx

BIT(B) src1.rx, src2.rx

Shift:

ASH reg, src.rw

ASHC reg, src.rw

If a register that is used in the source operand specifier in autoincreme or autodecrement modes is also used in the destination (or source 2 operand specifier, the updated value of the register is used to evaluate the destination specifier. Side effects caused by a destinatic address calculation have no effect on source values.

MOV   Move

Format:

opcode src.rx, dst.wx

Operation:

dst ← src;

Condition Codes:

N ← dst LSS 0;

Z ← dst EQL 0;

V ← 0;

C ← C;

Exceptions:

Opcodes (octal):

```
01   MOV    Move Word
11   MOVB   Move Byte
```

Description:
The destination operand is replaced by the source operand. The
instruction is double operand format with two address mode specifiers.
See Figure 9.2.

Note:
The low byte is sign-extended on a MOVB to a register; that is, bits
⟨15:8⟩ of the destination register are replaced by bit ⟨7⟩ of the source
operand.

Add

Format:

```
opcode src.rw, dst.mw
```

Operation:

```
dst ← dst + src;
```

Condition Codes:

```
N ← dst LSS 0;
Z ← dst EQL 0;
V ← {integer overflow};
C ← {carry from most significant digit};
```

Exceptions:
none

Opcode (octal):

```
06   ADD   Add Word
```

Description:
The source operand is added to the destination operand, and the
destination operand is replaced by the result. The instruction is double
operand format with two address mode specifiers. See Figure 9.2.

Note:
Integer overflow occurs if the input operands have the same sign and
the result has the opposite sign. On overflow, the destination
operand is replaced by the low-order bits of the true result.

SUB

Subtract

Format:

```
opcode src.rw, dst.mw
```

Operation:

dst ← dst − src;

Condition Codes:

N ← dst LSS 0;
Z ← dst EQL 0;
V ← {integer overflow};
C ← {borrow into most significant digit};

Exceptions:
none

Opcode (octal):

```
16   SUB   Subtract Word
```

Description:
The source operand is subtracted from the destination operand, and the destination operand is replaced by the result. The instruction is double operand format with two address mode specifiers. See Figure 9.2.

Note:
Integer overflow occurs if the input operands are of different signs and the result has the sign of the source. On overflow, the destination operand is replaced by the low-order bits of the true result.

CMP

Compare

Format:

```
opcode src1.rx, src2.rx
```

Operation:

tmp ← src1 − src2;

Condition Codes:

N ← tmp LSS 0;

```
Z ← tmp EQL 0;
V ← {integer overflow};
C ← {borrow into most significant digit};
```

Exceptions:
none

Opcodes (octal):

```
02   CMP    Compare Word
12   CMPB   Compare Byte
```

Description:
The source 1 operand is compared with the source 2 operand. The only action is to set the condition codes. The instruction is double operand format with two address mode specifiers. See Figure 9.2.

Note:
Integer overflow occurs if the operands are of different sign and the result of the subtraction (src1 − src2) has the same sign as the source 2 operand.

UL

Multiply

Format:

```
opcode reg, src.rw
```

Operation:

```
tmp⟨31:0⟩ ← Rn * src;
Rn ← tmp⟨31:16⟩;
R[n OR 1] ← tmp⟨15:0⟩;
```

Condition Codes:

```
N ← tmp LSS 0;
Z ← tmp EQL 0;
V ← 0;
C ← {result cannot be represented in 16 bits};
```

Exceptions:
none

Opcode (octal):

```
070   MUL   Multiply Word
```

Description:

The destination register is multiplied by the source operand. The most significant 16 bits of the 32-bit product are stored in register Rn. Then the least significant 16 bits are stored in R[n OR 1]. The condition codes are set based on the 32-bit result. The instruction is double operand format with register and address mode specifiers. See Figure 9.2.

Note:

1. The C-bit is set if the result of the multiplication cannot be represented in 16 bits; that is, if the 32-bit product is less than -2^{15} or greater than or equal to 2^{15}.

2. If an odd-numbered register is used as the destination, the low-order 16 bits are stored as the result.

3. If R6 or PC is used as the destination, the next instruction execute and the result are UNPREDICTABLE.

DIV Divide

Format:

```
opcode reg, src.rw
```

Operation:

```
tmp ← Rn'R[n OR 1]
Rn ← tmp / src;
R[n OR 1] ← REM(tmp , src);
```

Condition Codes:

```
N ← Rn LSS 0;   !UNPREDICTABLE if V is set
Z ← Rn EQL 0;   !UNPREDICTABLE if V is set
V ← {src EQL 0} OR {integer overflow};
C ← {src EQL 0};
```

Exceptions:

Opcode (octal):

```
071  DIV  Divide
```

Description:

If the source operand is not zero, the 32-bit integer in Rn'R[n OR 1] is divided by the source operand. The quotient is stored in Rn, and the remainder is stored in R[n OR 1]. The remainder has the same sign as the dividend. If the source operand is zero, the instruction terminates without modifying the destination registers.

Notes:

1. Integer overflow occurs if the quotient is less than -2^{15} or greater than or equal to 2^{15}. On integer overflow, the contents of the destination registers are UNPREDICTABLE.

2. If an odd register or R6 is used as the destination, the results are UNPREDICTABLE. Furthermore, if R6 or PC is used as the destination, the next instruction executed is UNPREDICTABLE.

OR

Exclusive-OR

Format:

```
opcode reg, dst.mw
```

Operation:

```
dst ← Rn XOR dst;
```

Condition Codes:

```
N ← dst LSS 0;
Z ← dst EQL 0;
V ← 0;
C ← C;
```

Exceptions:

Opcode (octal):

```
074  XOR  Exclusive-OR Word
```

Description:

The source register is XORed with the destination operand, and the destination operand is replaced by the result. The instruction is double operand format with register and address mode specifiers. See Figure 9.2.

BIS

Bit Set

Format:

```
opcode src.rx, dst.mx
```

Operation:

dst ← dst OR src;

Condition Codes:

N ← dst LSS 0;
Z ← dst EQL 0;
V ← 0;
C ← C;

Exceptions:
none

Opcodes (octal):

05 BIS   Bit Set Word
15 BISB Bit Set Byte

Description:
The source operand is ORed with the destination operand, and the destination operand is replaced by the result. The instruction is doubl operand format with two address mode specifiers. See Figure 9.2.

BIC   Bit Clear

Format:

opcode src.rx, dst.mx

Operation:

dst ← dst AND {NOT src};

Condition Codes:

N ← dst LSS 0;
Z ← dst EQL 0;
V ← 0;
C ← C;

Exceptions:
none

Opcodes (octal):

04 BIC   Bit Clear Word
14 BICB Bit Clear Byte

Description:
The destination operand is ANDed with the one's complement of the source operand, and the destination operand is replaced by the result. The instruction is double operand format with two address mode specifiers. See Figure 9.2.

IT

Bit Test

Format:

```
opcode srcl.rx, src2.rx
```

Operation:

```
tmp ← srcl AND src2;
```

Condition Codes:

```
N ← tmp LSS 0;
Z ← tmp EQL 0;
V ← 0;
C ← C;
```

Exceptions:
none

Opcodes (octal):

```
03  BIT   Bit Test Word
13  BITB  Bit Test Byte
```

Description:
The source 1 operand is ANDed with the source 2 operand. The only action is to set the condition codes. The instruction is double operand format with two address mode specifiers. See Figure 9.2.

SH

Arithmetic Shift

Format:

```
opcode reg, src.rw
```

Operation:

```
Rn ← Rn shifted src⟨5:0⟩ bits;
```

Condition Codes:

```
N ← Rn LSS 0;
Z ← Rn EQL 0;
V ← if src⟨5:0⟩ EQL 0 then 0 else {integer overflow};
C ← if src⟨5:0⟩ EQL 0 then 0 else {last bit shifted out};
```

Exceptions:
none

Opcode (octal):

```
072   ASH   Arithmetic Shift
```

Description:
The specified register is arithmetically shifted by the number of bits specified by the count operand (bits ⟨5:0⟩ of the source operand), and the register is replaced by the result. The count ranges from −32 to +31. A negative count signifies a right shift. A positive count signifies a left shift. A zero count implies no shift, but condition codes are affected. The instruction is double operand format with register and address mode specifiers. See Figure 9.2.

Notes:
1. The sign bit of Rn is replicated in shifts to the right. The least significant bit is filled with zero in shifts to the left. The C-bit stores the last bit shifted out.
2. Integer overflow occurs on a left shift if any bit shifted into the sign position differs from the initial sign bit of the register.
3. If the PC is used as the destination operand, the result and the next instruction executed are UNPREDICTABLE.

ASHC   Arithmetic Shift Combined

Format:

```
opcode reg, src.rw
```

Operation:

```
tmp ← Rn'R[n OR 1];
tmp ← tmp shifted src⟨5:0⟩ bits;
Rn ← tmp⟨31:16⟩;
R[n OR 1] ← tmp⟨15:0⟩;
```

Condition Codes:

```
N ← tmp LSS 0;
Z ← tmp EQL 0;
V ← if src⟨5:0⟩ EQL 0 then 0 else {integer overflow};
C ← if src⟨5:0⟩ EQL 0 then 0 else {last bit shifted out};
```

Exceptions:
none

Opcode (octal):

073   ASHC   Arithmetic Shift Combined

Description:
The contents of the specified register, Rn, and the register R[n OR 1] are treated as a single 32-bit operand and are shifted by the number of bits specified by the count operand (bits ⟨5:0⟩ of the source operand); the registers are replaced by the result. First, bits ⟨31:16⟩ of the result are stored in register Rn. Then, bits ⟨15:0⟩ of the result are stored in register R[n OR 1]. The count ranges from −32 to +31. A negative count signifies a right shift. A positive count signifies a left shift. A zero count implies no shift, but condition codes are affected. Condition codes are always set on the 32-bit result. The instruction is double operand format with register and address mode specifiers. See Figure 9.2.

Notes:
1. The sign bit of Rn is replicated in shifts to the right. The least significant bit is filled with zero in shifts to the left. The C-bit stores the last bit shifted out.

2. Integer overflow occurs on a left shift if any bit shifted into the sign position differs from the initial sign bit of the 32-bit operand.

3. If the SP or PC is used as the destination operand, the result and the next instruction executed are UNPREDICTABLE.

Branch Instructions

The following PDP-11 compatibility mode branch instructions are described in this section.

BCC displ.bb

BCS displ.bb

BEQ displ.bb

BGE displ.bb

BGT displ.bb

BHI displ.bb

BHIS displ.bb

BLE displ.bb
BLO displ.bb
BLOS displ.bb
BLT displ.bb
BMI displ.bb
BNE displ.bb
BPL displ.bb
BR displ.bb
BVC displ.bb
BVS displ.bb
SOB reg, displ.b6

BR

Branch

Format:

```
opcode displ.bb
```

Operation:

```
PC ← PC + SEXT(2*displ);
```

Condition Codes:

```
N ← N;
Z ← Z;
V ← V;
C ← C;
```

Exceptions:
none

Opcode (octal):

```
0004  BR  Branch
```

Description:
Twice the sign-extended displacement is added to the PC, and the PC is replaced by the result. The instruction is branch format with 8-bit displacement. See Figure 9.2.

B

Branch on (condition)

Format:

opcode displ.bb

Operation:

if condition then PC ← PC + SEXT(2*displ);

Condition Codes:

N ← N;
Z ← Z;
V ← V;
C ← C;

Exceptions:
none

Opcodes (octal):
Condition

0014	BEQ	Z EQL 1	Branch on Equal
0010	BNE	Z EQL 0	Branch Not Equal
1004	BMI	N EQL 1	Branch on Minus
1000	BPL	N EQL 0	Branch on Plus
1034	BCS,	C EQL 1	Branch on Carry Set,
	BLO		Branch on Lower
1030	BCC,	C EQL 0	Branch on Carry Clear,
	BHIS		Branch on Higher or Same
1024	BVS	V EQL 1	Branch on Overflow Set
1020	BVC	V EQL 0	Branch on Overflow Clear
0024	BLT	{N XOR V} EQL 1	Branch on Less Than
0020	BGE	{N XOR V} EQL 0	Branch on Greater Than or Equal
0034	BLE	{Z OR {N XOR V}}	
		EQL 1	Branch on Less Than or Equal
0030	BGT	{Z OR {N XOR V}}	
		EQL 0	Branch on Greater Than
1010	BHI	{C OR Z} EQL 0	Branch on Higher
1014	BLOS	{C OR Z} EQL 1	Branch on Lower or Same

Description:
The condition codes are tested and, if the condition indicated by the
instruction is met, twice the sign-extended displacement is added
to the PC; the PC is replaced by the result. These instructions are
branch format with 8-bit displacement. See Figure 9.2.

SOB   Subtract One and Branch

Format:

```
opcode reg, displ.b6
```

Operation:

```
Rn ← Rn - 1;
if Rn NEQ 0 then PC ← PC - ZEXT(2*displ);
```

Condition Codes:

```
N ← N;
Z ← Z;
V ← V;
C ← C;
```

Exceptions:
none

Opcode (octal):

```
077   SOB   Subtract One and Branch
```

Description:
One is subtracted from the specified register, and the register is replaced by the result. If the register is not equal to zero, twice the zero-extended displacement is subtracted from the PC; the PC is replaced by the result. The instruction is loop format. See Figure 9.2.

Notes:
1. If the PC is specified as the register, the results and the next instruction executed are UNPREDICTABLE.
2. The 6-bit displacement operand is contained in bits ⟨5:0⟩ of the instruction.

Jump and Subroutine Instructions

The following PDP-11 compatibility mode jump and subroutine instructions are described in this section.

JMP dst.aw

JSR reg, dst.aw

RTS reg

Jump

Format:

opcode dst.aw

Operation:

PC ← dst;

Condition Codes:

N ← N;
Z ← Z;
V ← V;
C ← C;

Exceptions:
compatibility mode illegal instruction

Opcode (octal):

0001   JMP   Jump

Description:
The PC is replaced by the destination operand. The instruction is single operand format with address mode specifier. See Figure 9.2.

Note:
A compatibility mode illegal instruction fault occurs if destination mode 0 is used.

Jump to Subroutine

Format:

opcode reg, dst.aw

Operation:

tmp ← dst;   ! Value of Rn is affected by
-(SP) ← Rn;   ! dst specifier evaluation.
Rn ← PC;
PC ← tmp;

Condition Codes:

```
N ← N;
Z ← Z;
V ← V;
C ← C;
```

Exceptions:
compatibility mode illegal instruction

Opcode (octal):

```
004   JJSR   Jump to Subroutine
```

Description:
The source register is pushed on the stack, and the source register is replaced by the PC. The PC is replaced by the destination operand. The instruction is double operand format with register and address mode specifier. See Figure 9.2.

Notes:
1. A compatibility mode illegal instruction fault occurs if destination mode 0 is used.
2. If the destination uses the same register as the source in the autoincrement or autodecrement addressing modes, the updated contents of the register are pushed on the stack.

RTS   Return from Subroutine

Format:

```
opcode reg
```

Operation:

```
PC ← Rn;
Rn ← (SP) + ;
```

Condition Codes:

```
N ← N;
Z ← Z;
V ← V;
C ← C;
```

Exceptions:

Opcode (octal):

```
00020   RTS   Return from Subroutine
```

Description:
The PC is replaced by the destination register. The destination register is replaced by a word popped from the stack. The instruction is single operand format with register specifier. See Figure 9.2.

Return from Interrupts and Traps

The following PDP-11 compatibility mode return-from-interrupts and return-from-trap instructions are described in this section.

RTI

RTT

RTI   Return from Interrupt

RTT   Return from Trap

Format:

```
opcode
```

Operation:

$PC \leftarrow (SP)+;$

$PSW\langle 4:0 \rangle \leftarrow \{(SP)+\}\langle 4:0 \rangle;$

Condition Codes:

$N \leftarrow saved\ PSW\langle 3 \rangle;$

$Z \leftarrow saved\ PSW\langle 2 \rangle;$

$V \leftarrow saved\ PSW\langle 1 \rangle;$

$C \leftarrow saved\ PSW\langle 0 \rangle;$

Exceptions:
none

Opcodes (octal):

```
000002   RTI   Return from Interrupt
000006   RTT   Return from Trap
```

Description:

The PC is replaced by the first word popped from the stack. The low five bits of the PSW are replaced by the corresponding bits of the second word popped from the stack. The instruction is zero operand format. See Figure 9.2.

Notes:

1. In compatibility mode, the RTI and RTT instructions ignore the high 11 bits of the PSW popped from the stack.

2. In compatibility mode, the RTI and RTT instructions are identical.

Miscellaneous Instructions

The following miscellaneous PDP-11 compatibility mode instructions are described in this section.

MTP{I,D} dst.ww	CLZ	SEV
MFP{I,D} src.rw	CLN	SEZ
NOP	CCC	SEN
CLC	SEC	SCC
CLV		

MTP

Move To Previous Space

Format:

```
opcode dst.ww
```

Operation:

```
tmp ← (SP)+;        !Pop source from stack (updating SP
dst ← tmp;          !Write source to destination
```

Condition Codes:

```
N ← dst LSS 0;
Z ← dst EQL 0;
V ← 0;
C ← C;
```

Exceptions:

```
none
```

Opcodes (octal):

```
0066  MTPI  Move To Previous Instruction Space
1066  MTPD  Move To Previous Data Space
```

Description:
In compatibility mode, this PDP-11 instruction works like a POP instruction. The destination operand is replaced by a word popped from the stack. The instruction is single operand format with address mode specifier. See Figure 9.2.

Note:
The implied source operand specifier is evaluated before the destination specifier.

FP

Move From Previous Space

Format:
opcode src.rw

Operation:
$-(SP) \leftarrow src;$

Condition Codes:
N ← src LSS 0;
Z ← src EQL 0;
V ← 0;
C ← C;

Exceptions:
none

Opcodes (octal):

0065 MFPI Move From Previous Instruction Space
1065 MFPD Move From Previous Data Space

Description:
In compatibility mode, this PDP-11 instruction works like a PUSH instruction. The source operand is pushed onto the stack. The instruction is single operand format with address mode specifier. See Figure 9.2.

C

Condition Code Operators

Format:
opcode mask

Operation:

```
if mask⟨4⟩ EQL 1 then PSW⟨3:0⟩ ← PSW⟨3:0⟩ OR mask⟨3:0⟩
          else PSW⟨3:0⟩ ← PSW⟨3:0⟩ AND {NOT mask⟨3:0⟩};
```

Condition Codes:

```
if mask⟨4⟩ EQL 1 then
        begin
        N ← N OR mask⟨3⟩;
        Z ← Z OR mask⟨2⟩;
        V ← V OR mask⟨1⟩;
        C ← C OR mask⟨0⟩;
        end
else
        begin
        N ← N AND {NOT mask⟨3⟩};
        Z ← Z AND {NOT mask⟨2⟩};
        V ← V AND {NOT mask⟨1⟩};
        C ← C AND {NOT mask⟨0⟩};
        end
```

Exceptions:
none

Opcodes (octal):

```
000240   NOP   No operation
000241   CLC   Clear C
000242   CLV   Clear V
000244   CLZ   Clear Z
000250   CLN   Clear N
000257   CCC   Clear all Condition Codes
000261   SEC   Set C
000262   SEV   Set V
000264   SEZ   Set Z
000270   SEN   Set N
000277   SCC   Set all Condition Codes
```

Combinations of the above set or clear operations may be ORed together to form combined instructions.

Description:
If the mask⟨4⟩ bit is set, the PSW condition code bits are ORed with mask⟨3:0⟩ and the condition codes are replaced by the result. If the mask⟨4⟩ bit is clear, the PSW condition code bits are ANDed with the one's complement of mask⟨3:0⟩ and the condition codes are replaced by the result. The instruction is zero operand format. See Figure 9.2. Bits ⟨4:0⟩ of the opcode are used as the mask operand.

NTERING ND LEAVING OMPATIBILITY ODE

Compatibility mode is entered by executing an REI instruction with the compatibility mode bit set in the PSL on the stack. Other bits in the PSL either have the effects they have in native mode or are required to have specific values in compatibility mode. PSL⟨TP⟩, ⟨T⟩, ⟨N⟩, ⟨Z⟩, ⟨V⟩, and ⟨C⟩ have the same effects and meanings as they have in native mode. PSL⟨FPD⟩, ⟨IS⟩, ⟨IPL⟩, ⟨IV⟩, ⟨FU⟩, ⟨DV⟩ must be 0, and ⟨CUR_MOD⟩ and ⟨PRV_MOD⟩ must be 3.

VAX native mode is returned to from compatibility mode by the compatibility mode program causing an exception, or by an interrupt.

Note that when an RTI or RTT instruction is executed in compatibility mode, the 11 high bits of the PSW are ignored. But when the PSW is restored as part of the PSL when going from VAX native mode to compatibility mode, those bits must be 0, or a reserved operand fault occurs.

ATIVE MODE ND OMPATIBILITY ODE EGISTERS

Compatibility mode registers R0 through R6 are bits ⟨15:0⟩ of VAX general registers R0 through R6, respectively. Compatibility mode register R7 (PC) is bits ⟨15:0⟩ of VAX general register R15 (PC). VAX registers R8 through R14 (SP) are not affected by compatibility mode. When entering compatibility mode, VAX register R7 and the upper halves of registers R0 through R6 and R15 are ignored. When an exception or interrupt occurs from compatibility mode, VAX register R7 is UNPREDICTABLE and the upper halves of R0 through R6 are either cleared or left unchanged; the upper half of the stacked R15 (PC) is zero. Since there are no FP11 floating-point instructions in compatibility mode, there are no floating accumulators.

OMPATIBILITY ODE MEMORY ANAGEMENT

PDP-11 addresses are 16-bit byte addresses. Hence, compatibility mode programs are confined to execute in the first 64K bytes of the per-process part of the virtual address space. A one-to-one corre-spondence exists between a compatibility mode virtual address and its VAX counterpart. (Virtual address 0, for example, references the same location in both modes.) A compatibility mode address is interpreted in the following paragraphs as a native mode address by appending zero in bits ⟨31:16⟩ to the compatibility mode address in bits ⟨15:0⟩.

PDP-11 segments can consist of 1 to 128 blocks of 64 bytes. VAX pages are 512 bytes long. The PDP-11 capability of providing differe access protection to different segments is provided in 8-block chunks since protection is specified at the page level in the VAX architecture

The memory management system protects and relocates compatibili mode addresses in the normal native mode manner. Thus, all of the memory management mechanisms available in VAX mode are available to the compatibility mode executive for managing both the virtual and physical memory of compatibility mode programs. All of th exception conditions that can be caused by memory management in VAX mode can also occur when relocating a compatibility mode address. See Chapter 4.

COMPATIBILITY MODE EXCEPTIONS AND INTERRUPTS

All interrupts and exception conditions that occur while the processor is in compatibility mode cause the processor to enter VAX mode. These conditions are serviced as indicated in Chapter 5 (note that thi includes backing up instruction side effects if necessary). The exception conditions discussed in this section are specific to compatibility mode. All these exceptions create a three-longword frame on the kernel stack containing PSL and PC, and one longword of exception-dependent information. Bits ⟨15⟩ through ⟨0⟩ of this longword contain a code indicating the specific type of exception, and bits ⟨31⟩ through ⟨16⟩ are zero. There are no compatibility mode exception conditions that result in traps. (See Chapter 5 for definitions of trap, fault, and abort.)

Odd Address Error Abort

An odd address error abort is caused in compatibility mode whenever a word reference is attempted on a byte boundary. The code for odd address errors is 6.

Faults

The following paragraphs give the compatibility mode instruction faults and their corresponding code numbers.

Reserved Instruction Fault—A reserved instruction fault occurs for opcodes that are defined as reserved in compatibility mode (see the section "Instructions" earlier in this chapter). The code for the reserved instruction fault is 0.

BPT Instruction Fault—The code for the BPT instruction fault is 1.

IOT Instruction Fault—The code for the IOT instruction fault is 2.

EMT Instruction Fault—The fault code for the group of EMT instruction is 3.

TRAP Instruction Fault—The fault code for the group of TRAP instructions is 4.

Illegal Instruction Fault—In compatibility mode, JMP and JSR instructions with a register destination are illegal. The fault code for illegal instructions is 5.

In compatibility mode, a trace fault occurs at the beginning of an instruction when the T-bit is set in the PSW at the beginning of the prior instruction. This effect is achieved by using the TP bit in the PSL (see Chapter 5). On trace faults, a two-longword kernel stack frame is created, containing PSL and PC. IPL and IS are 0 and CM is 1 in the stacked PSL. Compatibility mode trace fault uses the same vector as VAX mode trace fault (see Chapter 5). The rules for trace fault generation in compatibility mode are identical to those for native mode. However, an odd address abort for an instruction fetch may precede the trace fault for that instruction.

There are two ways to get the T-bit set at the beginning of a compatibility mode instruction:

- An RTT or RTI instruction is executed in compatibility mode with the T-bit set in the PSW image on the stack. In this case, the next instruction is executed (the 1 pointed to by the PC on the stack), and a trace fault is taken before the following instruction.
- An REI instruction is executed in VAX mode which has both the T-bit and CM bit set (and TP clear) in the saved PSL image on the stack. Again, one instruction is executed, and the trace fault is taken. (See Chapter 5 for a complete description of the interaction of REI, T-bit, and TP bit. The operations that occur as a function of these conditions are the same whether or not compatibility mode is being entered from the REI.)

The T-bit interacts with other compatibility mode operations as follows. For interaction with other than compatibility mode, see Chapter 5.

1. T-bit is set (but TP is clear) at the beginning of any compatibility mode instruction that does not cause a compatibility mode fault.

   In this case, the instruction sets TP and executes. A trace fault is taken before the next instruction. The saved PSL has the T-bit set and TP clear. The compatibility mode executive can take one of the following courses of action:

   a. If it services the exception directly, it can clear the T-bit in the saved PSL on the kernel stack if it no longer wants to trace the program; or it can leave it set if it wants to continue tracing the program. It exits with an REI.

b. If it returns the trace exception to compatibility mode, it pushes
    a (16-bit) PC and (16-bit) PSW with the T-bit set on the
    compatibility mode user stack to simulate the effect of the
    PDP-11 trace trap. It then clears the T-bit in the saved PSL
    image on the kernel stack, changes the saved PC to point to
    the compatibility mode service routine, and does an REI.
    The compatibility mode service routine can then clear the T-bit
    in the PSW image on its stack if it does not want to continue
    tracing. The compatibility mode routine returns with RTT or
    RTI.

2. T-bit is set (but TP is clear) at the beginning of an RTI or RTT.

   The RTT or RTI instruction executes, and TP is set. A trace fault
   occurs before the next instruction is executed. Two different cases
   exist depending on whether or not the T-bit was set in the image of
   the PSW which was popped from the stack by the RTT or RTI
   instruction:

   a. T-bit is not set. Neither TP nor T will be set in the saved PSL
       on the kernel stack.

   b. T-bit is set. TP will not be set, and T will be set, as is the case
       for other compatibility mode instructions.

3. T-bit is set (but TP is clear) at the beginning of any instruction
   which causes a compatibility mode fault.

   The fault condition is serviced first. TP is clear and T is set in the
   saved PSL pushed on the kernel stack.

UNIMPLE-MENTED PDP-11 TRAPS

Several traps that occur in PDP-11 systems are not implemented in
compatibility mode:

• There is no stack overflow trap. This is equivalent to the user mode
  of the KT11 where there is also no overflow protection. Stack
  overflow can be provided by the compatibility mode executive using
  the memory management mechanisms.

• There is no concept of a double error trap in compatibility mode,
  since the first error always puts the processor in VAX mode.

• All other exception conditions such as power failure, memory parity,
  and memory management exceptions cause the processor to
  enter VAX mode.

COMPATI-BILITY MODE I/O REFERENCES

Neither instruction stream references nor data reads or writes can
be to I/O space. The results are UNPREDICTABLE if I/O space
is referenced from compatibility mode.

PROCESSOR REGISTERS

The only processor register available in compatibility mode is part of
the PSW, and it maybe explicitly referenced only with the condition

code instructions, RTI, and RTT. Access to all other registers must be done in VAX mode.

All PDP-11 systems guarantee that read-modify-write operations to I/O device registers are interlocked; that is, the device can determine at the time of the read that the same register will be written as the next bus cycle. This synchronization also works in memory on most PDP-11 systems. In compatibility mode, instructions that have modify destinations will perform this synchronization for UNIBUS I/O device registers and never for memory.

Compatibility mode procedures can write data that is to be subsequently executed as an instruction without requiring any additional synchronization.

System Bootstrapping and Console 10

A VAX processor can be in one of five major states: attempting to load and start (bootstrap) the operating system, attempting to restart the operating system, powered off, halted, or running. This chapter describes the processor when it is not running and describes the transitions between major states.

The four major states described in this chapter are differentiated from the running state. When the processor is running, it interprets instructions, services interrupts and exceptions, and initiates I/O operations. The console acts like a normal operating system terminal (the console is in program I/O mode).

When the processor is halted, it does not interpret instructions, service interrupts or exceptions, or initiate I/O operations. The console interprets a command language that provides control over the system (the console is in console I/O mode).

When system power supplies are unable to provide power to the processor, the processor halts, and is powered off.

The console can restart a halted operating system and can also load and start (bootstrap) an operating system. How the console handles these states is described in the following sections.

SYSTEM BOOT- TRAPPING

System bootstrap can occur as the result of a powerfail recovery, a processor halt, or the operator entering a BOOT command at the console. See the section "Major System State Transitions" in this chapter for a complete description of these state transitions.

To prevent repeated attempts and failures to bootstrap or restart the operating system, the console maintains two flags called the bootstrap-in-progress flag and the restart-in-progress flag. If a system bootstrap or restart would occur automatically but the corresponding flag is already set, the console assumes that an attempt has already been made and has failed. The console therefore does not try again.

To load and start (bootstrap) the operating system, the console searches for a section of correctly functioning system memory large enough to hold a primary bootstrap program (called VMB). If a sectio of memory is found, the console loads and starts VMB. VMB loads and starts the operating system.

The console uses this algorithm to bootstrap the operating system:

1. If this bootstrap is the result of a console BOOT command, skip to step 4.

2. Print the message "Attempting system bootstrap" on the console terminal.

3. Check to see if the bootstrap-in-progress flag is set. If so, boot fails.

4. Set the bootstrap-in-progress flag.

5. Locate a page-aligned 64-kilobyte block of good memory. Testing memory leaves the contents of memory UNPREDICTABLE. If suc a block cannot be found, boot fails.

6. Load a bootstrap program into that good memory, starting 512 bytes from the beginning. The name of the bootstrap program is VMB.EXE. If VMB cannot be found on the load device, or if there is an error during loading, boot fails.

7. Load the general registers:

R0	
R1	Together, R0 through R3 specify a boot device.
R2	They are interpreted by VMB.
R3	
R4	Reserved for future use.
R5	Boot control parameter. Contains the value specifiedby the BOOT command, if any; otherwise, zero.
R6	Reserved for future use.
R7	Reserved for future use.
R8	Reserved for future use.
R9	Reserved for future use.
R10	The halt PC.
R11	The halt PSL.
AP	The halt code.
FP	Reserved for future use.
SP	The address of 512 bytes past the start ofgood memory.

8. Start VMB at the address in SP. VMB loads and starts the operating system.

If bootstrap fails, the console prints a message reporting the failure. The message may explain the cause of the failure, or it may just report "System bootstrap failed."

If the bootstrap is successful, the operating system sends a message to the console, causing the console to clear the bootstrap-in-progress flag. See the section on "System Running" for a description of the messages the operating system can pass to the console.

SYSTEM RESTART

The console can restart a halted operating system. To do so, the console searches system memory for the Restart Parameter Block (RPB), a data structure constructed for this purpose by the operating system. If a valid RPB is found, the console restarts the operating system at an address specified in the RPB.

The console keeps an internal flag called restart-in-progress, which it uses to avoid repeated attempts to restart a failing operating system. An additional restart-in-progress flag may be maintained by software in the RPB.

A system restart can occur as the result of a powerfail restart, or as the result of a processor halt. See the section "Major System State Transitions" for a complete description.

The console uses this algorithm to restart the operating system:

1. Print the message "Attempting system restart" on the console terminal.
2. Check to see if the internal restart-in-progress flag is set. If so, restart fails.
3. Set the internal restart-in-progress flag.
4. Check to see if memory has been preserved by battery backup. If not, restart fails.
5. Look for an RPB left in memory by the operating system. If none is found, restart fails.
6. Read the software restart-in-progress flag from bit ⟨0⟩ of the fourth longword of the RPB. If it is set, restart fails.
7. Load SP with the address of the RPB plus 512.

   Boad AP with the halt code.
9. Start the processor at the restart address, which is read from the second longword in the RPB.

physical address of the RPB	:RPB
physical address of the restart routine	
checksum of the first 31 longwords of the restart routine	
software restart in progress flag (bit 0)	

Figure 10.1
Restart Parameter Block (RPB)

If restart fails, the console prints a message reporting the failure. The message may explain the cause of the failure, or it may just report "System restart failed."

If the restart is successful, the operating system sends a message to the console, causing the console to clear its internal restart-in-progress flag. See the section "System Running" later in this chapter for a description of the messages the operating system can pass to the console.

The RPB is a page-aligned control block created by the operating system. Its format is this shown in Figure 10.1.

The console uses this algorithm to find an RPB:

1. Search for a page of memory that contains its address in the first longword. If none is found, the search for an RPB has failed.

2. Read the second longword in the page (the physical address of the restart routine). If it is not a valid physical address, or if it is 0, return to step 1. The check for 0 is necessary to ensure that a page of zeros does not pass the test for a valid RPB.

3. Calculate the 32-bit two's complement sum (ignoring overflows) of the first 31 longwords of the restart routine. If the sum does not match the third longword of the RPB, return to step 1.

4. A valid RPB has been found.

SYSTEM POWERFAIL AND RECOVERY

The system requires power to operate. The system power supply conditions external power and transforms it for use by the processor. When external power fails, the power supply requests a powerfail interrupt of the processor. The power supply continues to provide power to the processor for at least 2 milliseconds after the interrupt is requested in order to allow the operating system to save state. When the power supply can no longer provide power to the processor the processor is halted and powered off. Battery backup options are available on some processors to supply power after external power fails, to maintain the contents of main memory, and to keep system time with the time-of-day clock.

When power is restored, the console initializes itself, initializes the processor, and examines the front panel console-lock and autorestart switches. If the console is locked, it attempts a system restart; if that fails, it attempts a system bootstrap. If the console is not locked, its action is determined by the setting of the autorestart switch.

Note that when the processor loses power, its state is lost. For example, if a processor is halted when power fails, the action on power-up is still determined by the front panel switches. So the system does not necessarily stay halted.

When power is restored, the processor initializes itself. There are three kinds of hardware initialization called processor initialization, system bus initialization, and power-up initialization. Processor initialization is the result of a console INITIALIZE and involves the initialization of registers internal to the processor and the console. System bus initialization is the result of a console UNJAM command and is implementation-dependent. Power-up initialization affects the system as a whole. It is the result of the restoration of power, and includes a processor initialization.

The processor must be initialized after an error halt. If the processor starts running after an error halt, without an intervening processor initialization, the operation of the processor is UNDEFINED.

The following processor registers are affected by a processor initialization. Registers not listed here are UNPREDICTABLE after a processor initialization.

PSL	041F0000 (hex)
IPL	1F (hex)
ASTLVL	4
SISR	0
ICCS	⟨6⟩ and ⟨0⟩ clear, the rest is UNPREDICTABLE
RXCS	0
TXCS	80 (hex)
MAPEN	0
PME	0
ACCS	0 if no accelerator; 8001 (hex) if a floating-point accelerator is installed
cache, instruction buffer, write buffer, etc.	empty or valid

console previous reference	physical address, longword size, address 0
KSP, ESP, SSP, USP, ISP	UNPREDICTABLE
P0BR, P0LR, P1BR, P1LR	UNPREDICTABLE
SBR, SLR	UNPREDICTABLE
PCBB	UNPREDICTABLE
SCBB	UNPREDICTABLE
translation buffer	UNPREDICTABLE
NICR, ICR	UNPREDICTABLE
TODR	unaffected
main memory	unaffected
registers R0 through PC	unaffected
halt code	unaffected
bootstrap-in-progress flag	unaffected
restart-in-progress flag	unaffected

In addition to what processor initialization does, power-up initializes the following:

bootstrap-in-progress flag	cleared
internal restart-in-progress flag	cleared
halt code	03 (power-up)
general registers	UNPREDICTABLE
system memory	unaffected if preserved by battery backup; otherwise, UNPREDICTABLE
TODR	unaffected if preserved by batterybackup; otherwise, 0

MAJOR SYSTEM STATE TRANSITIONS

The transitions between major system states are determined by the current state and by a number of variables and events, including:

- Whether power is available to the system
- The console front panel autorestart switch
- The console lock switch
- The bootstrap-in-progress flag
- The restart-in-progress flag
- Processor error halts
- The HALT instruction
- Console commands.

Table 10.1 shows the actions that cause major system state transitions. The processor follows these rules:

	Final State				
tial ate	Powered Off	Halted	Booting	Restarting	Running
wered f		A and power restored	B and power restored	C and power restored	
lted	powerfail		BOOT command and unlocked		START or CONTINUE and unlocked
oting	powerfail	boot fails, or D			boot succeeds
start	powerfail	D	restart fails		restart succeeds
nning	powerfail	A and processor halts, or D	B and processor halts	C and processor halts	

y: A The console is unlocked and the halt action switch is set to Halt.
   B The console is unlocked and the halt action switch is set to Boot.
   C The console is unlocked and the halt action switch is set to Restart, or the console is locked.
   D The console is unlocked, and the operator types CTRL/P and HALT.

- If the console is not locked when power is restored or when the processor halts, enter the state selected by the console front panel autorestart switch.
- If the console is locked when power is restored or when the processor halts, attempt a system restart.
- When system restart fails, attempt a system bootstrap.
- When system bootstrap fails, halt.
- When system bootstrap or system restart succeed, the processor starts running.
- When the processor is halted and the console is not locked, the console BOOT command causes a system bootstrap.
- When the processor is halted and the console is not locked, the console START and CONTINUE commands cause the processor to start running.
- If the console is not locked and is running or booting or restarting, typing CTRL/P followed by a HALT command at the console halts the processor.

STEM
LTED
ONSOLE I/O
ODE)

Included in this section about the system-halted state are descriptions of the console; command syntax, keywords, language subsets; errors and error messages; and halt and halt messages.

nsole

Traditionally, computers have had a panel of lights and switches on the front for processor diagnosis and for operation of standalone programs. On VAX, this function is provided by an ASCII console through which the operator controls the processor. The ASCII console may be envisioned as a virtual console processor attached to the main processor, to a console terminal, and to a console file-storage device. Note that the console processor need not be physically separate from the main processor. It may be implemented in main processor microcode, as in the VAX-11/750 computer system. The console processor interprets commands typed on the console terminal and controls the operation of the main processor.

Through the console terminal, an operator can boot the operating system, a field service engineer can maintain the system, and a system user can communicate with running programs. Sophisticated users may also use the console for developing software.

The processor can halt as the result of an operator command, a serious system error, a HALT instruction, or a powerfail recovery. (See the section "Major System State Transitions" earlier in this chapter for a complete description.) When the processor is halted, the operator controls the system through the console command language. The console is in console I/O mode. The console prompts the operator for input with the string of right angle brackets (>>>).

It may be possible for the operator to put the system in an inconsistent state through the use of the console commands. For example, it may be possible to use the console to set bits in MBZ fields or to set conflicting control bits. The operation of the processor in such a state is UNDEFINED.

Special Characters

In console I/O mode, several characters have special meanings. Some of these characters are produced by pressing a single key, while others, like the control characters, are produced by pressing the character while simultaneously pressing the control key (CTRL).

- Carriage return—Typing a carriage return ends a command line. No action is taken on a command until after it is terminated by a carriage return. A null line terminated by a carriage return is treated as a valid, null command. No action is taken, and the console again prompts for input. Carriage return is echoed as carriage return line feed.

- Rubout—When the operator types rubout, the console deletes the character that the operator previously typed. The console echoes with a backslash (/), followed by the character being deleted. If the operator types additional rubouts, the additional characters deleted are echoed. When the operator types a non-rubout character, the console echoes another backslash, followed by the character typed.

The result is to echo the characters deleted, surrounding them with backslashes. For example:

The operator types: EXAMI;E⟨rubout⟩⟨rubout⟩NE⟨CR⟩

The console echoes: EXAMI;E\E;\NE⟨CR⟩

The console sees the command line: EXAMINE⟨CR⟩

The console does not delete characters past the beginning of a command line. If the operator types more rubouts than there are characters on the line, the extra rubouts are ignored. If a rubout is typed on a blank line, it is ignored.

- CTRL/U—The console echoes ^U and deletes the entire line. If CTRL/U is typed on an empty line, it is echoed; otherwise, it is ignored. The console prompts for another command.

- CTRL/S—Typing CTRL/S stops console transmissions to the console terminal until CTRL/Q is typed. Additional input between CTRL/S and CTRL/Q is buffered as input but not echoed until CTRL/Q is typed. CTRL/S typed again before the CTRL/Q is ignored. CTRL/S and CTRL/Q are not echoed.

- CTRL/Q—Typing CTRL/Q resumes console transmissions stopped by CTRL/S. Additional typing of CTRL/Q is ignored. CTRL/S and CTRL/Q are not echoed.

- CTRL/O— Typing CTRL/O causes the console to throw away transmissions to the console terminal until the next CTRL/O is entered. CTRL/O is echoed as ^O⟨CR⟩ when it disables output; it is not echoed when it reenables output. Output is reenabled if the console prints an error message or if it promptsfor a command from the terminal. Reading a command from a command file and displaying a REPEAT command do not reenable output. When output is reenabled for reading a command, the console prompt is displayed. Output is also enabled by entering program I/O mode by CTRL/P and by CTRL/C.

- CTRL/C—Typing CTRL/C causes the console to echo ^C and to abort processing of a command. CTRL/C has no effect as part of a binary load data stream. CTRL/C reenables output stopped by CTRL/O. When CTRL/C is typed as part of a command line, the console deletes the line as it does with CTRL/U.

- CTRL/P—If the console is in console I/O mode, CTRL/P is equivalent to CTRL/C and is echoed as ^P. If the console is in program I/O mode and is locked, CTRL/P is not echoed but is passed to the operating system like any other character. If the console is in program I/O mode and is not locked, CTRL/P is not echoed but causes the processor to enter console I/O mode. It is UNPREDICT-ABLE whether CTRL/P also causes the processor to halt. HALT must subsequently be typed to halt the processor.

If an unrecognized control character is typed (a control character here means a character with an ASCII code less than 32 decimal), it is echoed as caret followed by the character with ASCII code 64 greater. For example, BEL (ASCII code 7) is echoed as Ĝ, since capital G is ASCII code 7+64=71. When a control character is deleted with rubout, it is echoed the same way. After echoing the control character, the console processes it as a normal character. Unless the control character is part of a comment, the command will be invalid and the console will respond with an error message.

The response of the console to characters with codes greater than 127 (decimal) is UNPREDICTABLE.

Command Syntax

The console accepts commands of lengths up to 80 characters. Longer commands are responded to with an error message.

Commands may be abbreviated. Abbreviations are formed by dropping characters from the end of a keyword. All commands but SET may be unambiguously abbreviated to one character. SET cannot be abbreviated to less than two characters, since it then conflicts with START. The console verifies all characters typed in a command, even when they are not needed to uniquely identify the command.

Multiple adjacent spaces and tabs are treated as a single space by the console. Leading and trailing spaces and tabs are ignored.

Command qualifiers can appear after the command keyword, or after any symbol or number in the command.

All numbers (addresses, data, counts) are in hexadecimal. (Note, though, that symbolic register names include decimal digits.) Hex digit are 0 through 9, and A through F. The console does not distinguish between upper- and lowercase either in numbers or in commands. Both are accepted.

Command Keywords

Following is a list of processor control, data transfer, and console control command keywords. These commands are described in the next section of this chapter.

Processor Control Commands

INITIALIZE

START⟨address⟩

CONTINUE

HALT

BOOT ⟨device⟩

NEXT ⟨count⟩

MICROSTEP ⟨count⟩

UNJAM

Data Transfer Commands

EXAMINE ⟨address⟩

DEPOSIT ⟨address⟩ ⟨data⟩

LOAD ⟨file⟩

X ⟨address⟩ ⟨count⟩

Console Control Commands

FIND

REPEAT ⟨command⟩

SET ⟨parameter⟩ ⟨value⟩

TEST

@ ⟨file⟩

! ⟨comment⟩

---

ommands

BOOT

The device specification is of the format "ddan," where "dd" is a two-letter device mnemonic, "a" is an optional alphabetic adapter identifier, and "n" is a one-digit unit number

The console initializes the processor and starts VMB running. (See the section "System Bootstrapping" earlier in this chapter.) VMB boots the operating system from the specified device. The default device is implementation dependent.

Format:

```
BOOT [⟨qualifier list⟩] [⟨device⟩]
```

Qualifier:

/   After initializing the processor and before starting
R5:⟨data⟩   VMB, R5 is loaded with the specified data. This
                     allows a command file containing a BOOT command
                     or a console user to pass a parameter to VMB.

CONTINUE

The processor begins instruction execution at the address currently contained in the program counter. Processor initialization is not performed. The console enters program I/O mode.

DEPOSIT

The command deposits the data into the address specified. If no
address space or data size qualifiers are specified, the defaults are
the last address space and data size used in a DEPOSIT or EXAMIN
command. After processor initialization, the default address space is
physical memory, the default data size is long, and the default
address is zero.

If the specified data is too large to fit in the data size to be deposited
the console ignores the command and issues an error response. If
the specified data is smaller that the data size to be deposited, it
is extended on the left with zeros.

Format:

DEPOSIT [⟨qualifier list⟩] ⟨address⟩ ⟨data⟩

Qualifiers:

/B	The data size is byte.
/W	The data size is word.
/L	The data size is longword.
/V	The address space is virtual memory. All access and protection checking occur. If the access would not be allowed to a program running with the current PSL, the console issues an error message This includes refusing odd address references if PSL⟨CM⟩ is set. Virtual space DEPOSITs cause th PTE⟨M⟩ bit to be set. If memory mapping is not enabled, virtual addresses are equal to physical addresses.
/P	The address space is physical memory.
/I	The address space is internal processor registers. These are the registers addressed by the MTPR and MFPR instructions.
/G	The address space is the general register set, R0 through PC.
/M	(Optional.) The address space is machine-dependent.
/C	The address space is microcode memory.
/U	(Optional.) The address space is console micro-processor memory.
/N:⟨count⟩	The address is the first of a range. The console deposits to the first address, then to the specified number of succeeding addresses. Even if the address is the symbolic address " − ", the succeed

ing addresses are at larger addresses. The symbolic address specifies only the starting address, not the direction of succession. For repeated references to preceding addresses, use "REPEAT DEPOSIT − ⟨data⟩."

For example:

`D/P/B/N:1FF 0 0`	Clears the first 512 bytes of physical memory.
`D/V/L/N:3 1234 5`	Deposits "5" into four longwords in virtual memory.
`D/N:8 R0 FFFFFFFF`	Loads general registers R0 through R8.
D/N:200 − 0	Clears the previous address, then the next 512.

If conflicting address space or data sizes are specified, the console ignores the command and issues an error response.

The address may also be one of the following symbolic addresses:

PSL   The processor status longword. No address space qualifier is legal. When PSL is examined, the address space is identified as M (machine dependent).

PC   program counter (general register 15). The address space is set to /G.

SP   The stack pointer (general register 14). The address space is /G.

Rn   General register n. The register number is in decimal. The address space is /G. For example:

D R5 1234 is equivalent to D/G 5 1234

D R10 6FF00 is equivalent to D/G A 6FF00

Plus sign (+)—The location immediately following the last location referenced in an examine or deposit. For references to physical or virtual memory spaces, the location referenced is the last address, plus the size of the last reference (1 for byte, 2 for word, 4 for long). For other address spaces, the address is the last addressed referenced, plus one.

Minus sign (−)—the location immediately preceding the last location referenced in an EXAMINE or DEPOSIT. For references to physical or virtual memory spaces, the location referenced is the last address minus the size of this reference (1 for byte, 2 for word, 4 for long). For other address spaces, the address is the last addressed referenced minus one.

Asterisk (*)—the location last referenced in an examine or deposit.

At sign (@)—the location addressed by the last location referenced ii an examine or deposit.

EXAMINE

This command examines the contents of the specified address. If no address is specified, The plus sign (+) is assumed. The same qualifiers may be used on EXAMINE as may be used on DEPOSIT. The address may also be one of the symbolic addresses described under DEPOSIT.

Format:

EXAMINE [⟨qualifier list⟩] [⟨address⟩]

Response:

⟨tab⟩⟨address space identifier⟩ ⟨address⟩ ⟨data⟩

The address space identifier can be:

P	Physical memory. Note that when virtual memory is examined, the address space and address in the response are the translated physical address.
G	General register.
I	Internal processor register.
M	Machine-dependent address space. When the PSL is examined, the address space identified is machir dependent.
C	Microcode memory.
U	(Optional.) Console microprocessor memory.

FIND

The console searches main memory starting at address zero for a page-aligned 64-kilobyte block of good memory, or a restart paramet block (RPB). If the block is found, its address plus 512 is left in SP. I the block is not found, an error message is issued, and the contents of SP are UNPREDICTABLE. If no qualifier is specified, /RPB is assumed.

Format:

FIND [⟨qualifier list⟩]

Qualifiers:

MEMORY	Search memory for a page-aligned block of good memory, 64 kilobytes in length. Since the search ma include a read and write test of memory, the search leaves the contents of memory UNPREDICTABLE.

/RPB   Search memory for a restart parameter block. See the section "System Restart" earlier in this chapter for the search algorithm. The search leaves the contents of memory unchanged.

HALT

The processor stops execution of macroinstructions after completing the current macroinstruction. Neither processor initialization nor I/O initialization occurs, so I/O operations already in progress are unaffected. If the processor is already halted, the HALT command has no affect.

On the VAX-11/750 and VAX-11/730 systems, the processor is halted whenever the console is in console I/O mode; the HALT command does not affect the processor. On the VAX-11/780 system, it is possible for the console to be in console I/O mode when the processor is running. The HALT command causes the VAX-11/780 console to halt the VAX-11/780 processor.

Response:

PC = ⟨PC⟩

If the processor is already halted, the response is preceded by a halt message.

Message:
Already halted

INITIALIZE

A processor initialization is performed. See the section "System Powerfail and Recovery" for initial register contents.

LOAD

The console loads data from the specified file into memory. If no qualifiers are specified, data is loaded into physical memory starting at address 0. If an unrecoverable device or memory error occurs during the load, the command is aborted and the console issues an error message.

Format:

LOAD [⟨qualifier list⟩] ⟨file⟩

Qualifiers:

/S:⟨address⟩   The data is loaded starting at the specified address.

/C   The data is to be loaded into microcode memory.

/U   (Optional.) The data is to be loaded into console
                      microprocessor memory.

MICROSTEP

The console causes the processor to execute the specified number of
microinstructions. If no count is specified, 1 is assumed. After the
last microinstruction is executed, the console enters space-bar-step
mode.

In space-bar-step mode, the console executes one microinstreuction
each time the operator presses the space bar. If the operator presses
any other key, the console exits space-bar-step mode, then
processes the character typed. Typing carriage return is the suggested
means of exiting from space-bar-step mode.

The operator can use the NEXT command to cause the console to
finish the macroinstruction executing.

Format:

MICROSTEP [⟨count⟩]

Response:

uPC = ⟨uPC⟩

NEXT

The console causes the processor to execute the specified number of
macroinstructions. If no count is specified, 1 is assumed. After the
last macroinstruction is executed, the console enters space-bar-step
mode.

In space-bar-step mode, the console executes one macroinstruction
each time the operator presses the space bar. If the operator presses
any other key, the console exits space-bar-step mode, then
processes the character typed. Typing carriage return is the suggested
means of exiting from space-bar-step mode.

The NEXT command can be used to finish a macroinstruction partially
executed by MICROSTEP. This partial execution is counted by
NEXT as though it were the execution of a full instruction.

Format:

NEXT [⟨count⟩]

Response:

PC = ⟨PC⟩

REPEAT

The console repeatedly displays and executes the specified command. The repeating is stopped when the operator types CTRL/C. Any valid console command may be specified for this command with the exceptions of the REPEAT command and the @ command. If the command is REPEAT or @, the results are UNPREDICTABLE.

Format:

REPEAT ⟨command⟩

Response:
⟨dependent upon command specified⟩

SET

Sets the console parameter to the indicated value. The console parameters and their meanings are all implementation-dependent.

Format:

SET ⟨parameter⟩ ⟨data⟩

START

The console starts instruction execution at the specified address. The default address is implementation-dependent. If no qualifier is present, macroinstruction execution is started. If memory mapping is enabled, macroinstructions are executed from virtual memory. The START command is equivalent to a DEPOSIT to PC followed by a CONTINUE. No INITIALIZE is performed.

Format:

START [⟨qualifier list⟩] [⟨address⟩]

Qualifiers:

/C	Microinstruction (rather than macro) execution is started.
/U	(Optional.) Console microprocessor instruction execution is started.

TEST

The console executes a self-test. All qualifiers are optional.

Format:

TEST [⟨qualifier list⟩]

UNJAM

A system bus initialization is performed. The effects of a system bus initialization are implementation-dependent.

Binary Load and Unload Command

The X command is for use by automatic systems communicating with the console. It is not intended for use by operators. The console load or unloads (that is, writes to memory or reads from memory) the specified number of data bytes, starting at the specified address. If no qualifiers specify otherwise, data is transferred to or from physical memory.

If bit ⟨31⟩ of the count is clear, data is to be received by the console and deposited into memory. If bit ⟨31⟩ of the count is set, data is to be read from memory and sent by the console. The remaining bits in the count are a positive number indicating the number of bytes to load or unload.

The console accepts the command upon receiving the carriage return. The next byte the console receives is the command checksum, which is not echoed. The command checksum is verified by adding all command characters, including the checksum (but not including the terminating carriage return or rubouts or characters deleted by rubout), into an 8-bit register initially set to zero. If no errors occur, the result is zero. If the command checksum is correct, the console responds with the input prompt and either sends data to the requester or prepares to receive data. If the command checksum is in error, the console responds with an error message. The intent is to prevent inadvertent operator entry into a mode where the console is accepting characters from the keyboard as data with no escape sequence possible.

If the command is a load (bit ⟨31⟩ of the count is clear), the console responds with the input prompt, then accepts the specified number of bytes of data for depositing to memory and an additional byte of received data checksum. The data is verified by adding all data characters and the checksum character into an 8-bit register initially set to zero. If the final contents of the register is non-zero, the data or checksum are in error, and the console responds with an error message.

If the command is a binary unload (bit ⟨31⟩ of the count is set), the console responds with the input prompt followed by the specified number of bytes of binary data. As each byte is sent, it is added to a checksum register initially set to zero. At the end of the transmission the two's complement of the low byte of the register is sent.

If the data checksum is incorrect on a load, or if memory errors or line errors occur during the transmission of data, the entire transmission is completed and then the console issues an error message. If an error occurs during loading, the contents of the memory being loaded are UNPREDICTABLE.

If the console implements SET TERMINAL ECHO and SET TERMINAL NOECHO commands, the state of the echo flag is unaffected by the X command. Regardless of the flag, echo is suppressed while data string and checksums are being received.

It is possible to control the console through the use of the console control characters (CTRL/C, CTRL/S, CTRL/O, etc.) during a binary unload. It is not possible during a binary load because all received characters are valid binary data.

Data being loaded with a binary load command must be received by the console at a rate of at least one byte per second. If the console does not receive a data byte for more than one second, the console aborts the transmission by issuing an error message and prompting for input.

The entire command, including the checksum, may be sent to the console as a single burst of characters at the console's specified character rate. To make this command useful in automated systems, the console is able to receive at least 4K bytes of data in a single X command.

Format:

X [⟨qualifier list⟩] ⟨address⟩ ⟨count⟩ ⟨CR⟩ ⟨checksum⟩

Qualifiers:

/P	Data is to be read from or written to physical memory.
/C	Data is to be read from or written to microcode memory.
/U	(Optional.) Data is to be read from or written to console microprocessor memory.

The Indirect Command

The console reads and executes commands from the specified file. The commands are displayed on the console terminal as they are read. When a BOOT, START, or CONTINUE command is executed, putting the console into program I/O mode, command file processing is suspended. If a "software done" message is received by the console (see the section "System Running" later in this chapter) and the processor halts, command file processing is continued. If the processor halts before a "software done" message is received by the console, the remainder of the command file is ignored.

Command files can be chained by using another @ command as the last command in a file. If an @ command is encountered in the middle of a command file, the console executes it but may ignore the remainder of the original command file. It is an implementation option whether or not the console resumes execution of the original command file on completion of the secondary.

Format:

@ ⟨file⟩

The comment

The comment is ignored.

Format:

! ⟨comment⟩

Command Language Subsets

To reduce cost, some implementations may not implement the full console command set. A subset implementation is defined.

The commands supported by a subset console are as follows:
- BOOT ⟨device⟩
- CONTINUE
- DEPOSIT ⟨address⟩ ⟨data⟩
- EXAMINE [⟨address⟩]
- INITIALIZE
- HALT
- START ⟨address⟩
- TEST
- X ⟨address⟩ ⟨count⟩
- ! ⟨comment⟩

EXAMINE and DEPOSIT support the qualifiers /B /W /L /P /V /I /G and the symbolic address PSL.

The control characters supported are carriage return, CTRL/P, CTRL/S CTRL/Q, CTRL/U, and rubout.

The subset console may perform range checking on addresses and data. If it does not, it truncates values that are too large and uses the lower digits.

The subset console may accept only abbreviated commands. It may also limit the command length to less than 80 characters. It may accept only uppercase commands. Automatic systems communicating with a console must limit themselves to the commands in the subset, must abbreviate all commands, and must use only uppercase if they are to communicate with any console implementation.

Some features are optional, such as the diagnosis mode and the /M and /U qualifiers. These may be implemented by any console, even by a subset.

The console can issue error messages in response to commands. The case (uppercase or lowercase) is implementation dependent.

The console responds to all commands within 1 second. If the processor does not respond to a console request, the console issues an error message within 1 second.

The following three messages indicate failure of the requested operation. Some implementations may abbreviate some or all of these messages to "Can't."

`Can't power up`	The console microprocessor cannot complete its own power-up initialization. The state of the console and that of the processor is UNDEFINED.
`File not found`	The file specified in a BOOT, LOAD, or @ command cannot be found.
`Reference not allowed`	The requested reference would violate virtual memory protection, or the address is not mapped, or the reference is invalid in the specified address space, or the value is invalid in the specified destination.

The messages below are responses to ill-formed commands. Some implementations may abbreviate some or all of these messages to "Illegal command."

`Illegal command`	The command string cannot be parsed.
`Invalid digit`	A number has an invalid digit.

`Line too long`	The command was too large for the console to buffer. The message is issued only after receipt of the terminating carriage return.
`Illegal address`	The address specified falls outside the limits of the address space.
`Value too big`	The value specified does not fit in the destination.
`Conflicting switches`	For example, two different data sizes are specified with an EXAMINE command.
`Unknown switch`	The switch is unrecognized.
`Unknown symbol`	The symbolic address in an EXAMINE or DEPOSIT is unrecognized.

The following message is produced when a binary transfer command is improperly specified.

Incorrect checksum	The command or data checksum of an X command is incorrect. If the data checksum is incorrect, this message is issued and is not abbreviated to "Illegal command."

The following message is produced when a HALT command is given to the console and the processor is already halted.

Already halted	The operator entered a HALT command and the processor was already halted.

Some console commands may result in errors. For example, if a memory error occurs as the result of a console command, the console will respond with an error message. Such errors do not affect the halted program. Specifically, the processor stays halted, and if it is started later, no exception or interrupt occurs as the result of the console error.

Halts and Halt Messages

Whenever the processor halts, the console prints the response "PC = "⟨PC⟩. Except when the halt was requested by a console HALT command or by a NEXT command, the response is preceded by a halt message. For example:

```
?06  HALT executed
     PC = 800050D3
```

The number preceding the halt message is the halt code, and is passed to the operating system on a restart. Halt code 03 does not have a corresponding message. It is passed by the console during powerfail restart.

The halt messages are:

?00 CPU halted	The operator entered a HALT command while the processor was running, so the console halted the processor.
?01 Microverify complete	The console quick-verify completed successfully.
?02 CPU halted	The operator typed CTRL/P while the console was in program I/O mode. The console was not locked, and the console halted the processor.
03	Halt code 03 does not appear in a halt message but is passed by the console on powerfail restart.
?04 I-stack not valid	In attempting to push state onto the interrupt stack during an interrupt or exception, the processor discovered that the interrupt stack was mapped NO ACCESS or NOT VALID.
?05 CPU double error	The processor attempted to report a machine-check to the operating system, and a second machine-check occurred.
?06 HALT executed	The processor executed a HALT instruction in kernel mode.
?07 Invalid SCB vector	The vector had bits $\langle 1{:}0 \rangle$ set.
?08 No user WCS	An SCB vector had bits $\langle 1{:}0 \rangle$ equal to 2, and no user writable control store was installed.
?09 Error pending on halt	The processor was halted (by CTRL/P) before it could perform an error halt.
?0A CHM from I-stack	A change mode instruction was executed when PSL$\langle$IS$\rangle$ was set.
?0B CHM to interrupt stack	The exception vector for a change mode had bit $\langle 0 \rangle$ set.
?0C SCB read error	A hard memory error occurred while the processor was trying to read an exception or interrupt vector.

When the processor is running, the console is in program I/O mode. In this mode, all terminal interaction is handled by the operating system. The console terminal becomes like any other operating system terminal and passes through all characters (except for CTRL/P). If the console is locked, even CTRL/P is passed through. the console is not locked, CTRL/P causes the processor to halt and the consoleto enter console I/O mode.

**Console
Terminal
Registers**

The console is accessed by the operating system through four internal processor registers. Two are associated with passing inform tion from the console to the processor (receive registers) and two with passing information from the processor to the console (transmit registers). In each direction, there is a control and status register an a data buffer register. The registers are shown in Figure 10.2. The fields of the registers are described in Table 10.2.

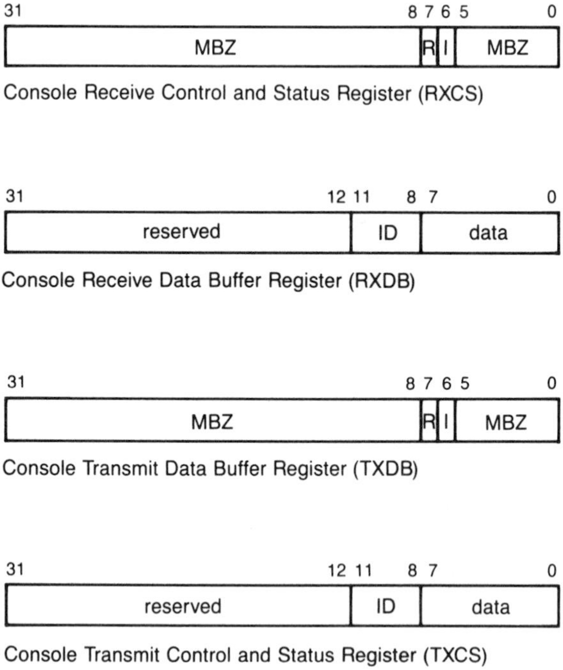

```
31                                       8 7 6 5      0
+----------------------------------------+-+-+------+
|                MBZ                     |R|I| MBZ  |
+----------------------------------------+-+-+------+
```
Console Receive Control and Status Register (RXCS)

```
31                          12 11   8 7            0
+---------------------------+------+--------------+
|         reserved          |  ID  |    data      |
+---------------------------+------+--------------+
```
Console Receive Data Buffer Register (RXDB)

```
31                                       8 7 6 5      0
+----------------------------------------+-+-+------+
|                MBZ                     |R|I| MBZ  |
+----------------------------------------+-+-+------+
```
Console Transmit Data Buffer Register (TXDB)

```
31                          12 11   8 7            0
+---------------------------+------+--------------+
|         reserved          |  ID  |    data      |
+---------------------------+------+--------------+
```
Console Transmit Control and Status Register (TXCS)

Figure 10.2
Four Console Terminal Registers

Table 10.2

Fields of the Console Terminal Registers

Name	Extent	Description
RXCS Register Fields		
ready	⟨7⟩	Cleared by processor initialization and by reading RXDB. When Ready is clear, RXDB is UNPREDICTABLE. When Ready is set, RXDB contains valid data to be read.
interrupt enable	⟨6⟩	Read/write. Cleared by processor initialization and by being written zero. If interrupt enable is set by software while RXDB Ready is already set, or if ready is set by the console while Interrupt enable is already set, then an interrupt is requested at IPL 14 (hex). That is, an interrupt is requested whenever the function [interrupt enable AND ready] changes from 0 to 1.
RXDB Register Fields		
error	⟨15⟩	An error occurred while receiving data, such as data overrun or loss of carrier. Cleared by processor initialization and by reading from RXDB.
identification	⟨11:8⟩	If zero, then data is from the console terminal. If nonzero, then the rest of the register is implementation dependent. Cleared by processor initialization and by reading from RXDB.
data	⟨7:0⟩	Data from the console terminal (if ID is zero). UNPREDICTABLE unless RXCS ready is set.
TXCS Register Fields		
ready	⟨7⟩	Read only. Set by processor initialization. Ready is clear when the console terminal is busy writing a character written to TXDB. Ready is set when the console terminal is ready to receive another character.
interrupt enable	⟨6⟩	Read/write. Cleared by processor initialization and by being written clear. If interrupt-enable is set when ready becomes set, or if interrupt-enable is set by software when ready is already set, an interrupt is requested at IPL 14 (hex). That is, an interrupt is requested whenever the function [interrupt enable AND ready] changes from 0 to 1.
TXDB Register Fields		
identification	⟨11:8⟩	If ID is written zero when TXDB is written, the data goes to the console terminal. If ID is written with 0F (hex), the data is a message to be sent to the console. If ID is neither zero nor 0f (hex), the meaning is implementation-dependent.

Table 10.2

Fields of the Console Terminal Registers (*continued*)

Name	Extent	Description
data	⟨7:0⟩	If ID is zero, the data is a character sent to the console terminal to type. If ID is 0f (hex), the data is a message to be sent to the console, with the following meaning: 1. Software done—A program started by a console indirect command file is signaling successful completion. When the processor halts, the console should resume processing the indirect command file. 2. Boot processor—The console should initiate a system bootstrap. 3. Clear "restart in progress" flag—A system restart has successfully completed. If a system restart would occur automatically, the attempt should be allowed. 4. Clear "bootstrap in progress" flag—A system bootstrap has successfully completed. If a system bootstrap would occur automatically, the attempt should be allowed.

Architectural Subsetting 11

This chapter describes those parts of the VAX architecture that may be included as standard features of a processor, provided as options to the processor, or omitted completely from the processor.

A processor implementing a subset of the VAX instructions, data types, or registers, as described in this chapter, is known as a subset VAX. Of the many subsets possible, the following are important enough to name:

- Full VAX—includes all VAX data types, instructions, and registers
- Kernel subset—the minimum allowed subset
- MicroVAX I subset—as implemented by the MicroVAX I
- MicroVAX chip subset—as implemented by the MicroVAX chip

For a description of the MicroVAX I and MicroVAX chip subsets, see Appendix B.

The subsetting of the architecture reflects the need to be able to trade-off manufacturing cost, software development cost, and performance of VAX processors. The following conflicting hardware and software goals influenced the design of the subsetting rules:

- Hardware goal—Permit an implementor of a low-end processor to omit instructions and other features in order to reduce manufacturing cost without losing the ability to run all of the system software. The decision to implement a subset will have some impact on the performance of various classes of software products.

- Software goal—Provide as small a number of classes of processor instruction sets as possible to reduce software development costs. In particular, a single version of each compiler or other layered software product should run on all processors in the VAX family. Also the combination of hardware and instruction emulation routines in operating systems must (as required) give the appearance of a complete architecture on all processors.

The features of the architecture that may be omitted can be divided into several groups, with different rules for subsetting.

The first group consists of the F__floating, D__floating, G__floating, and H__floating data types, and the associated instructions. Each of these data types may only be subset as an entity. This means that if one of these data types is included, all the instructions that operate on that data type must be included.

Twenty-two F__floating instructions: MOVF, MNEGF, CVTF{B,W,L}, CVT{B,W,L}F, CMPF, TSTF, ADDF2, ADDF3, SUBF2, SUBF3, MULF2, MULF3, DIVF2, DIVF3, CVTRFL, EMODF, POLYF, ACBF

Twenty-four D__floating instructions: MOVD, MNEGD, CVTD{B,W,L,F} CVT{B,W,L,F}D, CMPD, TSTD, ADDD2, ADDD3, SUBD2, SUBD3, MULD2, MULD3, DIVD2, DIVD3, CVTRDL, EMODD, POLYD, ACBD

Twenty-four G__floating instructions: MOVG, MNEGG, CVTG{B,W,L,F} CVT{B,W,L,F}G, CMPG, TSTG, ADDG2, ADDG3, SUBG2, SUBG3, MULG2, MULG3, DIVG2, DIVG3, CVTRGL, EMODG, POLYG, ACBG

Thirty-two H__floating instructions: MOVH, MNEGH, CVTH{B,W,L,F,D,G}, CVT{B,W,L,F,D,G}H, CMPH, TSTH, ADDH2, ADDH3, SUBH2, SUBH3, MULH2, MULH3, DIVH2, DIVH3, CVTRHL EMODH, POLYH, ACBH, MOVO, CLRH (CLRO), MOVAH (MOVAO), PUSHAH (PUSHAO)

If an instruction in this group is omitted by a processor, execution of the instruction results in a reserved-instruction fault.

The second group, listed below, consists of the string instructions and their associated data types, including the decimal string, EDITPC, CRC, and character-string instructions, but not including MOVC3 or MOVC5. (That is, MOVC3 and MOVC5 are part of the kernel instruction set, and may not be omitted.) Instructions in this second class may be subset individually.

Nine character string instructions: MOVTC, MOVTUC, CMPC3, CMPC5, SCANC, SPANC, LOCC, SKPC, MATCHC

Sixteen decimal string instructions: MOVP, CMPP3, CMPP4, ADDP4, ADDP6, SUBP4, SUBP6, CVTLP, CVTPL, CVTPT, CVTTP, CVTPS, CVTSP, ASHP, MULP, DIVP

One other decimal string instruction: EDITPC

One other string instruction: CRC

If an instruction in this group is omitted by a processor, execution of the instruction results in a subset-emulation exception.

The third group consists of the compatibility mode instruction set. If compatibility mode is omitted by a processor, the execution of an REI instruction attempting to enter compatibility mode results in a reserved-operand fault.

The fourth group consists of internal processor registers. The registers described below may be omitted from subset processors. If any of the registers named on one of the following lines is included, all the registers on that line must be included.

- Interval timer registers: NICR, ICR, ICCS except for ⟨IE⟩. (That is, ICCS⟨IE⟩ is part of the kernel subset and may not be omitted.)
- Time-of-Year clock register: TODR
- Console registers: RXCS, RXDB, TXCS, TXDB
- Performance Monitor Enable register: PME

THE KERNEL INSTRUCTION SET

The kernel instruction set is defined by exception; it is those instructions that may not be omitted. For convenience, the kernel set is listed here. There are 304 native mode instructions in the full VAX instruction set. Of these, 129 may be omitted, leaving 175 instructions in the kernel instruction set. They are:

Eighty-nine integer arithmetic and logical instructions: ADAWI, ADD{B,W,L}{2,3}, ADWC, ASH{L,Q}, BIC{B,W,L}{2,3}, BIS{B,W,L}{2,3}, BIT{B,W,L}, CLR{B,W,L,Q}, CMP{B,W,L}, CVTB{W,L}, CVTW{B,L}, CVTL{B,W}, DEC{B,W,L}, DIV{B,W,L}{2,3}, EDIV, EMUL, INC{B,W,L}, MCOM{B,W,L}, MNEG{B,W,L}, MOV{B,W,L,Q}, MOVZ{BW,BL,WL}, MUL{B,W,L}{2,3}, PUSHL, ROTL, SBWC, SUB{B,W,L}{2,3}, TST{B,W,L}, XOR{B,W,L}{2,3}
Eight address instructions: MOVA{B,W,L,Q}, PUSHA{B,W,L,Q}.

Seven variable-length bit field instructions: CMPV, CMPZV, EXTV, EXTZV, FF{S,C}, INSV.

Thirty-nine branch and control instructions: ACB{B,W,L}, AOBLEQ, AOBLSS, BLSS, BLEQ, BEQL, BNEQ, BGEQ, BGTR, BLSSU, BLEQU, BGEQU, BGTRU, BVS, BVC, BB{S,C}, BB{S,C}{S,C}, BB{SS,CC}I, BLB{S,C}, BR{B,W}, BSB{B,W}, CASE{B,W,L}, JMP, JSB, RSB, SOBGEQ, SOBGTR.

Three procedure call instructions: CALLG, CALLS, RET.

Six queue instructions: INSQHI, INSQTI, INSQUE, REMQHI, REMQTI, REMQUE.

Two character string instructions: MOVC3, MOVC5.

Twelve instructions for use by operating systems: PROBE{R,W}, CHM{K,E,S,U}, HALT, REI, LDPCTX, SVPCTX, MTPR, MFPR.

Nine miscellaneous instructions: BI{C,S}PSW, BPT, INDEX, MOVPSL, NOP, POPR, PUSHR, XFC.

Byte, word, longword, and quadword operand sizes have been included in the kernel instruction set. The octaword operand size has not been included.

INSTRUCTION EMULATION

Subset VAX processors and their operating systems cooperate to support emulation of those instructions that are omitted from the processor's instruction set. Programs running under the operating system can make use of these instructions as though they were supported directly by the processor. The process of emulating an omitted instruction depends on the instruction type. Emulation of string instructions is assisted by the processor through the instruction-emulation exception. Emulation of compatibility mode instructions and floating-point instructions is done entirely by software.

The process of emulating an omitted string instruction consists of the following steps:

1. The processor reads the instruction opcode and finds that this is an omitted instruction. The processor saves the opcode.

2. The processor evaluates the operand specifiers in order of instruction stream occurrence. The processor saves the operand address for each operand of write-access type or address type, and it reads and saves the operand itself for operands of read-access type.

3. The processor initiates a subset-emulation trap, pushing an emulation trap frame onto the stack. The opcode and operands (or their addresses) are part of the trap frame. Unlike many exceptions, subset emulation trap does not cause the processor to enter kernel mode. The exception handler runs in the same mode as the trapped instruction, and the trap frame is pushed onto the current stack.

4. The emulation-exception handler in the operating system examines the opcode of the trapped instruction and dispatches to the appropriate emulation routine.

5. The instruction-emulation routine reads and writes the instruction operands, as appropriate to the instruction being emulated. The operands need not be probed, since the emulation handler is running in the same mode as the emulated instruction.

6. The instruction-emulation routine sets the condition codes in the PSL on the stack, pops the emulation trap frame (except for the new PC and PSL) from the stack, and returns with REI.

7. Emulation is now complete, and the instruction following the emulated instruction begins execution.

If, during the emulation of an instruction, an exception such as access violation occurs, the emulation code must gain control, save state in the registers just as the emulated instruction would, set FPD in the saved PSL, and reflect the exception to the user's current exception handler. If the conditions causing the exception are corrected and the exception was a fault, the instruction can be restarted. In this case, PSL⟨FPD⟩ will be set when instruction execution begins. Emulation consists of the following steps:

1. The processor reads the opcode and finds that this is an omitted instruction and that PSL⟨FPD⟩ is set.

2. The processor initiates a suspended-emulation fault, pushing PC and PSL onto the stack.

3. The emulation-exception handler rebuilds the intermediate state of the instruction, using the information saved in the general registers at the time the emulated instruction was faulted.

4. The emulation handler resumes emulation of the instruction, as in steps 5 through 7 in the previous list above.

Emulation software runs in the mode of the emulated instruction and uses the same stack. Emulation software may allocate and use up to five pages of stack space for temporary storage. The contents of this area are UNPREDICTABLE after execution of an emulated instruction. If an emulated instruction addresses part of this area as an operand without first allocating it, or if an emulated instruction uses SP as an operand, the results of the instruction are UNPREDICTABLE. That is, the instructions DIVF3 R1, R2, −50(SP) and DIVF3 R1, R2, SP produce UNPREDICTABLE results. The instruction DIVF3 R1, R2, −(SP) allocates the area on top of the stack before using it and is legal.

Instruction-Emulation Exceptions

When a subset processor executes a string instruction that is omitted from its instruction set, an emulation exception results. An emulation exception occurs through one of two SCB vectors, depending on whether or not PSL⟨FPD⟩ is set at the beginning of the instruction. If PSL⟨FPD⟩ is clear, a subset-emulation trap occurs through the SCB vector at offset C8 (hex), and a subset-emulation trap frame is pushed onto the stack. The PC pushed points to the instruction following the omitted instruction. If PSL⟨FPD⟩ is set, a suspended-emulation fault occurs through the SCB vector at offset CC (hex), and

PC and PSL are pushed onto the stack. The PC pushed points to the faulted instruction.

In either case, if PSL⟨T⟩ is set at the time of the trap, PSL⟨TP⟩ is set in the PSL pushed onto the stack. All other bits in the pushed PSL are unchanged. If PSL⟨FPD⟩ was set, it is set in the saved PSL.

The new PSL has ⟨TP,FPD,IV,DV,FU,T⟩ clear. All other fields are unchanged, including PSL⟨CUR_MOD,PRV_MOD,IS,IPL⟩. That is, the emulation-exception handler runs in the mode of the emulated instruction, on the same stack, and at the same IPL. The exception parameters are pushed onto the current stack. (If the current stack cannot be written, the processor takes a memory management fault rather than an emulation exception.)

If either emulation-exception vector has bits ⟨1:0⟩ set to 1 (indicating that the exception is to be taken on the interrupt stack), the operation of the processor is UNDEFINED.

The emulation-exception stack frame is shown in Figure 11.1 and includes the following:

- Opcode—contains the opcode of the trapped instruction.
- Old PC—contains the address of the trapped instruction.
- Specifiers 1 through 8—contain the addresses of corresponding instruction operands or contain the operands themselves. For each operand of the trapped instruction, if the operand is of read access type (.rx), the parameter contains the operand value; if the operand

opcode	:(SP)
old PC	
specifier #1	
specifier #2	
specifier #3	
specifier #4	
specifier #5	
specifier #6	
specifier #7	
specifier #8	
new PC	
saved PSL	

Figure 11.1
Subset-Emulation Trap Frame

is writeaccess type (.wx) or address type (.ax), the parameter contains the operand address. For read-type operands of byte size, bits $\langle 31:8 \rangle$ of the longword are UNPREDICTABLE. For read-type operands of word size, bits $\langle 31:16 \rangle$ are UNPREDICTABLE. When an operand is in a register, the register is denoted by a reserved system space address corresponding to the one's complement of the register number. The parameter corresponding to an instruction operand that does not exist is UNPREDICTABLE. For example, if the trapped instruction has four operands, the parameters for specifiers 5 through 8 are UNPREDICTABLE.

- New PC—contains the address of the instruction following the trapped instruction.
- Saved PSL—contains the PSL at the time of the trap. If PSL$\langle T \rangle$ was set at the beginning of the instruction, saved PSL$\langle TP \rangle$ is set.

Opcode Assignments

A

Binary	Hex	Mnemonic	Binary	Hex	Mnemonic
00000000	00	HALT	00100000	20	ADDP4
00000001	01	NOP	00100001	21	ADDP6
00000010	02	REI	00100010	22	SUBP4
00000011	03	BPT	00100011	23	SUBP6
00000100	04	RET	00100100	24	CVTPT
00000101	05	RSB	00100101	25	MULP
00000110	06	LDPCTX	00100110	26	CVTTP
00000111	07	SVPCTX	00100111	27	DIVP
00001000	08	CVTPS	00101000	28	MOVC3
00001001	09	CVTSP	00101001	29	CMPC3
00001010	0A	INDEX	00101010	2A	SCANC
00001011	0B	CRC	00101011	2B	SPANC
00001100	0C	PROBER	00101100	2C	MOVC5
00001101	0D	PROBEW	00101101	2D	CMPC5
00001110	0E	INSQUE	00101110	2E	MOVTC
00001111	0F	REMQUE	00101111	2F	MOVTUC
00010000	10	BSBB	00110000	30	BSBW
00010001	11	BRB	00110001	31	BRW
00010010	12	BNEQ, BNEQU	00110010	32	CVTWL
00010011	13	BEQL, BEQLU	00110011	33	CVTWB
00010100	14	BGTR	00110100	34	MOVP
00010101	15	BLEQ	00110101	35	CMPP3
00010110	16	JSB	00110110	36	CVTPL
00010111	17	JMP	00110111	37	CMPP4
00011000	18	BGEQ	00111000	38	EDITPC
00011001	19	BLSS	00111001	39	MATCHC
00011010	1A	BGTRU	00111010	3A	LOCC
00011011	1B	BLEQU	00111011	3B	SKPC
00011100	1C	BVC	00111100	3C	MOVZWL
00011101	1D	BVS	00111101	3D	ACBW
00011110	1E	BGEQU, BCC	00111110	3E	MOVAW
00011111	1F	BLSSU, BCS	00111111	3F	PUSHAW

Binary	Hex	Mnemonic	Binary	Hex	Mnemonic
01000000	40	ADDF2	01110000	70	MOVD
01000001	41	ADDF3	01110001	71	CMPD
01000010	42	SUBF2	01110010	72	MNEGD
01000011	43	SUBF3	01110011	73	TSTD
01000100	44	MULF2	01110100	74	EMODD
01000101	45	MULF3	01110101	75	POLYD
01000110	46	DIVF2	01110110	76	CVTDF
01000111	47	DIVF3	01110111	77	Reserved to DIGITAL
01001000	48	CVTFB	01111000	78	ASHL
01001001	49	CVTFW	01111001	79	ASHQ
01001010	4A	CVTFL	01111010	7A	EMUL
01001011	4B	CVTRFL	01111011	7B	EDIV
01001100	4C	CVTBF	01111100	7C	CLRQ, CLRD, CLRG
01001101	4D	CVTWF	01111101	7D	MOVQ
01001110	4E	CVTLF	01111110	7E	MOVA {Q, D, G}
01001111	4F	ACBF	01111111	7F	PUSHA {Q, D, G}
01010000	50	MOVF	10000000	80	ADDB2
01010001	51	CMPF	10000001	81	ADDB3
01010010	52	MNEGF	10000010	82	SUBB2
01010011	53	TSTF	10000011	83	SUBB3
01010100	54	EMODF	10000100	84	MULB2
01010101	55	POLYF	10000101	85	MULB3
01010110	56	CVTFD	10000110	86	DIVB2
01010111	57	Reserved to DIGITAL	10000111	87	DIVB3
01011000	58	ADAWI	10001000	88	BISB2
01011001	59	Reserved to DIGITAL	10001001	89	BISB3
01011010	5A	Reserved to DIGITAL	10001010	8A	BICB2
01011011	5B	Reserved to DIGITAL	10001011	8B	BICB3
01011100	5C	INSQHI	10001100	8C	XORB2
01011101	5D	INSQTI	10001101	8D	XORB3
01011110	5E	REMQHI	10001110	8E	MNEGB
01011111	5F	REMQTI	10001111	8F	CASEB
01100000	60	ADDD2	10010000	90	MOVB
01100001	61	ADDD3	10010001	91	CMPB
01100010	62	SUBD2	10010010	92	MCOMB
01100011	63	SUBD3	10010011	93	BITB
01100100	64	MULD2	10010100	94	CLRB
01100101	65	MULD3	10010101	95	TSTB
01100110	66	DIVD2	10010110	96	INCB
01100111	67	DIVD3	10010111	97	DECB
01101000	68	CVTDB	10011000	98	CVTBL
01101001	69	CVTDW	10011001	99	CVTBW
01101010	6A	CVTDL	10011010	9A	MOVZBL
01101011	6B	CVTRDL	10011011	9B	MOVZBW
01101100	6C	CVTBD	10011100	9C	ROTL
01101101	6D	CVTWD	10011101	9D	ACBB
01101110	6E	CVTLD	10011110	9E	MOVAB
01101111	6F	ACBD	10011111	9F	PUSHAB

Binary	Hex	Mnemonic		Binary	Hex	Mnemonic
10100000	A0	ADDW2		11010000	D0	MOVL
10100001	A1	ADDW3		11010001	D1	CMPL
10100010	A2	SUBW2		11010010	D2	MCOML
10100011	A3	SUBW3		11010011	D3	BITL
10100100	A4	MULW2		11010100	D4	CLRL, CLRF
10100101	A5	MULW3		11010101	D5	TSTL
10100110	A6	DIVW2		11010110	D6	INCL
10100111	A7	DIVW3		11010111	D7	DECL
10101000	A8	BISW2		11011000	D8	ADWC
10101001	A9	BISW3		11011001	D9	SBWC
10101010	AA	BICW2		11011010	DA	MTPR
10101011	AB	BICW3		11011011	DB	MFPR
10101100	AC	XORW2		11011100	DC	MOVPSL
10101101	AD	XORW3		11011101	DD	PUSHL
10101110	AE	MNEGW		11011110	DE	MOVAL, MOVAF
10101111	AF	CASEW		11011111	DF	PUSHAL, PUSHAF
10110000	B0	MOVW		11100000	E0	BBS
10110001	B1	CMPW		11100001	E1	BBC
10110010	B2	MCOMW		11100010	E2	BBSS
10110011	B3	BITW		11100011	E3	BBCS
10110100	B4	CLRW		11100100	E4	BBSC
10110101	B5	TSTW		11100101	E5	BBCC
10110110	B6	INCW		11100110	E6	BBSSI
10110111	B7	DECW		11100111	E7	BBCCI
10111000	B8	BISPSW		11101000	E8	BLBS
10111001	B9	BICPSW		11101001	E9	BLBC
10111010	BA	POPR		11101010	EA	FFS
10111011	BB	PUSHR		11101011	EB	FFC
10111100	BC	CHMK		11101100	EC	CMPV
10111101	BD	CHME		11101101	ED	CMPZV
10111110	BE	CHMS		11101110	EE	EXTV
10111111	BF	CHMU		11101111	EF	EXTZV
11000000	C0	ADDL2		11110000	F0	INSV
11000001	C1	ADDL3		11110001	F1	ACBL
11000010	C2	SUBL2		11110010	F2	AOBLSS
11000011	C3	SUBL3		11110011	F3	AOBLEQ
11000100	C4	MULL2		11110100	F4	SOBGEQ
11000101	C5	MULL3		11110101	F5	SOBGTR
11000110	C6	DIVL2		11110110	F6	CVTLB
11000111	C7	DIVL3		11110111	F7	CVTLW
11001000	C8	BISL2		11111000	F8	ASHP
11001001	C9	BISL3		11111001	F9	CVTLP
11001010	CA	BICL2		11111010	FA	CALLG
11001011	CB	BICL3		11111011	FB	CALLS
11001100	CC	XORL2		11111100	FC	XFC
11001101	CD	XORL3		11111101	FD	Two-byte opcode
11001110	CE	MNEGL		11111110	FE	Two-byte opcode
11001111	CF	CASEL		11111111	FF	Two-byte opcode

Hex	Mnemonic	Hex	Mnemonic
00FD to 31FD	Reserved to DIGITAL		
32FD	CVTDH	33FD	CVTGF
34FD to 3FFD	Reserved to DIGITAL		
40FD	ADDG2	60FD	ADDH2
41FD	ADDG3	61FD	ADDH3
42FD	SUBG2	62FD	SUBH2
43FD	SUBG3	63FD	SUBH3
44FD	MULG2	64FD	MULH2
45FD	MULG3	65FD	MULH3
46FD	DIVG2	66FD	DIVH2
47FD	DIVG3	67FD	DIVH3
48FD	CVTGB	68FD	CVTHB
49FD	CVTGW	69FD	CVTHW
4AFD	CVTGL	6AFD	CVTHL
4BFD	CVTRGL	6BFD	CVTRHL
4CFD	CVTBG	6CFD	CVTBH
4DFD	CVTWG	6DFD	CVTWH
4EFD	CVTLG	6EFD	CVTLH
4FFD	ACBG	6FFD	ACBH
50FD	MOVG	70FD	MOVH
51FD	CMPG	71FD	CMPH
52FD	MNEGG	72FD	MNEGH
53FD	TSTG	73FD	TSTH
54FD	EMODG	74FD	EMODH
55FD	POLYG	75FD	POLYH
56FD	CVTGH	76FD	CVTHG
57FD	Reserved to DIGITAL	77FD	Reserved to DIGITAL
58FD	Reserved to DIGITAL	78FD	Reserved to DIGITAL
59FD	Reserved to DIGITAL	79FD	Reserved to DIGITAL
5AFD	Reserved to DIGITAL	7AFD	Reserved to DIGITAL
5BFD	Reserved to DIGITAL	7BFD	Reserved to DIGITAL
5CFD	Reserved to DIGITAL	7CFD	CLRH, CLRO
5DFD	Reserved to DIGITAL	7DFD	MOVO
5EFD	Reserved to DIGITAL	7EFD	MOVAH, MOVAO
5FFD	Reserved to DIGITAL	7FFD	PUSHAH, PUSHAO
80FD to 97FD	Reserved to DIGITAL		
98FD	CVTFH	99FD	CVTFG
9AFD to F5FD	Reserved to DIGITAL		
F6FD	CVTHF	F7FD	CVTHD

Hex	Mnemonic	Hex	Mnemonic
F8FD to FFFD	Reserved to DIGITAL	00FE to FFFE	Reserved to DIGITAL
00FF to FCFF	Reserved to DIGITAL		
FDFF	BUGL (used by VMS for BUGCHECK)	FEFF	BUGW
FFFF	Reserved for all time		

Implementation Dependencies

B

The VAX family of processors shares a common architecture, including data types, instructions and addressing modes, and registers. Software written to depend only on these features will run on any VAX processor. Some software, however, typically operating system software, by necessity depends on features that vary from implementation to implementation.

This appendix describes individual VAX processors, in particular those features that are typically of interest to operating systems programmers. Such features include:

- Instruction subset
- Layout of physical memory
- System control block
- Codes for the halt conditions
- Internal processor registers
- Contents of the machine-check stack frame
- Operations that are specified UNDEFINED or UNPREDICTABLE.

Instruction Subsetting

Some instructions, data types, and processor registers described in this book may be omitted from VAX processors. Chapter 11 describes the subsetting rules and the allowed subsets.

The Physical Address Space

VAX virtual addresses are 32 bits in length. When memory mapping is enabled, virtual addresses are translated to physical addresses as described in Chapter 4, Memory Management.

VAX physical addresses are at most 30 bits in length, so as to fit in a PTE. Implementations may recognize fewer address bits, in which case the additional bits are ignored. When memory mapping is disabled, virtual addresses are translated to physical addresses by ignoring virtual address bits ⟨31:30⟩.

The physical address space consists of two parts: memory space and I/O space. Memory space starts at address zero and continues to an implementation-dependent limit. I/O space begins at that limit and continues to the end of the physical address space. Neither memory space nor I/O space are necessarily filled and typically will be sparsely filled.

Both memory space and I/O space are addressed by bytes. Aligned and unaligned references to memory of byte, word, and longword size are supported. Only aligned longword references are necessarily supported to I/O space. References of other sizes may be supported on some implementations.

Typically, I/O space consists of several "adapter spaces" and one or more address spaces. The adapter spaces are sections of the address space set aside for the registers of various bus adapters and memory controllers. Many adapter spaces begin with an "adapter configuration register" which contains an adapter type code. This is for use by the operating system during power-up initialization to help it determine the system hardware configuration.

UNIBUS address spaces are sections of the I/O address space which directly map to a UNIBUS address space. UNIBUS addresses are 18 bits in length, so a UNIBUS address space is 256 kilobytes in length. Within the UNIBUS address space, the low 248 Kbytes is UNIBUS memory space. Typically, UNIBUS references to UNIBUS memory space are translated by a set of UNIBUS map registers to references in the VAX physical address space. This allows UNIBUS devices to directly access VAX physical memory.

The System Control Block

The system control block is a block of physical memory that contains vectors for exceptions and interrupts. Chapter 5 describes its format and interpretation. VAX processors may include exception and interrupt vectors in addition to those described in Chapter 5.

Halt Codes

Chapter 10 describes halting. When a VAX processor halts, the reason for the halt is saved in a halt code. A processor may report halt codes in addition to those described in Chapter 10.

Internal Processor Registers

Chapter 8, Privileged Registers, describes the internal processor register address space and the registers found there on every machine. Processors may include internal processor registers in addition to those described in Chapter 8.

Chapter 5 describes the overall format of the machine-check stack frame. Included in the stack frame is space for implementation-dependent error report information. The circumstances that cause machine-check are different for each processor, and the information reported is different as well.

As used in this book, the terms UNPREDICTABLE and UNDEFINED have particular meanings. Results specified as UNPREDICTABLE may vary from one execution to the next. Software must not depend on any UNPREDICTABLE results. The results of an instruction include:

• Explicit destination operands (those with operand specifiers)

• Implicit destination operands

• Registers modified by operand specifier evaluation, including specifiers for implied operands

• PSL condition codes

• PSL⟨FPD⟩

• PSL⟨TP⟩, if PSL⟨T⟩ was set at the beginning of the instruction

• PTE⟨M⟩ for pages mapping write or modify type operands (PTE⟨M⟩ will be set if the instruction modified the page, or if PTE⟨M⟩ was set before the instruction started.)

PC and unlisted fields of the PSL are specifically excluded from this list. They are UNPREDICTABLE only when they appear as explicit or implicit operands.

UNPREDICTABLE results are constrained by memory mapping and access protection. That is, if correctly operating instructions cannot affect a memory location or privileged register, then an instruction with UNPREDICTABLE results cannot either.

UNPREDICTABLE results include:

• Any instruction whose operands wrap around from PC to R0

• Any native mode VAX instruction that is modified by writing into the instruction stream, until the instruction stream is resynchronized by REI

• Any instruction mapped by a PTE that has been modified in memory, until the translation buffer is updated. See Chapter 5, Memory Management

• Any instruction that uses PC in register mode, register deferred mode, or autodecrement mode

• Any instruction that writes or modifies an immediate mode operand

- Any instruction that uses the same register twice in autoincrement indexed mode, autodecrement indexed mode, or autoincrement deferred indexed mode
- Any instruction that uses the same register as a floating-point number and as an address in autoincrement mode, autodecrement mode, or autoincrement deferred mode
- Any instruction that uses immediate indexed mode
- Any instruction whose operands, general registers, or PSL is modified while PSL⟨FPD⟩ is set
- Any instruction that is started with PSL⟨FPD⟩ set if PSL⟨FPD⟩ was not set as a result of the instruction's previous execution
- The condition codes after a fault or interrupt. The condition codes are preserved only to the extent necessary to ensure correct completion of the instruction when it is resumed.
- ADAWI when the operands overlap
- Five pages above the top of the current stack, after the execution of an omitted instruction that is emulated by software
- Any emulated instruction that references the five pages above the top of the stack without allocating it first
- Any emulated instruction that references SP as an operand
- MOVTC and MOVTUC when the destination operand overlaps the table operand or the escape operand
- CRC when the table operand is not well formed
- Any packed decimal-string instruction that encounters an invalid packed decimal digit in a source operand
- Any decimal-string instruction that encounters a reserved operand
- Any decimal-string instruction whose operands overlap, except as noted in CVTPL and CVTLP
- ASHP when the round operand is greater than 9
- EDITPC when used incorrectly; see the description of EDITPC, Chapter 3
- DIVP when the divisor is 0
- Any compatibility mode byte instruction that writes or modifies PC
- Compatibility mode ASR, SXT, SWAB, ASH, and SOB, when the operand is PC
- Compatibility mode MUL, DIV, and ASHC, when the operand is SP or PC
- Compatibility mode DIV when integer overflow occurs
- The order of multiple exceptions within a single instruction
- Saved condition codes and general registers when PSL⟨FPD⟩ is set
- Memory from −1(SP) through −16(SP) after DIVP; see the description of DIVP in Chapter 3

- The order of access of pages in operands that cross page boundaries
- The contents of many privileged registers after processor initialization
- PTE⟨M⟩ after PROBEW, if it was zero at the start of the instruction, and access is allowed
- PTE⟨M⟩ in PTEs that map destination operands in instructions that fault, when the operands could have been written but were not written, and PTE⟨M⟩ was clear at the beginning of the instruction
- Clearing PSL⟨TP⟩ without clearing PSL⟨T⟩
- PSL⟨T⟩ viewed by software.
- The order of trace fault and page fault on an instruction opcode
- VAX native mode R7 after executing in compatibility mode
- Whether the top half of R0 through R6 are zeroed or left unchanged by executing in compatibility mode
- Whether an instruction reads any operand it does not need to complete correctly. Completing correctly includes having the specified values in all explicit and implicit operands, including PSL and registers modified by operand specifier evaluation; completing correctly does not include page faults or reserved operand exceptions resulting from reading operands not needed to otherwise complete the instruction.

UNDEFINED operations result from privileged software performing proscribed actions. The effects may be widespread and are not necessarily constrained by memory mapping or access control. UNDEFINED operations may affect the contents of memory, the operation of peripherals, and the operation of the processor. UNDE-FINED operations are constrained only to not hang the processor and console. Control of the machine can be regained by reinitializing the processor from the console.

The complete list of UNDEFINED operations is implementation-dependent but includes:
- Writing non-zero values into fields specified as MBZ
- Writing values specified as reserved into privileged registers
- An exception or interrupt whose SCB vector has bits ⟨1:0⟩ both set
- Restarting an instruction that references an I/O register with side effects
- Unaligned references to I/O space
- References to I/O space registers in which the reference size is not the register size
- Console START or CONTINUE after an error halt and before a processor initialization
- Page tables, the PCB, or the SCB in I/O space
- LDPCTX when the new kernel stack is invalid or inaccessible.

MicroVAX I

The MicroVAX I computer system is the first subset VAX. Announced in 1984, it is packaged in a box about 6 inches by 28 inches by 22 inches.

The MicroVAX I comes in two versions; one includes F—floating and G—floating instructions, the other includes F—floating and D—floating instructions. Neither version includes H—floating instructions. The MicroVAX I processor includes some of the optional string instructions (CMPC3, LOCC, SCANC, SKPC, SPANC) but does not include any of the optional processor registers or compatibility mode.

Implementation-dependent features of the MicroVAX I are described in Figures B.1–B.3 and Tables B.1–B.4.

MicroVAX II

The MicroVAX II computer system is the first VAX with the processor on a single chip. F—floating, D—floating, and G—floating instructions are provided by a floating-point unit (another chip). The MicroVAX II is a subset VAX, and includes none of the optional string instructions, optional processor registers, H-floating instructions, or compatibility mode.

Implementation-dependent features of the MicroVAX II are described in Figures B.4–B.6 and Tables B.5–B.8.

VAX-11/725

The VAX-11/725 computer system, announced in 1984, is a repackaged version of the VAX-11/730 processor. The cabinet is 25 inches high and 18 inches wide, and includes memory, two TU58 tape cartridge drives, and an RC25 disk.

VAX-11/730

The VAX-11/730 computer system, announced in 1982, was the third processor in the VAX family, and the first to include G—floating and H—floating as standard. It is packaged with two disks in a cabinet 42 inches tall and 22 inches wide.

The VAX-11/730 includes all the instructions, all the architecturally defined processor registers, and compatibility mode.

Implementation-dependent features of the VAX-11/730 are described in Figures B.7–B.9 and Tables B.9–B.12.

VAX-11/750

The VAX-11/750, announced in 1980, was the second processor in the VAX family. It is packaged in a cabinet 42 inches tall and 29 inches wide.

The VAX-11/750 includes all the instructions (G—floating and H—floating are available as an option), all architecturally defined processor registers, and compatibility mode.

Implementation-dependent features of the VAX-11/750 are described in Figures B.10 through B.12 and Tables B.13 through B.16.

AX-11/780

The VAX-11/780 computer, announced in 1978, was the first processor of the VAX family. It is packaged in a cabinet 60 inches tall and 47 inches wide.

The VAX-11/780 includes all the instructions (G_floating and H_floating instructions are available as an option), all the architecturally defined processor registers, and compatibility mode.

Implementation-dependent features of the VAX-11/780 are described in Figures B.13 through B.15 and Tables B.17 through B.20.

AX-11/782

The VAX-11/782 computer system, announced in 1982, is a dual processor VAX-11/780 with shared memory. The cabinets containing the processor, I/O adapters, and shared memory are 60 inches tall and 190 inches wide.

AX-11/785

The VAX-11/785 computer system, announced in 1984, is available as a field upgrade of the VAX-11/780. It is packaged in a cabinet 60 inches tall and 80 inches wide, including processor, memory, and I/O adapters. The VAX-11/785 is identical to the VAX-11/780 from the point of view of software, except that the VAX-11/785 has increased performance and has a bit set in the SID internal processor register, by which software can differentiate between the two processor types.

AX 8200

The VAX 8200, announced in 1986, is packaged with two disks in a cabinet 42 inches tall and 22 inches wide.

The 8200 includes all the instructions and architecturally defined processor registers, but does not include compatibility mode.

Implementation-dependent features of the VAX 8200 are described in Figures B.16–B.18 and Tables B.21–B.22.

AX 8300

The VAX 8300, announced in 1986, is a dual-processor version of the VAX 8200, packaged in the same cabinet.

AX 8500

The VAX 8500, announced in 1986, is a single-processor version of the VAX 8800. It is packaged in a cabinet 60 inches tall and about 27 inches wide.

VAX 8600

The 8600, announced in 1984, is packaged in a cabinet 60 inches ta and about 80 inches wide.

The 8600 includes all the instructions, architecturally defined process registers, and compatibility mode.

Implementation-dependent features of the VAX 8600 are described i Figures B.19–B.21 and Tables B.23–B.26.

VAX 8650

The 8650, announced in 1985, is available as a field upgrade of the 8600. The 8650 is packaged in the same cabinet as the 8600 and offers higher performance.

VAX 8800

The dual-processor 8800, announced in 1986, is the highest performance member of the VAX family. It is packaged in a cabinet 60 inches tall and about 80 inches wide.

The 8800 includes all the instructions and architecturally defined processor registers. The 8800 does not include PDP-11 compatibility mode.

Implementation-dependent features of the VAX 8800 are described i Figures B.22–B.24 and Tables B.27–B.29.

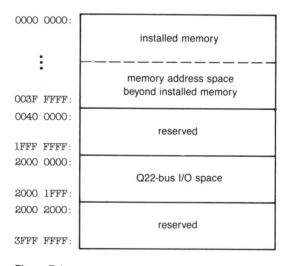

Figure B.1
MicroVAX I Physical Address Space

Table B.1

MicroVAX I Implementation-Dependent System Control Block Vectors

Offset	Vector Name	IPL	Notes
60	write-bus timeout	1D	
C0	interval timer	16	
200–3FC	Q22 bus interrupts	14–17	IPL corresponds to bus request levels 4 through 7.

Table B.2

MicroVAX I Halt Codes

Code	Meaning
1	microverify succeeded
2	processor halted by HALT button or console break
3	powerup
4	interrupt stack not valid
5	double machine-check
6	HALT instruction executed
A	change mode from the interrupt stack
C	SCB vector read error
FF	microverify failed

Table B.3

MicroVAX I Implementation-Dependent Internal Processor Registers

IPR	Mnemonic	Name
18	ICCS	Interval-clock control and status (1)
19	NICR	Next interval count (2)
1A	ICR	Interval count (2)
1B	TODR	Time-of-year clock (2)
24	TBDR	Translation-buffer disable (2)
25	CDR	Cache disable
26	MCESR	Machine-check error summary
27	CAER	Cache error (2)
30	SBIFS	SBI fault status (2)
31	SBIS	SBI silo (2)
32	SBISC	SBI silo comparator (2)
33	SBIMT	SBI maintenance (2)
34	SBIER	SBI error (2)
35	SBITA	SBI timeout address (2)
36	SBIQC	SBI quadword clear (2)
37	IORESET	I/O reset
3B	TBDATA	Translation-buffer data
3C	MBRK	Microprogram breakpoint
3D	PME	Performance-monitor enable
3E	SID	System identification
3F	TBCHK	Translation-buffer check (3)

(1) Subset implementation. (3) Always returns "TB miss."
(2) Reads as zero, ignores writes.

```
31          24 23         17 16 15         8 7            0
┌──────────────┬──────────┬─┬────────────┬──────────────┐
│      7       │ reserved │D│microcode rev│ hardware rev │
└──────────────┴──────────┴─┴────────────┴──────────────┘
```

Figure B.2
MicroVAX I System Identification Register (SID)

```
┌────────────────────────────────────────────────┐
│         byte count (0000000C hex)               │ :SP
├────────────────────────────────────────────────┤
│           machine-check type code               │
├────────────────────────────────────────────────┤
│              first parameter                    │
├────────────────────────────────────────────────┤
│              second parameter                   │
├────────────────────────────────────────────────┤
│                    PC                           │
├────────────────────────────────────────────────┤
│                    PSL                          │
└────────────────────────────────────────────────┘
```

Figure B.3
MicroVAX I Machine-Check Stack Frame

Table B.4
MicroVAX I Machine-Check Type Codes

Code	Meaning
0	memory controller bug check*
1	unrecoverable memory read error*
2	nonexistent memory*
3	illegal I/O space operation*
4	unrecoverable PTE read error*
5	unrecoverable PTE write error*
6	control store parity error†
7	micromachine bug check†
8	Q22 bus vector read error†
9	write parameter error‡

*Bits$\langle 29,21{:}0 \rangle$ of the first parameter contain the corresponding bits of the physical address of the last memory reference, and the second parameter contains the address presented to the memory controller.
†Both parameters are zero.
‡The first parameter contains the virtual address that was being written, and the second parameter is zero.

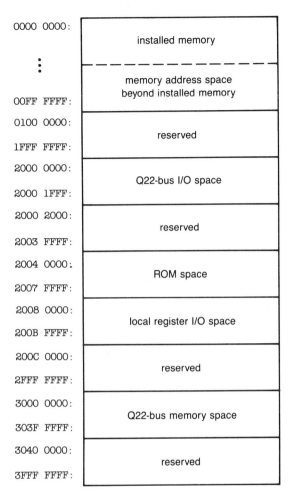

Figure B.4
MicroVAX II Physical Address Space

Table B.5
MicroVAX II Implementation-Dependent System Control Block Vectors

Offset	Vector Name	IPL	Notes
CO	interval timer	16	
200–3FC	Q22 bus interrupts	14–17	IPL corresponds to bus request levels 4 through 7.

Table B.6

MicroVAX II Implementation-Dependent Internal Processor Registers

IPR	Mnemonic	Name
18	ICCS	Interval-clock control and status (1)
19	NICR	Next interval count (2)
1A	ICR	Interval count (2)
1B	TODR	Time-of-year clock (2)
1C	CSRS	Console storage receiver status (2)
1D	CSRD	Console storage receiver data (2)
1E	CSTS	Console storage transmitter status (2)
1F	CSTD	Console storage transmitter data (2)
20	RXCS	Console receiver status (2)
21	RXDB	Console receiver data (2)
22	TXCS	Console transmitter status (2)
23	TXDB	Console transmitter data (2)
24	TBDR	Translation-buffer disable (2)
25	CADR	Cache disable (2)
26	MCESR	Machine-check error summary (2)
27	CAER	Cache error (2)
20	SAVISP	Console saved interrupt stack pointer
2A	SAVPC	Console saved PC
2B	SAVPSL	Console saved PSL
30	SBIFS	SBI fault status (2)
31	SBIS	SBI silo (2)
32	SBISC	SBI silo comparator (2)
33	SBIMT	SBI maintenance (2)
34	SBIER	SBI error (2)
35	SBITA	SBI timeout address (2)
36	SBIQC	SBI quadword clear (2)
37	IORESET	I/O reset (2)
3B	TBDATA	Translation-buffer data (2)
3C	MBRK	Microprogram breakpoint (2)
3D	PME	Performance-monitor enable (2)
3E	SID	System identification
3F	TBCHK	Translation-buffer check

(1) Subset implementation.
(2) Reads as zero, ignores writes.

```
31        24 23                                    0
+-------------+--------------------------------------+
|      8      |                  0                   |
+-------------+--------------------------------------+
```

Figure B.5
MicroVAX II System Identification Register (SID)

byte count (0000000C hex)	:SP
machine-check code	
most recent virtual address	
internal state information	
PC	
PSL	

Figure B.6
MicroVAX II Machine-Check Stack Frame

Table B.7
MicroVAX II Machine-Check Type Codes

Code	Meaning
1	impossible microcode state (FSD)
2	impossible microcode state (SSD)
3	undefined FPU error code 0
4	undefined FPU error code 7
5	undefined memory management status (TB miss)
6	undefined memory management status (M = 0)
7	process PTE in PO space
8	process PTE in P1 space
9	undefined interrupt ID code
80	read bus error, address parameter is virtual
81	read bus error, address parameter is physical
82	write bus error, address parameter is virtual
83	write bus error, address parameter is physical

Table B.8
MicroVAX II Halt Codes

Code	Meaning
2	HALT L asserted
3	Initial power on
4	Interrupt stack not valid during exception
5	Machine-check during machine-check or kernel-stack-not-valid exception
6	HALT instruction executed in kernel mode
7	SCB vector bits $\langle 1{:}0 \rangle$ = 11
8	SCB vector bits $\langle 1{:}0 \rangle$ = 10
A	CHMx executed while on interrupt stack
10	Access-control-violation or translation-not-valid during machine-check exception
11	Access-control-violation or translation-not-valid during kernel-stack-not-valid exception

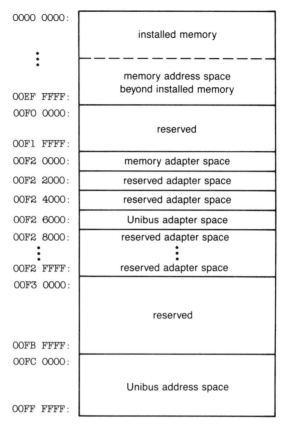

```
0000 0000:  ┌─────────────────────────────┐
            │                             │
            │       installed memory      │
     ⋮      │                             │
            ├ ─ ─ ─ ─ ─ ─ ─ ─ ─ ─ ─ ─ ─ ─┤
            │      memory address space   │
            │     beyond installed memory │
OOEF FFFF:  │                             │
OOFO 0000:  ├─────────────────────────────┤
            │                             │
            │           reserved          │
OOF1 FFFF:  │                             │
OOF2 0000:  ├─────────────────────────────┤
            │      memory adapter space   │
OOF2 2000:  ├─────────────────────────────┤
            │     reserved adapter space  │
OOF2 4000:  ├─────────────────────────────┤
            │     reserved adapter space  │
OOF2 6000:  ├─────────────────────────────┤
            │      Unibus adapter space   │
OOF2 8000:  ├─────────────────────────────┤
            │     reserved adapter space  │
     ⋮      │              ⋮              │
OOF2 FFFF:  │     reserved adapter space  │
OOF3 0000:  ├─────────────────────────────┤
            │                             │
            │                             │
            │           reserved          │
            │                             │
OOFB FFFF:  │                             │
OOFC 0000:  ├─────────────────────────────┤
            │                             │
            │      Unibus address space   │
            │                             │
OOFF FFFF:  └─────────────────────────────┘
```

Figure B.7
VAX-11/730 Physical Address Space

Table B.9
VAX-11/730 Implementation-Dependent System Control Block Vectors

Offset	Vector Name	IPL	Notes
54	Corrected Read Data	1A	Corrected memory error.
F0	Console Storage Device (TU58) Receive	14	Console load device signalling read complete.
F4	Console Storage Device (TU58) Transmit	14	Console load device signalling write complete.
200–3FC	Unibus interrupts	14	IPL corresponds to bus request levels 4 through 7.

Table B.10

VAX-11/730 Halt Codes

Code	Meaning
02	CTRL/P was typed at the console.
03	Does not appear in a halt message, but is passed by the console during powerfail restart.
04	The interrupt stack was not valid when the processor tried to push PC and PSL from an exception or an interrupt.
05	While the processor was trying to process a machine-check, a second machine-check occurred.
06	A HALT instruction was executed, while the processor was in kernel mode.
07	An exception or interrupt occurred and the SCB vector had bit⟨1⟩ set.
0A	A CHMx instruction was executed when the processor was executing on the interrupt stack.
0B	A CHMx instruction was executed and the SCB vector had bit⟨0⟩ set.
0C	A hard memory error occurred while the processor was trying to read an SCB vector.

Table B.11

VAX-11/730 Implementation-Dependent Internal Processor Registers

IPR	Mnemonic	Name
1C	CSRS	Console storage receive status
1D	CSRD	Console storage receive data
1E	CSTS	Console storage transmit status
1F	CSTD	Console storage transmit data
24	TBDR	Translation-buffer disable (1)
25	CDR	Cache disable (1)
26	MCESR	Machine-check error summary (2)
27	CAER	Cache error (1)
28	ACCS	Accelerator control and status
30	SBIFS	SBI fault status (1)
31	SBIS	SBI silo (3)
32	SBISC	SBI silo comparator (1)
33	SBIMT	SBI maintenance (1)
34	SBIER	SBI error (1)
35	SBITA	SBI timeout address (3)
36	SBIQC	SBI quadword clear (4)
37	IORESET	I/O reset
3D	PME	Performance-monitor enable
3E	SID	System identification
3F	TBCHK	Translation-buffer check

(1) Reads as zero, ignores writes.
(2) Reads as zero, any write clears the "machine-check in progress" flag.
(3) Reads as zero, writes cause reserved-operand fault.
(4) Ignores writes, reads cause reserved-operand fault.

3	reserved	microcode rev	reserved

Figure B.8
VAX-11/730 System Identification Register (SID)

byte count (0000000C hex)	:SP
machine-check type code	
first parameter	
second parameter	
PC	
PSL	

Figure B.9
VAX-11/730 Machine-Check Stack Frame

0000 0000 :	installed memory
⋮	memory address space beyond installed memory
00EF FFFF :	
00F0 0000 :	reserved for loading WCS
00F2 0000 :	memory adapter space
00F2 2000 :	reserved adapter space
00F2 4000 :	reserved adapter space
00F2 6000 :	reserved adapter space
00F2 8000 :	MASSBUS 0 adapter space
00F2 A000 :	MASSBUS 1 adapter space
00F2 C000 :	MASSBUS 2 adapter space
00F2 E000 :	MASSBUS 3 adapter space
00F3 0000 :	UNIBUS 0 adapter space
00F3 2000 :	UNIBUS 1 adapter space
00F3 4000 : ⋮ 00F3 E000 :	reserved adapter spaces
00F4 0000 : ⋮ 00F7 FFFF :	reserved
00F8 0000 : ⋮ 00FB FFFF :	UNIBUS 1 address space
00FC 0000 : ⋮ 00FF FFFF :	UNIBUS 0 address space

Figure B.10
VAX-11/750 Physical Address Space

Table B.12

VAX-11/730 Machine-Check Error Type Codes

Code	Meaning
0	Microcode shouldn't be here. If the first parameter is zero, no other information is available. If the first parameter is two, the problem was inability to write back a PTE$\langle$M$\rangle$ bit. If the parameter is three, the problem was a bad 8085 interrupt. The second parameter is always zero.
1	Translation buffer parity error. The first parameter is the bad value from the TB. PFN is in bits $\langle 23:0 \rangle$. PTE$\langle$V$\rangle$, the protection code, and PTE$\langle$M$\rangle$ are in bits $\langle 31:26 \rangle$. TB valid bit is in bit $\langle 25 \rangle$. The second parameter is the virtual address referenced.
3	Impossible value in memory CSR. The first parameter is the virtual address referenced. The second parameter is the bad value of the CSR.
4	Fast interrupt without support. A fast interrupt was requested and no microcode was loaded to handle it. Both parameters are zero.
5	FPA parity error. The FPA control store had a parity error. The first parameter has parity error summary in bit$\langle 0 \rangle$, group 0 parity in bit $\langle 1 \rangle$, group 1 parity in bit $\langle 2 \rangle$, and in unpredictable in bits$\langle 31:3 \rangle$. The second parameter is zero.
6	Error on SPTE read. The first parameter is the physical address of the SPTE. The second parameter contains the error syndrome bits.
7	Uncorrectable ECC error. The first parameter is the physical address of the reference. The second parameter contains the error syndrome bits.
8	Nonexistent memory. The first parameter is the physical address referenced. The second parameter is zero.
9	Unaligned or non-longword reference to I/O space. The first parameter is the physical address referenced. The second parameter is zero.
A	Illegal I/O space address. The first parameter is the physical address referenced. The second parameter is zero.
B	Illegal UNIBUS reference. The first parameter is the physical address referenced. The second parameter is zero.

Table B.13

VAX-11/750 Implementation-Dependent System Control Block Vectors

Offset	Vector Name	IPL	Notes
54	corrected read data, or read data substitute	1A	Corrected memory error and uncorrected memory error.
60	write bus error	1D	Taken regardless of current IPL if error occurs during exception or interrupt.
F0	console storage device (TU58) receive	17	Console load device signalling read complete.
F4	console storage device (TU58) transmit	17	Console load device signalling write complete.
100–13C	adapter interrupts, adapters 0 through 15	14	Adapter interrupt.
140–17C	adapter interrupts, adapters 0 through 15	15	Adapter interrupt.
180–1BC	adapter interrupts, adapters 0 through 15	16	Adapter interrupt.
1C0–1FC	adapter interrupts, adapters 0 through 15	17	Adapter interrupt.
200–3FC	Unibus interrupts	14–17	IPL corresponds to bus request levels 4 through 7.

Table B.14

VAX-11/750 Halt Codes

Code	Meaning
1	successful completion of console TEST command
2	processor halted by fIP or single step
3	powerup
4	interrupt stack not valid, or SCB read failure
5	double bus write error
6	HALT instruction executed
7	illegal interrupt or exception vector (bits$\langle 1{:}0 \rangle$ = 3)
8	jump to nonexistent user writable control store (SCB vector bits$\langle 1{:}0 \rangle$ = 2, and no user WCS installed)
A	change mode from the interrupt stack
B	change mode to the interrupt stack
11	can't find a valid Restart Parameter Block during powerup restart, and powerup action switch set to RESTART/HALT
12	"system restart in progress" flag already set during powerup restart, and powerup action switch set to RESTART/HALT
13	can't find 64K bytes of good memory during system bootstrap
14	bad boot ROM or no boot ROM during powerup bootstrap
15	"system bootstrap in progress" flag already set during boot
16	powerup and powerup action switch set to HALT
FF	self-test failure

Table B.15

VAX-11/750 Implementation-Dependent Internal Processor Registers

IPR	Mnemonic	Name
17	CMIERR	CMI error
1C	CSRS	Console storage receive status
1D	CSRD	Console storage receive data
1E	CSTS	Console storage transmit status
1F	CSTD	Console storage transmit data
24	TBDR	Translation-buffer disable
25	CADR	Cache disable
26	MCESR	Machine-check error summary
27	CAER	Cache error
28	ACCS	Accelerator control and status
27	IORESET	Initialize UNIBUS
3B	TB	Translation-buffer test
3D	PME	Performance-monitor enable
3E	SID	System identification
3F	TBCHK	Translation-buffer check

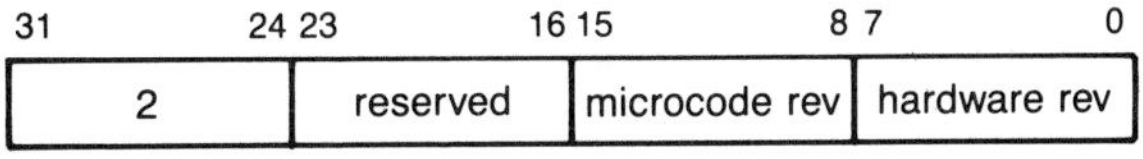

31	24 23	16 15	8 7	0
2	reserved	microcode rev	hardware rev	

Figure B.11

VAX-11/750 System Identification Register (SID)

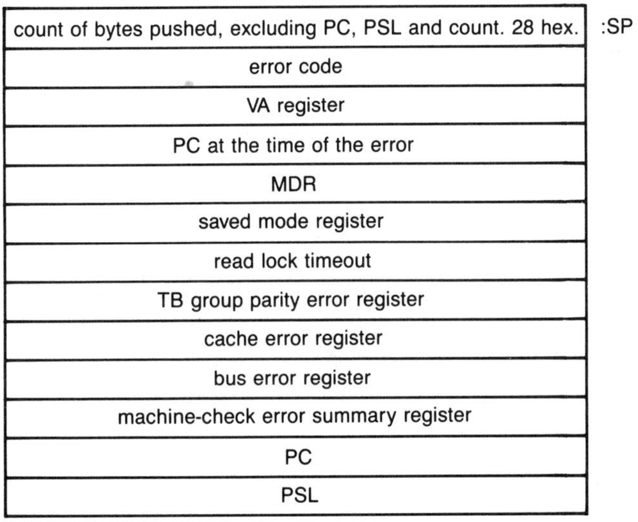

count of bytes pushed, excluding PC, PSL and count. 28 hex. :SP
error code
VA register
PC at the time of the error
MDR
saved mode register
read lock timeout
TB group parity error register
cache error register
bus error register
machine-check error summary register
PC
PSL

Figure B.12

VAX-11/750 Machine-Check Stack Frame

Table B.16
VAX-11/750 Machine-Check Error Summary Register

Code	Meaning
1	control store parity error
2	translation buffer parity error, bus error, or cache parity error
6	"microcode shouldn't be here" error
7	"unused IRD ROM slot" error

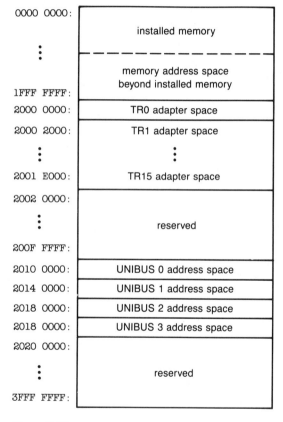

Figure B.13
VAX-11/780 Physical Address Space

Table B.17

VAX-11/780 Implementation-Dependent System Control Block Vectors

Offset	Vector Name	IPL	Notes
50	SBI silo compare	19	System bus error.
54	corrected read data, or read data substitute	1A	Corrected memory error, or uncorrected memory error.
58	SBI alert	1B	System bus error.
5C	SBI fault	1C	System bus error.
60	memory write timeout	1D	Memory error.
100–13C	nexus interrupts, nexuses 0 through 15	14	Device or adapter interrupt.
140–17C	nexus interrupts, nexuses 0 through 15	15	Device or adapter interrupt.
180–1BC	nexus interrupts, nexuses 0 through 15	16	Device or adapter interrupt.
1C0–1FC	nexus interrupts, nexuses 0 through 15	17	Device or adapter interrupt.

Table B.18

VAX-11/780 Halt Codes

Code	Message	Meaning
3	none	Powerup.
4	?INT-STK INVLD	The interrupt stack was not valid when the processor attempted to take an exception or interrupt.
5	?CPU DBLE-ERR HLT	A second processor error occurred during the processing of a previous error.
7	?ILL I/E VEC	Illegal interrupt or exception vector. (Vector bits⟨1:0⟩ were 3.)
8	?NO USR WCS	Jump to nonexistent user writable control store.
OA	?CHM ERR	Change mode from the interrupt stack.

Table B.19

VAX-11/780 Implementation-Dependent Internal Processor Registers

IPR	Mnemonic	Name
20	RXCS	Console terminal receive control and status
21	RXDB	Console terminal receive data buffer
22	TXCS	Console terminal transmit control and status
23	TXDB	Console terminal transmit data buffer
28	ACCS	Accelerator control and status
29	ACCR	Accelerator maintenance
2C	WCSA	Writable-control-store address
2D	WCSD	Writable-control-store data
30	SBIFS	SBI fault status
31	SBIS	SBI silo
32	SBISC	SBI silo comparator
33	SBIMT	SBI maintenance
34	SBIER	SBI error
35	SBITA	SBI timeout address
36	SBIQC	SBI quadword clear
3C	MBRK	Microprogram breakpoint
3D	PME	Performance-monitor enable
3E	SID	System identification
3F	TBCHK	Translation-buffer check

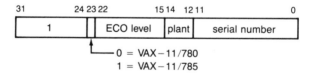

Figure B.14

VAX-11/780 System Identification Register (SID)

```
┌─────────────────────────────────────────────────────────────┐
│ count of bytes pushed, excluding PC, PSL and count. 28 hex.  │ :SP
├─────────────────────────────────────────────────────────────┤
│                    summary parameter                          │
├─────────────────────────────────────────────────────────────┤
│                  CPU error status register                    │
├─────────────────────────────────────────────────────────────┤
│                    trapped microPC                            │
├─────────────────────────────────────────────────────────────┤
│                     VA or VIBA                                │
├─────────────────────────────────────────────────────────────┤
│                      D register                               │
├─────────────────────────────────────────────────────────────┤
│                   TB ERR 0 register                           │
├─────────────────────────────────────────────────────────────┤
│                   TB ERR 1 register                           │
├─────────────────────────────────────────────────────────────┤
│                    timeout address                            │
├─────────────────────────────────────────────────────────────┤
│                    parity register                            │
├─────────────────────────────────────────────────────────────┤
│                   SBI error register                          │
├─────────────────────────────────────────────────────────────┤
│                        PC                                     │
├─────────────────────────────────────────────────────────────┤
│                        PSL                                    │
└─────────────────────────────────────────────────────────────┘
```

Figure B.15
VAX-11/780 Machine-Check Stack Frame

Table B.20
VAX-11/780 Machine-Check Error Summary Parameter

Code	Meaning
00	central processor read timeout or error confirmation fault
02	central processor translation buffer parity error fault
03	central processor cache parity error fault
05	central processor read data substitute fault
0A	instruction buffer translation buffer parity error fault
0C	instruction buffer read data substitute fault
0D	instruction buffer read timeout or error confirmation fault
0F	instruction buffer cache parity error fault
F1	control store parity error abort
F2	central processor translation buffer parity error abort
F3	central processor cache parity error abort
F4	central processor read timeout or error confirmation abort
F5	central processor read data substitute abort
F6	"microcode not supposed to get here" abort

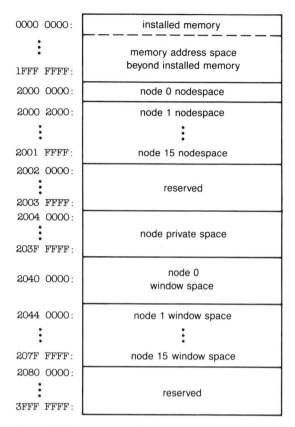

Figure B.16
VAX 8200 Physical Address Space

Table B.21
VAX 8200 Implementation-Dependent SCB Vectors

Offset	Vector Name	IPL
50	BI bus-error interrupt	14
54	Corrected read data	1A
58	RXCD (receive data register)	14
80	Interprocessor interrupt	14
C0	Interval timer interrupt	16
C8	Serial line #1 RX interrupt	14
CC	Serial line #1 TX interrupt	14
D0	Serial line #2 RX interrupt	14
D4	Serial line #2 TX interrupt	14
D8	Serial line #3 RX interrupt	14
DC	Serial line #3 TX interrupt	14
F0	Console storage device	14
F8	Console terminal RX interrupt	14
FC	Console terminal TX interrupt	14
100–3FFC	BI defined, loaded by software	14–17

Table B.22
VAX 8200 Implementation-Dependent Internal Processor Registers

IPR	Mnemonic	Name
16	IPIR	Interprocessor interrupt request
20	RXCS	Console terminal receive control and status
21	RXDB	Console terminal receive data buffer
22	TXCS	Console terminal transmit control and status
23	TXDB	Console terminal transmit data buffer
24	TBDR	Translation-buffer disable
25	CADR	Cache disable
26	MCESR	Machine-check error summary
28	ACCS	Accelerator control and status
2C	WCSA	Writable-control-store address
2D	WCSD	Writable-control-store data
2E	WCSL	Writable-control-store load
3E	SID	System identification
50	RXCS1	Serial line 1 receive control and status
51	RXDB1	Serial line 1 receive data buffer
52	TXCS1	Serial line 1 transmit control and status
53	TXDB1	Serial line 1 transmit data buffer
54	RXCS2	Serial line 2 receive control and status
55	RXDB2	Serial line 2 receive data buffer
56	TXCS2	Serial line 2 transmit control and status
57	TXDB2	Serial line 2 transmit data buffer
58	RXCS2	Serial line 3 receive control and status
59	RXDB3	Serial line 3 receive data buffer
5A	TXCS3	Serial line 3 transmit control and status
5B	TXDB3	Serial line 3 transmit data buffer
5C	RXCD	Receive console data
5D	CACHEX	Cache invalidate
5E	BINID	BI node identification
5F	BISTOP	BI stop

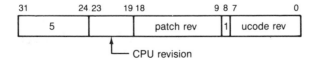

Figure B.17
VAX 8200 System Identification Register (SID)

count of bytes pushed, excluding PC, PSL, and count. 20 hex. :SP
machine-check type code
parameter 1
VA
VA prime
MAR
status word
PC at failure
micro-PC at failure
PC
PSL

Figure B.18 VAX 8200 Machine-Check Stack Frame

0000 0000 :	installed memory
⋮	
1FFF FFFF :	nonexistent-memory space
2000 0000 :	SBI0.TR0 adapter space
2000 2000 :	SBI0.TR1 adapter space
⋮	⋮
2001 FFFF :	SBI0.TR15 adapter space
2002 0000 :	reserved
2008 0000 :	SBIA #0 registers
2008 00C0 :	reserved
2010 0000 :	UNIBUS 0 address space
2014 0000 :	UNIBUS 1 address space
	⋮
201F FFFF :	UNIBUS 3 address space
2020 0000 :	reserved
2200 0000 :	SBI1.TR0 adapter space
2200 2000 :	SBI1.TR1 adapter space
⋮	⋮
2201 FFFF :	SBI1.TR15 adapter space
2202 0000 :	reserved
2208 0000 :	SBIA #1 registers
2208 00C0 :	reserved
2210 0000 :	UNIBUS 4 address space
2214 0000 :	UNIBUS 5 address space
	⋮
221F FFFF :	UNIBUS 7 address space
2220 0000 :	reserved
2400 0000 :	SBIA #2 address space
2600 0000 :	SBIA #3 address space
2800 0000 :	reserved

Figure B.19 VAX 8600 Physical Address Space

Table B.23 VAX 8600 Implementation-Dependent SCB Vectors

Offset	Vector Name	IPL	Notes
04	machine checks	1D or 1F	At IPL 1D only if the error is unrelated to the current instruction
50	SBI0 silo compare	19	System-bus memory error
54	Corrected read data	1D	Corrected memory error
58	SBI0 alert	1B	System-bus error
5C	SBI0 fault	1C	System-bus error
60	SBIA0 internal fail	1D	Abus-to-SBI-adapter error
64	SBI0 power fail	1E	
100–13C	SBIA0 nexus interrupts at BR4, nexus 0 thru 15	14	Device or adapter interrupt
140–17C	SBIA0 nexus interrupts at BR5, nexus 0 thru 15	15	Device or adapter interrupt
180–1BC	SBIA0 nexus interrupts at BR6, nexus 0 thru 15	16	Device or adapter interrupt
1C0–1FC	SBIA0 nexus interrupts at BR7, nexus 0 thru 15	17	Device or adapter interrupt
250	SBI1 silo compare	19	System-bus error
258	SBI1 alert	1B	System-bus error
25C	SBI1 fault	1C	System-bus error
260	SBIA1 internal error	1D	Abus-to-SBI-adapter error
264	SBI1 power fail	1E	
300–33C	SBIA1 nexus interrupts at BR4, nexus 0 thru 15	14	Device or adapter interrupt
340–37C	SBIA1 nexus interrupts at BR5, nexus 0 thru 15	15	Device or adapter interrupt
380–3BC	SBIA1 nexus interrupts at BR6, nexus 0 thru 15	16	Device or adapter interrupt
3C0–3FC	SBIA1 nexus interrupts at BR7, nexus 0 thru 15	17	Device or adapter interrupt
400–5FC	IOA #2 vectors		Correspond to 200–3FC
600–7FC	IOA # 3 vectors		Correspond to 200–3FC

Table B.24 VAX 8600 Implementation-Dependent Halt Codes

Code	Message	Meaning
0	UNRECOVERABLE MACHINE HANG	Console-support microcode is not running
4	INTERRUPT STACK INVALID	Interrupt stack not valid during the initiation of an exception or interrupt.
5	NON-EBOX DOUBLE ERROR	While initiating a machine check, a second machine check occurred.
6	KERNEL MODE HALT	HALT instruction in kernel mode.
7	SCB VECTOR<1:0>=3, INVALID	Illegal SCB vector (bits<1:0>=3).
8	SCB VECTOR<1:0>=2, NO USER WCS	Illegal SCB vector (bits<1:0>=2, no WCS microcode).
9	ERROR PENDING ON HALT	Pending error on HALT.
A	CHM WITH IS=1	CHMx from the interrupt stack.
B	CHM WITH VECTOR<1:0> NOT 0	CHMx to the interrupt stack.
11	INVOKED BY CONSOLE	Operator typed HALT at console.

Table B.25
VAX 8600 Implementation-Dependent Internal Processor Registers

IPR	Mnemonic	Name
20	RXCS	Console terminal receive control and status
21	RXDB	Console terminal receive data buffer
22	TXCS	Console terminal transmit control and status
23	TXDB	Console terminal transmit data buffer
28	ACCS	Accelerator control and status
3D	PME	Performance-monitor enable
3E	SID	System identification
3F	TBCHK	Translation-buffer check
40	PAMACC	Physical address memory map access
41	PAMLOC	Physical address memory map location
42	CSWP	Cache sweep
43	MDECC	M-box data ECC
44	MENA	M-box error enable
45	MDCTL	M-box data control
46	MCCTL	M-box MCC control
47	MERG	M-box error generator
48	CRBT	Console reboot
49	DFI	Diagnostic fault insertion
4A	EHSR	Error handling status
4C	STXCS	Console block storage control and status
4D	STXDB	Console block storage data buffer
4E	ESPA	E-box scratchpad address
4F	ESPD	E-box scratchpad data

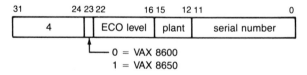

Figure B.20
VAX 8600 System Identification Register (SID)

count of bytes pushed, excluding PC, PSL, and count. 58 hex.
EHM.STS
EVMQSAV
EBCS
EDPSR
CSLINT
IBESR
EBXWD1
EBXWD2
IVASAV
VIBASAV
ESASAV
ISASAV
CPC
MSTAT1
MSTAT2
MDECC
MERG
CSHCTL
MEAR
MEDR
FBXERR
CSES
PC
PSL

Figure B.21
VAX 8600 Machine-Check Stack Frame

Table B.26
VAX 8600 Machine-Check Stack Frame Contents

Field	Offset	Extent	Meaning
COUNT	00	<31:0>	Bytes pushed, excluding PC, PSL, and count
EHM.STS	04	<31:24>	Error-handling status
		<23:19>	Control-store correction request
		<15:8>	Trap vector
		<7:0>	Status code
EVMQSAV	08	<31:0>	E-box virtual address
EBCS	0C	<31:27>	E-box control-store parity error
		<15:8>	E-box, I-box, M-box error
		<4:0>	Abort flags
EDPSR	10	<31:28>	A-mux byte in error
		<27:24>	B-mux byte in error
		<15:12>	VMQ byte in error
		<11:0>	E-box datapath error flags
CSLINT	14	<29:23>	Interrupt request flags
		<22:21>	IOA number
		<20:16>	Interrupt priority requests
		<15:8>	C-bus data
		<7:6>	C-bus control
		<5:0>	C-bus addresss
IBESR	18	<31:21>	I-box error flags
		<15:8>	Diagnostic and maintenance flags
EBXWD1	1C	<31:0>	Top of scratch-pad stack
EBXWD2	20	<31:0>	Next on scratch-pad stack
IVASAV	24	<31:0>	Virtual address for operand fetch
VIBASAV	28	<31:0>	Virtual address of next IB port request to fill IB
ESASAV	2C	<31:0>	PC being evaluated by E-box

Table B.26
VAX 8600 Machine-Check Stack Frame Contents *(continued)*

Field	Offset	Extent	Meaning
ISASAV	30	<31:0>	PC being evaluated by operand fetch unit
CPC	34	<31:0>	PC being evaluated by I-buffer
MSTAT1	38	<31:26>	M-box cycle in error
		<25:24>	Word count
		<23:16>	M-box error conditions
		<15:12>	Cache hit/miss history
		<11:8>	TB errors
		<7:0>	M-box datapath error summary
MSTAT2	3C	<20:16>	PAMM data
		<15:8>	SBIA diagnostic status
		<7:0>	M-box error information
MDECC	40	<22:16>	Data ECC error flags
		<14:9>	Data ECC syndrome
		<7:1>	Data ECC check bit invert
		<0>	Longword parity invert
MERG	44	<12:9>	Diagnostic bits
		<8>	Memory management enable
		<5:0>	M-box diagnostic error-insertion bits
CSHCTL	48	<3:0>	Cache control
MEAR	4C	<29:2>	Physical address latched
MEDR	50	<31:00>	Data word latched
FBXERR	54	<25:9>	Accelerator status
CSES	58	<28:16>	Control-store address
		<15:8>	Control-store syndrome
		<2:0>	Control-store code
PC	5C	<31:0>	PC
PSL	60	<31:0>	PSL

0000 0000:	installed memory
⋮	
	memory address space beyond installed memory
1FFF FFFF:	
2000 0000:	BI#0 node 0 nodespace
2000 2000:	BI#0 node 1 nodespace
⋮	⋮
2001 FFFF:	BI#0 node 15 nodespace
2002 0000:	multicast space
2004 0000:	boot ROM
2006 0000:	reserved
2008 0000:	node private space
2010 0000:	reserved
2040 0000:	node 0 window space
207F FFFF:	node 1 window space
⋮	⋮
2044 0000:	node 15 window space
2080 0000:	reserved
2200 0000:	BI #1 space
2400 0000:	BI #2 space
2600 0000:	BI #3 space
2800 0000:	reserved
⋮	
3FFF FFFF:	

Figure B.22
VAX 8800 Physical Address Space

ıX 8800 Implementation-Dependent SCB Vectors

ïset	Vector Name	IPL	Notes
5C	NMI fault	1C	System-bus error
80	interprocessor interrupt	14	Not included in 8500
48	memory error	15	Corrected or uncorrected error, interlock timeout, or controller error.
00–13C	SBIA0 nexus interrupts at BR4, nexus 0 thru 15	14	Device or adapter interrupr
40–17C	SBIA0 nexus interrupts at BR5, nexus 0 thru 15	15	Device or adapter interrupt
80–1BC	SBIA0 nexus interrupts at BR6, nexus 0 thru 15	16	Device or adapter interrupt
C0–1FC	SBIA0 nexus interrupts at BR7, nexus 0 thru 15	17	Device or adapter interrupt
ʹ00–3FC	UNIBUS device interrupts	14–17	Devices on UNIBUS 0
00–5FC	UNIBUS device interrupts	14–17	Devices on UNIBUS 1
00–38FC			Unused
00–393C	BI#0 interrupts, nodes 0 through 15	14–17	Device or adapter interrupt
40–397C	BI#0 interrupts, nodes 0 through 15	14–17	Device or adapter interrupt
80–39BC	BI#0 interrupts, nodes 0 through 15	14–17	Device or adapter interrupt
C0–39FC	BI#0 interrupts, nodes 0 through 15	14–17	Device or adapter interrupt
00–3BFC	BI#1 interrupt vectors	14–17	Device or adapter interrupt
00–3DFC	BI#2 interrupt vectors	14–17	Device or adapter interrupt
00–3FFC	BI#3 interrupt vectors	14–17	Device or adapter interrupt

Table B.28
VAX 8800 Implementation-Dependent Internal Processor Registers

IPR	Mnemonic	Name
26	MCSTS	Machine check status
80	NICTRL	NMI interrupt control
81	INOP	Interrupt other processor
82	NMIFSR	NMI fault/status
83	NMISILO	NMI bus silo
84	NMIEAR	NMI error address
85	COR	Cache on
86	REVR1	Revision register #1
87	REVR2	Revision register #2
88	CLRTOSTS	Clear timeout status

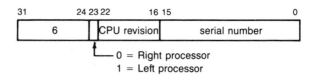

Figure B.23
VAX 8800 System Identification Register (SID)

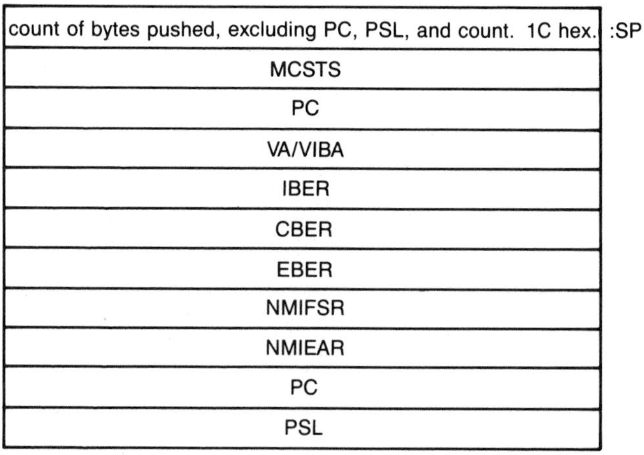

count of bytes pushed, excluding PC, PSL, and count. 1C hex.	:SP
MCSTS	
PC	
VA/VIBA	
IBER	
CBER	
EBER	
NMIFSR	
NMIEAR	
PC	
PSL	

Figure B.24
VAX 8800 Machine-Check Stack Frame

Table B.29
VAX 8800 Machine-Check Stack Frame Contents

Mnemonic	Offset	Contents
COUNT	00	Count of bytes pushed, excluding PC, PSL, and count
MCSTS	04	Machine-check status
PC	08	Current PC
VA/VIBA	0C	Virtual address/virtual instruction-buffer address
IBER	10	IBOX error
CBER	14	CBOX error
EBER	18	EBOX error
NMIFSR	1C	NMI fault summary
MNIEAR	20	NMI error address
PC	24	PC of faulted opcode
PSL	28	Processor status longword

Index

CLR (clear instructions):
compatibility mode, 297–298
floating point, 122–123
integer and logical, 51
CMP (compare instructions):
character string, 141–144
CMPC (compare characters),
141–144
CMPP (compare packed),
168–169
compatibility mode, 310–311
floating point, 123–124
integer and logical, 52
packed decimal, 168–169
variable length bit field, 68–69
COM (complement instruction), 301
Command files (@ console
command), 352
Compatibility mode (CM):
addresses, 327
address modes, 289–293
bit in PSL, 21
entering, 327
exceptions, 235–236,
328–330
instructions, 293–327
interrupts, 328–330
I/O, 330
leaving, 327
memory management, 327–328
omission of, 327, 361
processor registers, 330–331
PSW, 293
register mapping, 327
registers, 289–293
stack, 293
synchronization, 331
tracing, 329–330
unimplemented traps, 330
Condition code(s), 21
UMPREDICTABLE after fault or
interrupt, 251
Condition code operators instruction
(CC), 325–327
Console, 339–340
commands, 342–355
console I/O mode, 340
registers, 356–358
@ console command, 352
Context, of a process, 259
Context switching, 226, 279–281

CONTINUE console command, 343
Control characters, as console
commands, 340–342
Control region, of process space,
201
CRC (calculate cyclic redundancy
check instruction), 160–162
CTRL/C console command, 341
CTRL/O console command, 341
CTRL/P console command, 341
CTRL/Q console command, 341
CTRL/S console command, 341
CTRL/U console command, 341
Current access mode (CUR MOD),
21
CVT (convert instructions):
decimal, 169–177
floating point, 124–126
integer, 52–53
Cyclic redundancy check instruc-
tion, 159–162

Data, separation of procedure and,
270
Data sharing, 269–270
Data types:
definitions of, 5–18
notation for, 42–43
in registers, 20
DEC (integer decrement instructions), 53–54, 298
Decimal overflow (DV), 22, 164
Decimal string:
data types, 15–18
divide-by-zero exception, 231
instructions, 163–182
overflow exception, 232
packed, 18, 165
in registers, 20
zero-length, 165
DEPOSIT console command,
344–346
Device interrupts, 227
D_floating:
data type, 8
notation for, 42
in registers, 20
Displacement deferred mode
operand specifier formats,
31, 34–35

Modify access type, 42
MOV (move instructions):
  compatibility mode, 308–309
  floating point, 130–131
  integer and logical, 59
  MCOM (move complemented),
    56–57
  MFP (move from previous
    space), 325
  MFPR (move from processor
    register), 283
  MNEG (move negated), 58, 130
  MOVA (move address), 66
  MOVC (move character),
    147–151
  move character string, 147–155
  move IPR, 229, 282, 283
  MOVP (move packed), 179
  MOVPSL (move PSL), 99
  MOVTC (move translated char-
    acters), 151–153
  MOVTUC (move translated until
    character), 153–155
  MOVZ (move zero-extended),
    59– 60
  MTP (move to previous space),
    324–325
  MTPR (move to processor
    register), 229, 282
  packed decimal, 179
MTP (move to previous space),
  324–325
MTPR (move to previous register
  instruction), 229, 282
MUL (multiply instructions):
  compatibility mode, 311–312
  EMOD (extended multiply and
    integerize), 128–130
  EMUL (extended multiply), 56
  floating point, 131–132
  integer, 60–61
  MULP (multiply packed),
    180–181
  packed decimal, 180–181
Multiprocessors:
  PTE, 204, 205
  restrictions on caches, 274–275
  synchronization, 224

NEG (negate instruction),
  299–300
Negative condition code (N), 22

NEXT console command, 348
Next interval count register (NICR),
  286, 288
No-access. See Access type
NOP (no operation instruction),
  98–99
Numeric decimal string. See
  Decimal string

OA (operand address notation), 27
Octaword:
  data type, 6, 7
  notation for, 43
  in registers, 20
Odd address error abort, 328
Opcode formats, 25, 26
Opcode reserved to customers
  fault, 234–235
Operand specifier, 25, 26–27
Operand specifier notation, 42–43
Operand description notation,
  43–45
Overflow, 22
Overflow exceptions, 230–232

P0 and P1 registers:
  in PCB, 261
  P0BR (P0 base register), 213
  P0LR (P0 length register), 213
  P1BR (P1 base register),
    214–215
  P1LR (P1 length register),
    214–215
  restrictions when changing,
    215–216
Packed decimal string, 18, 165
  See also Decimal string
Page, 200
Page boundaries, 209
Page frame number field of PTE
  (PFN), 204
Page table(s):
  paging of, 212, 220–221
  process page tables, 212, 214
  restrictions when changing, 216
  system page table, 209
Page table entry (PTE), 203–207
  changes to, 206–207
  global page table index, 205
  for I/O devices, 205–206
PC. See Program counter

ORDERING INFORMATION

To order additional copies of this book and related titles, fill in and mail this form or call the toll-free telephone number below. Orders under $50 must be prepaid by check or credit card; postage and handling are free on prepaid orders. There is a 10 percent discount on orders of two or more copies of each title.

Digital Press/Order Processing
Digital Equipment Corporation
12A Esquire Road
Billerica, MA 01862

QTY.	AUTHOR/TITLE	ORDER NO.	PRICE*	TOTAL
	Leonard: VAX Architecture	EY-3459E-DP	$36.00	
	Kenah/Bate: VAX/VMS Internals	EY-00014-DP	55.00	
	Levy/Eckhouse: VAX-11	EY-AX008-DP	28.00	
	Digital Journal: VAX 8600	EY-3435E-DP	15.00	
	Digital Journal: MicroVAX II	EY-3474E-DP	15.00	
			Total	
			Discount	
		Add state sales tax		
		Total remitted		

METHOD OF PAYMENT

___ Check included (Make checks   ___ MasterCard/Visa
payable to Digital Equipment   Charge Card Acc't No. _____
Corporation)   Expiration Date _____

___ Purchase order (Please attach)   Authorized Signature _____

Name _____ Phone _____

Address _____

City _____ State _____ Zip _____

TOLL-FREE ORDER NUMBER

To order books by MasterCard or VISA, call 1-800-343-8321. Phone lines are open from 8:00 A.M. to 8:00 P.M., Eastern time.

Price and terms quoted are U.S. only and are subject to change without notice. For prices outside the U.S., contact the nearest office of Educational Services, Digital Equipment Corporation.

VAX System Family Tree

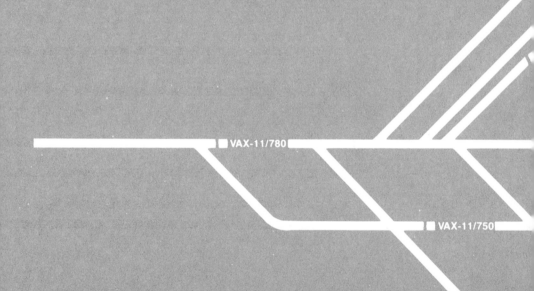

VAX-11/780

VAX-11/750

1975   1980